Health, Safety, and Nutrition for the Young Child

9th Edition

Lynn R. Marotz

CENGAGE
Learning

Australia • Brazil • Japan • Korea • Mexico • Singapore • Spain • United Kingdom • United States

Health, Safety, and Nutrition for the Young Child: 9th Edition

Lynn R. Marotz

Senior Manager, Student Engagement:

Linda deStefano

Janey Moeller

Manager, Student Engagement:

Julie Dierig

Marketing Manager:

Rachael Kloos

Manager, Production Editorial:

Kim Fry

Manager, Intellectual Property Project Manager:

Brian Methe

Senior Manager, Production and Manufacturing:

Donna M. Brown

Manager, Production:

Terri Daley

For product information and technology assistance, contact us at
Cengage Learning Customer & Sales Support, 1-800-354-9706
For permission to use material from this text or product,
submit all requests online at **cengage.com/permissions**
Further permissions questions can be emailed to
permissionrequest@cengage.com

This book contains select works from existing Cengage Learning resources and was produced by Cengage Learning Custom Solutions for collegiate use. As such, those adopting and/or contributing to this work are responsible for editorial content accuracy, continuity and completeness.

Compilation © 2014 Cengage Learning

ISBN-13: 978-1-305-28819-5
ISBN-10: 1-305-28819-X

WCN: 01-100-101

Cengage Learning
5191 Natorp Boulevard
Mason, Ohio 45040
USA

Cengage Learning is a leading provider of customized learning solutions with office locations around the globe, including Singapore, the United Kingdom, Australia, Mexico, Brazil, and Japan. Locate your local office at:
international.cengage.com/region.

Cengage Learning products are represented in Canada by Nelson Education, Ltd.
For your lifelong learning solutions, visit **www.cengage.com/custom.**
Visit our corporate website at **www.cengage.com.**

Brief Contents

Preface

Children's state of wellness has an unquestionable effect on their development and ability to learn. Our understanding of the factors that shape and influence a child's well-being, including nutrition, environmental conditions, and emotional and social health, continues to improve as a result of ongoing research. In turn, this information has led to noteworthy changes in our views about health, approaches to health care, and the critical importance of addressing health education during the early years. It has also contributed to the development of numerous resources (e.g., National Health Education Standards, MyPlate, Healthy People 2020, NAEYC's Standards for Early Childhood Professional Preparation, National Health and Safety Performance Standards for Child Care) that currently guide personal and classroom practices. Additionally, our knowledge of wellness and the importance of promoting healthy lifestyle behaviors draw increasing attention to the pivotal role teachers play in identifying children's health needs, creating high-quality environments that are safe and support learning, and providing comprehensive health education in schools.

Health, Safety, and Nutrition for the Young Child, now in its ninth edition, has become the standard text in the early childhood field. Its comprehensive approach and well-documented student/teacher-oriented focus continue to make it the best-selling, full-color textbook about children's well-being. Most importantly, this book provides students and teachers with a functional understanding of children's health, safety, and nutrition needs and guides them in implementing effective classroom practices. It also emphasizes the importance of respecting and partnering with all families to help children establish healthy lifestyles and achieve their learning potential. *Health, Safety, and Nutrition for the Young Child* accomplishes this by addressing all three essential components of children's wellness in one book:

- promoting children's **health** through awareness, assessment, early identification of special health needs, and meaningful health education
- creating and maintaining **safe learning environments** and fostering children's understanding and development of protective behaviors
- meeting children's essential **nutrition needs** by planning healthy meals, providing safe and nutritious food, and educating children about consuming a nutritious diet.

Extensive resources, lesson plans, teacher checklists, video clips, references, and family education materials are also provided throughout the book to aid busy students and practicing teachers in making a difference in children's lives.

The Intended Audience

First and foremost, *Health, Safety, and Nutrition for the Young Child* is written on behalf of young children everywhere. Ultimately, it is the children who benefit from having families and teachers who know how to protect and promote their safety and well-being. The term *families* is used throughout the text in reference to the diverse caring environments in which children are currently being raised and that may or may not include their biological parents. The term *teachers* is used inclusively to describe all adults who care for and work with young children-including educators, therapists, coaches, camp leaders, administrators, health care providers, legislators, and concerned citizens, whether they work in early education centers, home-based programs, recreation activities, public or private schools, community agencies, or after-school programs. The term *teacher* acknowledges the important educational role that families play in their children's daily lives. Its use also recognizes the valuable contributions of the many educators who dedicate their lives to children.

Health, Safety, and Nutrition for the Young Child is written for several primary audiences:

- Students and preservice teachers who have chosen a career in early education
- Experienced teachers in community schools, home-based programs, early childhood centers, Head Start programs, agencies that serve young children, and before- and after-school programs
- Allied health professionals and child advocates who work in any role that touches children's lives
- Families, who are children's most important teachers!

Organization and Key Content

The ninth edition of *Health, Safety, and Nutrition for the Young Child* maintains its original purpose to focus attention on the three critical areas that influence children's well-being: promoting children's health (Unit 1); creating high-quality, safe environments (Unit 2); and, supporting children's nutrition (basic and applied), healthy eating behaviors, and nutrition education (Units 3 and 4). This arrangement maximizes student learning and offers instructors flexibility in designing their courses. However, the interrelatedness of these three subject areas must not be overlooked despite their artificial separation.

Chapter content is presented in a clear, concise, and thought-provoking manner. It reflects the latest research developments and applications regarding children and wellness within a diverse and family-oriented framework. Key topics, including national health initiatives, children's mental health, bullying, fostering resilience and social-emotional competence, brain development, childhood obesity, emergency and disaster preparedness, and food safety have been added and updated. More information about children with special health challenges and school-aged children has also been provided. Without a doubt, this comprehensive book is a resource that no teacher (new or experienced) should be without!

New Content and Special Features

The ninth edition continues to include numerous features, tables, and checklists designed to engage students, reinforce learning, and enhance their ability to apply the information in contemporary educational settings:

- **Chapter Content Linked to National Association for the Education of Young Children Professional Preparation Standards**—NAEYC standards, identified at the onset of each chapter, enable students to relate chapter content to the association's professional education framework.

- **New Learning Objectives**—correlated to the main sections in each chapter show students what they need to know to process and understand the content. After completing the chapter, students should be able to demonstrate how they can use and apply their new knowledge and skills.

- **New Digital Downloads**—include most of the Teacher Checklists presented in the textbook for students to download, often customize, and use in the classroom! Look for the Digital Downloads label that identifies these items.

- **New Did You Get It? quizzes**—allow students to measure their performance against the learning objectives in each chapter. One question for each learning objective is featured in the textbook to encourage students to go to CengageBrain.com, take the full quiz, and check their understanding.

▸ **New Chapters**—Several chapters have been rewritten, reorganized, and expanded to improve student learning. A new section, *Emergency and Disaster Preparedness*, has been added to Chapter 8. Former Chapters 14 and 15 have been combined into a new Chapter 14, "*Nutrients That Promote Growth and Regulate Body Functions (Proteins, Vitamins, Minerals, and Water.*" Technical detail has been replaced with material that is easier for students to understand. Chapter 18, "*Food Safety,*" has been reorganized and new information added to draw attention to a serious health concern.

▸ **New Teach Source Video Connections**—feature footage from the classroom to help students relate key chapter content to real-life scenarios. Critical-thinking questions provide opportunities for in-class or online discussion and reflection.

▸ **New Partnering with Families**—is a feature designed to address the importance of family engagement and inclusion in children's health, safety, and nutrition education. Information on a variety of topics is provided in letter format for busy teachers to copy and send home or share with families in a newsletter, program handbook, website posting, parent conference, or bulletin board display.

▸ **Additional Teacher Checklists**—are a well-received feature that has been expanded in every chapter to provide teachers with quick, efficient access to critical information and best practices. Beginning practitioners will find these concise reference lists especially helpful in learning new material. Experienced teachers and administrators will appreciate their easy access for classroom use and staff training purposes. Most of the Teacher Checklists are also available as Digital Downloads.

▸ **New Connecting to Everyday Practice**—presents real-life situations that challenge students to resolve common dilemmas by applying chapter content. Thought-provoking questions encourage self-reflection and group discussion.

▸ **Classroom Corner Teacher Activities**—showcases lesson plans aligned with the National Health Education Standards. Learning objectives, materials lists, and step-by-step procedures are provided to save teachers preparation time and present children with meaningful learning experiences.

▸ **New Did You Know . . . ?**—offers interesting facts in a new marginal feature to increase student curiosity and interest in chapter content.

▸ **Monthly Calendar of National Health, Safety, and Nutrition Observances**—provides a month-by-month listing of national observances and related website resources that teachers can use when planning learning experiences for children. This information is located in Appendix B.

▸ **Children's Book List**—is an extensive, updated collection of children's books that can be used for teaching about health, safety, and nutrition while also encouraging literacy skills. This resource is located in Appendix D and includes titles that address topics such as dental health, mental health, self-care, safety, nutrition, special needs, and physical activity.

Chapter-by-Chapter Changes

Chapter 1 *Children's Well-Being: What It Is and How to Achieve It*

▸ *New* information on national health programs and initiatives, including National Health Education Standards, Coordinated School Health Program, Healthy People 2020, Children's Health Insurance Program, and Let's Move.

▸ Emphasis placed on health promotion and its effect on children's learning, development, and behavior.

▸ *New* information on early brain development, cultural influences on health, childhood stress, bullying, and cyber-bullying.

▸ *New TeachSource Video Connections* feature: "Infancy Brain Development."

Chapter 2 *Daily Health Observations*

▶ Additional *Teacher Checklists* highlighting key information for easy access.
▶ *New* references reinforcing teachers' role in early identification.
▶ *New TeachSource Video Connections* features: "Infants and Toddlers: Daily Health Checks" and "Communicating with Parents about Health in Early Childhood: A Parent-Teacher Meeting."

Chapter 3 *Assessing Children's Health*

▶ Greater emphasis placed on the teacher's role in identifying health problems (e.g., vision, hearing, language, nutrition) that affect learning.
▶ *New Teacher Checklists* for easy access to critical information.
▶ Additional content on childhood obesity and the short- and long-term consequences on health and learning.
▶ *New TeachSource Video Connections* features: "0–2 Years: Sensation and Perception, Vision in Infants and Toddlers" and "Students with Special Needs: The Referral and Evaluation Process."

Chapter 4 *Caring for Children with Special Medical Conditions*

▶ *New section* on inclusive classrooms and special education services, including a discussion of the Individuals with Disabilities Education Improvement Act (IDEA), Individualized Education Plans (IEPs), Individualized Family Service Plans (IFSPs), and Individualized Health Services Plans (IHSP).
▶ Updated information on the signs, symptoms, and management strategies for common chronic childhood diseases and medical conditions.
▶ *New TeachSource Video Connections* features: "Preschool: IEP and Transition Planning for a Young Child with Special Needs" and "Promoting Children's Health: Teacher Takes Care of Child With Asthma."

Chapter 5 *The Infectious Process and Environmental Control*

▶ The latest national childhood immunization recommendations (and chart).
▶ *New* information on classroom infection control practices, including hand washing and green cleaning products.
▶ *Newly issued warnings* and recommendations on mixing bleach solutions.
▶ *New TeachSource Video Connections* feature: "Promoting Children's Health: A Focus on Nutrition in Early Childhood Settings."

Chapter 6 *Childhood Illnesses: Identification and Management*

▶ *New* information on Sudden Infant Death Syndrome (SIDS).
▶ *New Teacher Checklists* highlighting critical information about childhood illnesses.
▶ *New TeachSource Video Connections* feature: "SIDS: Is There a Biological Cause?"

Chapter 7 *Creating High-Quality Environments*

▶ *New* information on safety features associated with high-quality environments, including outdoor play areas for children.
▶ More emphasis on the importance of outdoor play and physical activity in the prevention of childhood obesity, diabetes, and behavior problems.
▶ Field-based activities and a new case study reinforce application of chapter content to everyday practice.
▶ *New TeachSource Video Connections* features: "The Quality of Child Care" and "Creating a Safe Physical Environment for Toddlers."

Chapter 8 *Safety Management*

▶ *New* section on emergency and disaster preparedness, including strategies for helping children to cope following such an event.
▶ Additional information on school security.
▶ *New TeachSource Video Connections* feature: "Preschool Safety and Disaster Preparedness."

Chapter 9 *Management of Injuries and Acute Illness*

- *Updated* emergency and first aid techniques from the American Heart Association and Red Cross
- *New* information on initial injury assessment and assembling first aid kits.
- *New* section on anaphylaxis (life-threatening allergic reaction).
- *New TeachSource Video Connections* feature: "Working with Children Who Have Physical Disabilities."

Chapter 10 *Maltreatment of Children: Abuse and Neglect*

- *New* research-based information about the immediate and long-term emotional, cognitive, and economic effects maltreatment has on children's development.
- *New* information on vulnerable children, cultural implications, strategies for increasing resilience, and anger management.
- Updated booklist that teachers and families can use to address maltreatment with children and to build resilience.
- *New TeachSource Video Connections* feature: "0–2 Years: Observation Module for Infants and Toddlers."

Chapter 11 *Planning for Children's Health and Safety Education*

- Updated information on the National Health Education Standards and Health Education Curriculum Analysis Tool (HECAT).
- *New* lesson plan on "Yoga and Wellness."
- Additional teacher resources and children's book lists to use for lesson planning.

Chapter 12 *Nutrition Guidelines*

- *New* information on the Dietary Guidelines for Americans, Dietary Reference Intakes (DRIs), MyPlate, Healthy People 2020, and food labels.
- Emphasis placed on eating locally and the role of physical activity in health promotion.
- *New TeachSource Video Connections* feature: "Young Children's Stages of Play: An Illustrated Guide."

Chapter 13 *Nutrients that Provide Energy (Carbohydrates, Fats, and Proteins)*

- Additional information on childhood obesity, excess energy consumption, and weight management strategies for children.
- *New Teacher Checklists* highlighting key nutrient information.
- *New TeachSource Video Connections* feature: "Child Obesity and School Nutrition."

Chapter 14 *Nutrients that Promote Growth and Regulate Body Functions (Proteins, Vitamins, Minerals, and Water)*

- *New* chapter that combines Chapters 14 and 15 from the eighth edition. Content is presented in less technical terms and restructured to promote better understanding.
- *New* section on at-risk nutrients in children's diets.
- Additional information about vegetarian meal patterns.
- *New* case study challenges students to apply chapter content to real-life situations.
- *New TeachSource Video Connections* feature: "School-Age Children: Teaching about Nutrition."

Chapter 15 *Feeding Infants*

- *New* emphasis on the feeding relationship and its effect on infant biological, learning, and developmental needs.
- Additional information on nutrient contributions and early brain development.
- *New* tables on behavioral signs of hunger and fullness (satiety).
- *New* recommendations regarding vitamin D and fluoride supplementation.
- *New TeachSource Video Connections* feature: "Infants and Toddlers: Health and Nutrition."

Chapter 16 *Feeding Toddlers and Young Children*

- *New* guidelines for feeding preschool and school-age children aligned with the national standards.
- *New* information on safety considerations for children who have special feeding challenges and/or health problems.

- Additional information on increasing children's acceptance of unfamiliar foods and media influence on children's food preferences and eating habits.
- Updated information on feeding challenges and health problems (e.g., cardiovascular heart disease, diabetes, hypertension) related to children's dietary habits.
- *New TeachSource Video Connections* feature: "Technology and Media Use by Children and Adolescents."

Chapter 17 *Planning and Serving Nutritious and Economical Meals*

- *New* meal planning guidelines based on revised National School Lunch Program and Healthy Hunger-Free Kids Act standards.
- *New* resource tables and additional *Teacher Checklists*.
- Suggestions for incorporating more whole grain products, fresh produce, and ethnic foods into children's meals.
- *New TeachSource Video Connections* feature: "School-Age Children: Cooking Activities."

Chapter 18 *Food Safety*

- Reorganized content that reflects contemporary food safety concerns, research, and practices.
- *New* tables highlighting pesticide residues on fresh produce and safe cooking temperatures.
- *New* section added on national and international efforts to improve the safety of food supplies, including commercial food production practices.
- *New TeachSource Video Connections* feature: "Promoting Children's Health: A Focus on Nutrition in an Early Childhood Setting."

Chapter 19 *Nutrition Education: Rationale, Concepts, and Lessons*

- Greater emphasis placed on family engagement and educating children about healthy eating and physical activity.
- Lesson plans that include children's book lists.
- *New Teacher Checklists* highlighting key nutrient information.
- New *TeachSource Video Connections* feature: "Preschool: Cooking Activities."

Pedagogy and Learning Aids

Each chapter includes additional pedagogical features based on sound educational principles that encourage active student-centered learning, mastery, and application. The features also reflect student differences in learning needs, abilities, and styles.

- **Bulleted lists** are used extensively throughout the book to present important information in a concise, easy-to-access format.

- **Multicultural color photographs** taken on location at centers and schools show children as they work and play in developmentally appropriate settings.

- **Full-color illustrations** and tables reinforce and expand on important chapter content.

- A bulleted **Summary** concludes each chapter and recaps the main points of discussion.

- **Terms to Know** are highlighted in color throughout the chapters. Each term is defined on the page where it initially appears and also in a comprehensive glossary located at the end of the book.

- **Chapter Review** offers thought-provoking questions to reinforce student learning and comprehension. Questions can also be used for group discussion.

- **Case Studies** present real-life situations that require students to analyze and apply basic theory to solving everyday problems.

- **Application Activities** provide in-class and field projects that encourage students to practice and reinforce what they have learned in each chapter.

- **Helpful Web Resources** take advantage of technology to extend student learning beyond the pages of this book and to access valuable resource materials.

Ancillaries for Students

Early Childhood Education CourseMate

Cengage Learning's Early Childhood Education CourseMate brings course concepts to life with interactive learning, study, and exam preparation tools that support the printed textbook. Access the eBook, Did You Get It? quizzes, Digital Downloads, TeachSource Videos, flashcards, and more in your Education CourseMate. Go to CengageBrain.com to register or purchase access.

TeachSource Videos

The TeachSource videos feature footage from the classroom to help students relate key chapter content to real-life scenarios. Critical-thinking questions provide opportunities for in-class or online discussion and reflection.

Ancillaries for Instructors

Early Childhood Education CourseMate

Cengage Learning's Early Childhood Education CourseMate brings course concepts to life with interactive learning, study, and exam preparation tools that support the printed textbook. CourseMate includes the eBook, quizzes, Digital Downloads, TeachSource Video Cases, flashcards, and more—as well as EngagementTracker, a first-of-its-kind tool that monitors student engagement in the course. The accompanying instructor website, available through http://login.cengage.com, offers access to password-protected resources such as Microsoft® PowerPoint® lecture slides and the online Instructor's Manual with Test Bank. CourseMate can be bundled with the student text. Contact your Cengage sales representative for information on getting access to CourseMate.

Instructor's Manual

An online Instructor's Manual accompanies this book. It contains information to assist the instructor in course design, including sample syllabi, discussion questions, teaching and learning activities, field experiences, learning objectives, and additional online resources.

Online Test Bank

Extensive multiple choice, true/false, short answer, completion, and essay questions accompany each chapter and provide instructors with varied strategies for assessing student learning.

Online PowerPoint Slides

These vibrant PowerPoint lecture slides for each chapter assist you with your lecture by providing concept coverage using images, figures, and tables directly from the textbook!

Cengage Learner Testing Powered by Cognero

▶ Author, edit, and manage test bank content from multiple Cengage Learning solutions.
▶ Create multiple test versions in an instant.
▶ Deliver tests from your LMS, your classroom, or wherever you want.

Acknowledgments

A special thank you is extended to the instructors, students, and colleagues who use *Health, Safety, and Nutrition for the Young Child* in their classes and professional endeavors. Their suggestions continue to influence and improve each new edition. I would also like to recognize the contributions of dedicated teachers and families everywhere who strive to better children's lives.

I am grateful to have had the opportunity to again work with Lisa Mafrici, who has been my developmental editor on several book editions. Her professional expertise, insight, and encouragement have always been exceptional and led to a well-deserved promotion in the midst of this revision project. Although she will truly be missed, I wish her the very best! I also want to acknowledge and thank Kate Scheinman, who bravely stepped into an ongoing revision. She made the transition smooth, has been a pleasure to work with, and helped to produce another beautiful and improved edition. I would also like to extend my gratitude to Mark Kerr for his continued support, vision, and enthusiasm. The field is a better place because of his hard work and dedication. I thank Teresa, Catherine, and the production staff at Wadsworth Cengage Learning, who exercised their "Cinderella effect" and turned manuscript pages into a thing of worth and beauty! Thank you, too, to the many other behind-the-scenes individuals who contributed so much to making this book a success and to getting the word out!

Finally, I want to thank my husband and family for their patience and understanding during times when writing took precedence over times spent together.

I also offer my sincere appreciation to the following reviewers for sharing so many constructive suggestions:

Margaret Annunziata,
Davidson County Community College

Vella Black-Roberts,
Ohlone College

Dawn Burgess,
San Diego Community College

Cindy Calhoun,
Southern Union State Community College

Johnny Castro,
Brookhaven College

Mary Cordell,
Navarro College

Karan Demchak,
Allan Hancock College

Irene Den Bleyker,
University of New Mexico Gallup

Heather Flatness,
Wenatchee Valley College

Adrienne Gunn,
Santa Monica College

Marissa Happ,
Waubonsee Community College

Sharon Hirschy,
Collin County Community College

Bridget Ingram,
Clark State Community College

Sharon Little,
South Piedmont Community College

Rajone Lyman,
Houston Community College

Janelle Meyers,
St. Charles Community College

Dawn Munson,
Elgin Community College

Sandra Owen,
Cincinnati State Technical and Community College

Olivia Wagner Wakefield,
Central Carolina Community College

Janette Wetsel,
University of Central Oklahoma

Andrea Zarate,
Hartnell College

About the Author

Lynn R. Marotz received a Ph.D. from the University of Kansas, an M.Ed. from the University of Illinois, and a B.S. in nursing from the University of Wisconsin. She served as the health and safety coordinator and associate director of the Edna A. Hill Child Development Center (University of Kansas) for 35 years. She has worked closely with students in the Early Childhood teacher education program and taught undergraduate and graduate courses in the Department of Applied Behavioral Science, including issues in parenting, health/safety/nutrition for the young child, administration, and foundations of early childhood education. She provides frequent inservice training in first aid, children's safety, recognizing child abuse, childhood obesity, and identifying children's health problems for early childhood students and community educators.

Lynn has authored several invited chapters on children's health and development, nutrition, and environmental safety in national and international publications and law books. In addition, she is the co-author of *Developmental Profiles-Pre-Birth through Adolescence, Motivational Leadership*, and *By the Ages*. She has been interviewed for numerous articles about children's nutrition and well-being that have appeared in national trade magazines, and has served as a consultant for children's museums and training film productions. Her research activities focus on childhood obesity and children's health, safety, and nutrition. She has presented extensively at international, national, and state conferences and held appointments on national, state, and local committees and initiatives that advocate on children's and families' behalf. However, it is her daily interactions with children and their families, students, colleagues, and her beloved family that bring true insight, meaning, and balance to the material in this book.

Children's Well-Being: What It Is and How to Achieve It

naeyc Standards Chapter Links

▶ **#1 a and b:** Promoting child development and learning
▶ **#2 a, b, and c:** Building family and community relationships
▶ **#4 a, b, c, and d:** Using developmentally effective approaches to connect with children and families
▶ **#5 a, b, and c:** Using content knowledge to build a meaningful curriculum
▶ **#6 b, c, d, and e:** Becoming a professional
▶ Field Experience

Learning Objectives

After studying this chapter, you should be able to:

LO 1-1 Define the preventive health concept and describe several national programs that address children's health needs.

LO 1-2 Explain how health, safety, and nutrition are interrelated and discuss factors that influence the quality of each.

LO 1-3 Describe typical growth and developmental characteristics of infants, toddlers, preschool-age, and school-age children.

LO 1-4 Discuss ways that teachers can be proactive in promoting children's wellness in the areas of injury prevention, oral health, physical activity, and mental health.

Our ideas about health, disease, and the health care system are undergoing significant change. Individuals are beginning to realize that they must assume a more proactive role in maintaining personal health, and cannot continue to rely on the medical profession to always make them well. In part, this change is fueled by escalating medical costs, a lack of health insurance, and disabling conditions for which there are no current cures. In addition, and perhaps even more significant, are research findings that demonstrate positive health outcomes when people adapt healthy life-style behaviors (Maxwell et al., 2012; Daniels, Pratt, & Hayman, 2011).

1-1 The Preventive Health Concept

The concept of **preventive health** recognizes that individuals are able to reduce or eliminate many factors that threaten personal wellness (Figure 1–1). It implies that children and adults are able to make choices and engage in behaviors that improve the quality of life and lessen the risk of disease. This includes practices such as establishing healthful dietary habits (eating more fruits, vegetables, whole grains, and low-fat dairy products), implementing safety behaviors (wearing seat belts, limiting sun exposure), engaging in daily physical activity, and seeking early treatment for occasional illness and injury.

preventive health *– personal and social behaviors that promote and maintain well-being.*

FIGURE 1–1   Examples of preventive health practices.

A preventive health approach involves a combination of personal practices and national initiatives.

On a personal scale:
- eating a diet low in animal fats
- consuming a wide variety of fruits, vegetables, and grains
- engaging in aerobic and muscle-strengthening activities regularly
- practicing good oral hygiene
- using proper hand washing techniques
- avoiding substance abuse (e.g., alcohol, tobacco, drugs)
- keeping immunizations up-to-date

On a national scale:
- regulating vehicle emissions
- preventing chemical dumping
- establishing safety standard and inspecting food supplies
- measuring air pollution
- providing immunization programs
- fluoridating drinking water
- monitoring disease outbreaks

The early years are a critical time for children to establish preventive behaviors. Young children are typically more receptive to new ideas, curious, eager to learn, and have fewer unhealthy habits to overcome. Teachers, families, and health care providers can capitalize on these qualities and help children to develop practices that will foster a healthy, safe, and productive lifetime.

Although the preventive approach emphasizes an individual role in health promotion, it also implies a shared responsibility for addressing social and environmental issues that affect the quality of everyone's well-being, including:

- poverty and homelessness
- food insecurity
- inequitable access to medical and dental care
- adverse effects of media advertising
- substance abuse (e.g., alcohol, tobacco, drugs)
- food safety
- air and water pollution
- discrimination based on diversity
- unsafe neighborhoods

In addition to helping children learn about these complex issues, adults must also demonstrate their commitment by supporting social actions, policies, and programs that contribute to healthier environments and lifestyles for society as a whole.

1-1a National Health Initiatives

The positive health outcomes that are achievable through preventive practices continue to attract increased public interest, especially with respect to young children. Poor standards of health, safety, and nutrition have long been known to interfere with children's ability to learn and to ultimately become healthy, productive adults. As a result, a number of large-scale programs have been established to address children's health needs and to improve their access to preventive services. Descriptions of several initiatives follow; information about federal food programs for children is located in Appendix C.

Healthy People 2020 The nation's plan for improving the standard of health for its citizens is outlined in the *Healthy People 2020* initiative. It supports and strengthens the same underlying philosophy of health promotion and disease prevention presented in the original *Healthy People 2000 document*. It challenges communities to increase public health awareness and improve accessibility to preventive health services by encouraging better collaboration and coordination among agencies. It urges individuals to assume a more active role in achieving personal wellness, especially with regard to the prevention of heart disease, obesity, and diabetes. Many of the goals and objectives targeted in the *Healthy People 2020* plan also have direct application for schools and early childhood programs (Table 1–1). For example, teaching anger management skills, increasing outdoor play and physical activity in children's daily schedules, serving nutritious foods, providing more health and nutrition education, and creating safe learning environments reflect teachers' commitment to the *Healthy People 2020* ideals.

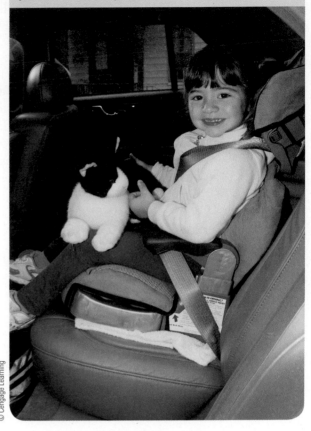

▼ **Early childhood is a prime time for teaching preventive health practices.**

© Cengage Learning

National Children's Agenda A similar Canadian proposal aimed at health promotion for children is outlined in a report entitled *A National Children's Agenda: Developing a Shared Vision*. This document presents a comprehensive agenda of goals and objectives for addressing children's health care and safety needs. It also embraces the importance of the early years and supports the vision of creating a unified approach to helping children achieve their full potential.

Children's Health Insurance Program The Children's Health Insurance Program (CHIP) provides low-cost health insurance to children in income-eligible families who don't qualify for Medicaid and cannot afford private coverage. The program is aimed at improving children's health and ability to learn through early identification and better access to preventive health care (Colby, Lipson, & Turchin, 2012). Services covered by the program include free or low-cost medical and dental care, immunizations, prescriptions, mental health treatment, and hospitalization.

CHIP is administered in each state through a combination of state and federal appropriations. Each state must submit a Child Health Plan describing how the program will be implemented, how eligibility will be determined, and how eligible children will be located. The Affordable Care Act extends reauthorization of the program through 2015 and expands service to an additional four million eligible children (Centers for Medicare & Medicaid Coverage, 2013).

TABLE 1–1   Healthy People 2020 Objectives

Areas targeted for improving children's health include the following:	
• physical activity and fitness	• immunizations and infectious diseases
• nutrition and weight status	• oral health
• substance abuse	• maternal, infant, and child health
• mental health	• access to health services
• sleep health	• health education
• environmental health	• vision, hearing, and communication disorders
• injury and violence prevention	

Source: Adapted from *Healthy People 2020*. (2012). U.S. Department of Health & Human Services.

Healthy Child Care America The primary objective of the Healthy Child Care America (HCCA) initiative is to foster high-quality improvements in out-of-home child care programs. HCCA, supported by the U.S. Department of Health and Human Services, the Child Care Bureau, and the Maternal and Child Health Bureau, was established in 1995 to coordinate the mutual interests of health professions, early education professionals, and families in addressing children's health and safety. The program is administered by the American Academy of Pediatrics (AAP) and has been instrumental in launching several large-scale educational campaigns, including Moving Kids Safely in Child Care, Tummy Time, Back to Sleep (for parents), Back to Sleep in Child Care Settings, and the Health Futures curriculum. Grant-supported offices, located in every state, have been established to evaluate and strengthen existing community infrastructure and to assist with new initiatives for improving children's health and safety in early childhood programs and access to preventive health care. Extensive resource information is available on their website (http://www.healthychildcare.org).

National Health and Safety Performance Standards for Child Care National concern for children's welfare led to a collaborative project among the American Academy of Pediatrics (AAP), the American Public Health Association (APHA), and the National Resource Center for Health and Safety in Child Care and Early Education (NRC) to develop health, safety, and nutrition guidelines for out-of-home child care settings. The resulting document, *Caring for Our Children: National Health and Safety Performance Standards: Guidelines for Out-of-Home Child Care* (3rd ed.), continues to identify quality standards and procedures for ensuring children's health and safety while they attend organized out-of-home care (Table 1–2) (AAP, APHA, & NRC, 2011). This document can be accessed at www.nrckids.org.

The current system allows individual states to establish their own child care licensing standards, which has resulted in significant differences in quality. The National Health and Safety Performance Standards attempt to address regulatory inconsistencies by proposing a uniform set of standards based on what research has identified as best practices. The National Association for the Education of Young Children (NAEYC) recently endorsed and aligned their accreditation criteria with the National Health and Safety Performance Standards (NAEYC, 2012).

TABLE 1–2   National Health and Safety Performance Standards

Comprehensive guidelines address the following areas of child care:

- staffing – child staff ratios, credentials, and training
- activities for healthy development – supervision, behavior management, partnerships with families, health education
- health promotion and protection – sanitation and hygiene practices, safe sleep, illness and medication management
- nutrition and food services – nutritional requirements, food safety, nutrition education
- facilities, supplies, equipment, and environmental health – space and equipment requirements, indoor/outdoor settings, maintenance
- playgrounds and transportation – space, water areas, toys, transportation safety
- infectious diseases – respiratory, blood-borne and skin conditions, immunizations
- children with special health care and disability needs – inclusion, eligibility for special services, facility modifications, assessment, service plans
- policies – health/safety, emergency plans, personnel, child records
- licensing and community action – regulatory agencies, teacher/caregiver support

Source: Adapted from AAP, APHA, & NRC. (2011). *Caring for our children: National health and safety performance standards* (3rd ed.). Elk Grove Village, IL: American Academy of Pediatrics; Washington, DC: American Public Health Association. Also available at http://nrckids.org.

No Child Left Behind The No Child Left Behind (NCLB) Act of 2001 authorized significant reforms of the K–12 educational system and strengthened partnerships with Head Start, Even Start, and early education programs in center- and home-based settings. It acknowledged families as children's first and most important teachers, the educational contributions of early childhood programs, and the importance of fostering early literacy skills (understanding and using language) to ensure children's readiness for, and success in, schools. The bill also provided funding to cover child care costs for low-income families, health care coverage for eligible children, and prenatal services for pregnant women. However, its main purpose was to improve educational outcomes for all children by holding educators more accountable. Several states were granted waivers in 2011 allowing them to opt out of the NCLB Act's required provisions if they agreed to establish their own performance standards.

Coordinated School Health Program In 1988, the Centers for Disease Control and Prevention (CDC) proposed a new school health services model called the Coordinated School Health program. At the time, teachers were being pressured to ensure children's success in school while studies demonstrated a strong association between children's health and academic outcomes. It became clear that traditional delivery methods were failing to address children's complex health needs and that a different approach was needed.

The Coordinated School Health program assumes a preventive health approach and emphasizes the collaborative involvement of teachers, administrators, staff, students, families, media, and community partners to promote children's well-being. Eight interactive standards and their corresponding performance indicators serve as curriculum guidelines for grades K–12 (Figure 1–2).

The National Children's Study One of the most comprehensive studies of children's health ever undertaken in the United States was authorized by the Children's Health Act of 2000. This longitudinal study is being led by the Eunice Kennedy Shriver National Institute of Child Health and Human Development (NICHD) and is currently following over 100,000 children from birth to age 21. The purpose of the study is to examine genetic and environmental effects on children's

FIGURE 1–2 Coordinated school health program components.

Health Education

Family/Community Involvement

Physical Education

Health Promotion for Staff

Health Services

Healthy & Safe School Environment

Nutrition Services

Counseling, Psychological, & Social Services

©Dmitriy Shironosov/Shutterstock.com

Did You Get It?

The Children's Health Insurance Program provides healthcare coverage, and the Healthy Child Care America initiative focuses on the _____ of child care programs.

  a. regulation
  b. improvement
  c. licensing
  d. insuring

Take the full quiz on CourseMate.

health and their potential contributions to disease. It will eventually yield one of the most expansive information databases ever compiled about children's growth and development, differences in access to health care, and the incidence of disease. Data obtained from the study will also be used to improve children's health and well-being through future policy formulation, funding, and service interventions.

Let's Move! The *Let's Move!* initiative was established by First Lady Michelle Obama in 2010 to address the problem of childhood obesity in the United States. The program encourages children and their families to achieve a healthier lifestyle by improving eating habits and increasing physical activity. Schools are challenged to provide healthier meals for children, increase opportunities for physical activity, and incorporate more health and nutrition education into their curriculum. A companion initiative, *Let's Move! Child Care*, was launched the following year and challenges all child care providers to adapt similar improvement measures. Informational resources can be accessed on the initiatives' websites.

▼ **Active play is essential for children's health and development.**

© Cengage Learning

1-2 Health, Safety, and Nutrition: An Interdependent Relationship

Health, safety, and nutrition are closely intertwined and dependent on one another. The status of each has a direct effect on the quality of the others. For example, children who receive all essential nutrients from a healthful diet are more likely to reach their growth potential, benefit from learning opportunities, experience fewer illnesses, and have ample energy for play. In contrast, children whose diet lacks critical nutrients such as protein and iron may develop anemia, which can lead to fatigue, diminished alertness, growth and academic failure, and loss of appetite. When children lack interest in eating, their iron intake is further compromised. In other words, nutritional status has a direct effect on children's health and safety, and, in turn, influences the dietary requirements needed to restore and maintain well-being.

A nutritious diet also plays an important role in injury prevention. The child or adult who arrives at school having eaten little or no breakfast may experience low blood sugar, which can cause fatigue, decreased alertness, and slowed reaction times and, thus, increase an individual's risk of accidental injury. Similarly, overweight children and adults are more likely to sustain injuries due to excess weight, which may restrict physical activity, slow reaction times, and increase fatigue with exertion.

1-2a What Is Health?

Definitions of **health** are as numerous as the factors that affect it. In years past, the term referred strictly to an individual's physical well-being and the absence of illness. Contemporary

health – *a state of wellness. Complete physical, mental, social, and emotional well-being; the quality of one health element affects the state of the others.*

definitions view health from a broader perspective and recognize it as a state of physical, emotional, social, economic, cultural, and spiritual well-being. Each interactive component is assumed to make an equally important contribution to health and to affect the functional activity of the others. For example, a stressful home environment may be contributing to a child's asthma attacks, stomachaches, or headaches; in turn, a child's repeated illnesses or chronic disability can profoundly affect the family's emotional, financial, social, and physical stability and well-being.

The current health concept also recognizes that children and adults do not live in isolation, but are active participants in multiple groups, including family, peer, neighborhood, ethnic, cultural, recreational, religious, and community. Children's health, development, and opportunities for learning are directly influenced by the positive and negative experiences that occur in each setting. For example, children growing up in a poor, urban neighborhood may be at greater risk for becoming obese because they have fewer safe places for outdoor play and limited access to fresh fruits and vegetables. In other words, children's health and development must be considered in the context of their social and environmental conditions.

1-2b What Factors Influence Children's Health?

Health is a dynamic and complex state. It is a product of continuous interactions between an individual's genetic makeup, environmental conditions, and personal experiences (Figure 1–3). For example, an infant's immediate and long-term health is influenced by his or her mother's personal lifestyle practices during pregnancy: her diet; use or avoidance of alcohol, tobacco, and certain medications; routine prenatal care; and exposure to communicable illnesses or toxic stress. Mothers who fail to maintain a healthy lifestyle during pregnancy are more likely to give birth to infants who are born prematurely, have low birth weight, or experience a range of special challenges (McCormick et al., 2011). These children also face a significantly greater risk of developing chronic health problems and early death. In contrast, a child who is born healthy, raised in a nurturing family, consumes a nutritious diet, lives in a safe environment, and has numerous opportunities for learning and recreation is more likely to enjoy a healthy life.

Heredity Characteristics transmitted from biological parents to their children at the time of conception determine all of the genetic traits of a new, unique individual. **Heredity** sets the limits for growth, development, and health potential. It explains, in part, why children in one family are short while those from another family are tall or why some individuals have allergies or require glasses while others do not.

Understanding how heredity influences health can also be useful for assessing a possible inherited tendency, or **predisposition**, to certain health problems, such as heart disease, deafness, cancer, diabetes, lactose intolerance, or mental health disorders. Although a family history of heart disease or diabetes may increase one's risk, it does not imply that an individual will actually develop the condition. Many lifestyle factors, including physical activity, diet, sleep, and stress levels, interact with genetic material (genes) and can alter the child's chances of ultimately developing heart disease or any number of other chronic health diseases.

Environment Although heredity provides the basic building materials that predetermine the limits of one's health, environment

FIGURE 1–3 Health is an interactive and continuously changing state.

Cultural · Physical · Mental · Economic · Social · Spiritual · **Health**

heredity – *the transmission of certain genetic material and characteristics from biological parents to a child at the time of conception.*
predisposition – *having an increased chance or susceptibility.*

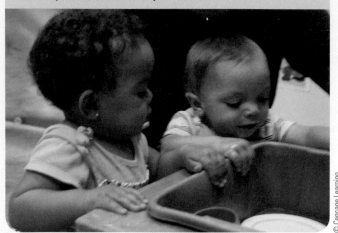

▼ **Heredity sets the limits for a child's growth, development, and health potentials.**

© Cengage Learning

plays an equally important role. Environment encompasses a combination of physical, psychological, social, economic, and cultural factors that collectively influence the way individuals perceive and respond to their surroundings. In turn, these experiences shape a person's behaviors and potential health outcomes. For example, two cyclists set off on a ride: One is wearing a helmet, the other is not. The choices each has made could potentially have quite different outcomes if they were to be involved in a serious collision. The helmet-wearing cyclist may suffer only minor scrapes and bruises while the cyclist without a helmet may sustain a serious head injury that could have significant health, economic, social, and psychological consequences.

Examples of several environmental factors that support and promote healthy outcomes include:

- making nutritious food choices
- participating in daily physical and recreational activities
- getting 8 to 9 hours of uninterrupted nighttime sleep
- having access to high-quality medical and dental care
- reducing stress levels
- residing in homes, child care facilities, schools, and workplaces that are clean and safe
- having friends and opportunities to form stable and meaningful relationships

There are also many environmental factors that have a negative effect on health. For example, exposure to chemicals and pollution, abuse, illness, obesity, prenatal alcohol exposure, **sedentary** lifestyles, poverty, acute and chronic stress, **food insecurity**, violence, or unhealthy dietary choices can interfere with children's optimal growth and development.

1-2c **Safety**

Safety refers to behaviors and measures taken to protect individuals from unnecessary harm. It is especially important that adults who work with young children view this responsibility seriously. Unintentional injuries are the leading cause of death among children from birth to 14 years in the United States and Canada and, sadly, many of these instances are avoidable (CDC, 2012; Safe Kids Canada, 2012). Young children are especially vulnerable to unexpected and serious injury because their developmental skills seldom match their level of enthusiasm and curiosity. Every adult who works with, or cares for, young children has a significant responsibility to maintain the highest standards of supervision and environmental safety.

Factors Affecting Children's Safety Protecting children's safety requires a keen awareness of their skills and abilities at each developmental stage (Marotz & Allen, 2013). For example, knowing that toddlers enjoy hand-to-mouth activities should alert teachers to continuously monitor the environment for small objects or poisonous substances that could be ingested. Understanding that preschoolers are spontaneous and exceedingly curious should cause adults to take extra precautions to prevent children from wandering away or straying into unsupervised water sources. Children who have developmental disabilities or sensory disorders are at increased risk of sustaining unintentional injury and must be monitored continuously (Cavalari & Romanczyk, 2012). In-depth discussions of environmental safety and safety management are presented in Chapters 7 and 8.

sedentary – *unusually slow or sluggish; a lifestyle that implies inactivity.*
food insecurity – *uncertain or limited access to a reliable source of food.*

1-2d Nutrition

The term *nutrition* refers to the science of food, its chemical components **nutrients**, and their relationship to health and disease. It includes all processes involved in obtaining nutrients from foods—from the ingestion, digestion, absorption, transportation, and utilization of nutrients to excretion of unused products. Nutrients are essential for life and have a direct effect on a child's nutritional status, behavior, health, and development.

Nutrients play critical roles in a variety of vital body functions, including:

- supplying energy
- promoting growth and development
- improving resistance to illness and infection
- building and repairing body tissue

A wide variety of foods must be consumed in the recommended amounts to meet the body's needs for essential nutrients. However, many family and environmental conditions, including financial resources, transportation, geographical location, cultural and religious preferences, convenience, and nutrition knowledge, can affect the quality of a child's diet. Most children in the United States live in a time and place where food is reasonably abundant. Yet, there is increasing concern about the number of children who may not be getting enough to eat or whose diets do not include the right foods (Okechukwu et al., 2012). Also, because many young children spend the majority of their waking hours in out-of-home child care programs or school classrooms, care must be taken to ensure that their nutrient needs are being met in these settings.

Nutrition's Effect on Children's Behavior, Learning, and Well-being Children's nutritional status has a significant effect on their behavior and cognitive development. Well-nourished children are typically more alert, attentive, physically active, and better able to benefit from learning experiences. Poorly nourished children may appear quiet and withdrawn, or exhibit hyperactive and disruptive behaviors in the classroom (Liu & Raine, 2011). They are also more prone to injury because of decreased alertness and slower reaction times. Children who are overweight also face a range of social, emotional, and physical challenges, including difficulty participating in physical activities, ridicule, emotional stress, and peer exclusion (Su & Aurelia, 2012). Additional information about children's specific nutrient needs and challenges associated with over- and under-consumption of foods is presented in Chapters 12 through 19.

Children's **resistance** to infection and illness is also directly influenced by their nutritional status (Weill, 2012). Well-nourished children experience fewer illnesses and recover more quickly when they are sick. Children who consume an unhealthy diet are more susceptible to infections and illness and often require longer time to recuperate. Frequent illness can interfere with a child's appetite, which may limit his or her intake of nutrients important for the recovery process. Thus, poor nutrition can create a cycle of increased susceptibility to illness and infection, nutritional deficiency, and prolonged recovery.

Teachers have an exceptional opportunity to protect and promote children's well-being. Their knowledge of children's development and health, safety, and nutritional needs can be applied when planning learning activities, classroom environments, meals and snacks, and supervision. In addition, teachers can implement sanitation and early identification practices to reduce children's unnecessary exposure to illness and infection. Furthermore, they can support the concept of preventive health by serving as positive role models and providing children with learning experiences that encourage a healthy lifestyle.

Did You Know...

that children who eat breakfast have better problem-solving skills, more energy, lower obesity rates, and feel more cheerful?

---

nutrients – *the chemical substances in food.*
resistance – *the ability to avoid infection or illness.*

▼ Nutritional status also affects children's behavior.

© Cengage Learning

Did You Get It?

What is the relationship between the roles of heredity and environment in determining an individual's health and well-being?
- **a.** They play equal, interrelated roles.
- **b.** They play unrelated roles.
- **c.** Heredity plays a greater role than environment.
- **d.** Environment plays a greater role than heredity.

Take the full quiz on CourseMate.

1-3 Children's Growth and Development

When teachers understand typical growth and developmental patterns, they are better able to identify and address children's diverse needs and to help children master critical skills. They can create learning experiences and set developmentally appropriate goals for children that foster positive self-esteem. They are able to design high-quality environments that are safe and encourage children's mastery of new skills. In addition, they are able to use this knowledge to promote children's well-being by identifying health problems and abnormal behaviors and teaching healthy practices.

The terms "average" or "normal" are often used to describe children's growth and development. However, such a child probably does not exist. Every child is a unique individual—a product of diverse experiences, environments, interactions, and heredity. Collectively, these factors can lead to significant differences in the rate at which children grow and acquire various skills and behaviors (Marotz & Allen, 2013).

Norms provide a useful reference for understanding, monitoring, and promoting children's growth and development. They represent the average or approximate age when the majority of children demonstrate a given skill or behavior. Thus, the term **normal** implies that although many children are able to perform a given skill by a specific age, some will be more advanced whereas others may take somewhat longer, yet they are still considered to be within the normal range.

....

norms – *an expression (e.g., weeks, months, years) of when a child is likely to demonstrate certain developmental skills.*
normal – *average; a characteristic or quality that is common to most individuals in a defined group.*

1-3a Growth

The term **growth** refers to the many physical changes that occur as a child matures. Although the growth process takes place without much conscious control, there are many factors that affect its quality and rate:

- genetic potential
- emotional stimulation and attachment
- cultural influences
- socioeconomic factors
- adequate nutrition
- parent responsiveness
- health status (i.e., illness)

Infants (0–12 months) The average newborn weighs approximately 7 to 8 pounds (3.2–3.6 kg) at birth and is approximately 20 inches (50.8 cm) in length. Growth is rapid during the first year; an infant's birth weight nearly doubles by the fifth month and triples by the end of the first year. For example, an infant who weighs 8 pounds (3.6 kg) at birth will weigh approximately 16 pounds (7.3 kg) at 5 months and 24 pounds (10.9 kg) at 12 months.

An infant's length increases by approximately 50 percent during the first year. Thus, an infant measuring 21 inches (53.3 cm) at birth should reach an approximate length of 31.5 inches (80 cm) by 12 months of age. A majority of this gain occurs during the first 6 months when an infant may grow as much as 1 inch (2.54 cm) per month.

An infant's head appears large in proportion to the rest of the body due to rapid brain growth. **Head circumference** is measured at regular intervals to ensure that brain growth is proceeding at a rate that is neither too fast nor too slow. Measurements should reflect a gradual increase in size so that by age 1, the head and chest circumferences are nearly equal.

Additional changes that occur during the first year include the growth of hair and eruption of teeth (four upper and four lower). The infant's eyes begin to focus and move together as a unit by the third month, and vision becomes more acute. Special health concerns for infants include the following:

- nutritional requirements
- adequate provisions for sleep
- **attachment**
- early brain development
- safety and injury prevention
- identification of birth defects and health impairments

At no other time in children's lives will they grow as much or as quickly as they do during the first year. A nutritious diet, adequate sleep, a nurturing environment, and responsive caregiving are especially important to foster growth during this critical period. (See Chapter 15.)

Toddlers (12–30 months) Toddlers continue to make steady gains in height and weight, but at a much slower rate than during infancy. Their weight increases an average of 6 to 7 pounds (2.7–3.2 kg) per year; by 2 years, toddlers have nearly quadrupled their birth weight. They also grow approximately 3 to 5 inches (7.6–12.7 cm) in height per year. Their body proportions begin to change and contribute to a more erect appearance.

Eruption of "baby teeth," or **deciduous teeth**, is complete by the end of the toddler period. (Deciduous teeth consist of a set of twenty temporary teeth.) Toddlers can begin learning how to brush their new teeth with close adult supervision. Special attention should also be paid to additional preventive measures such as providing foods that promote dental health; are colorful, appealing, and easily chewed; and, include all of the essential nutrients. Foods from all food groups—fruits,

---

growth – *increase in size of any body part or of the entire body.*
head circumference – *distance around the largest part of the head; used to monitor brain growth and development.*
attachment – *an emotional connection established between infants and their parents and/or primary caregivers.*
deciduous teeth – *a child's initial set of teeth; these teeth are temporary and gradually begin to fall out at around 5 years of age.*

▼ **Toddlers need plenty of sleep to meet their high energy demands.**

© Cengage Learning

▶❚❚ **TeachSource Video Connections**

© 2015 Cengage Learning

Infancy Brain Development

You might be surprised to learn that infants have many more brain cells than you do! Discover why this occurs and what you can do to keep all of those you currently have. As you watch the learning video, *Infancy Brain Development*, consider to the following questions:

1. What enables neurons to communicate with one another?

2. What happens to neurons when they aren't used?

3. What functions are performed by the left side of the brain? What roles does the right side have?

4. How is brain size affected by environment and learning opportunities?

Watch on CourseMate.

vegetables, dairy, protein, whole-grains—should always be part of the toddler's daily meal pattern.

High activity levels make it essential for toddlers to get at least 10 to 12 hours of uninterrupted nighttime sleep and 1 to 2 hour-long naps each day. Insufficient sleep has been linked to an increase in learning and behavior problems, risk of injury, and a variety of health problems including obesity (Blunden, 2012). Safety awareness and injury prevention continue to be major concerns that demand close adult supervision.

Preschoolers/Early School-age (2 1/2–8 years) During the preschool and early school-age years, a child's appearance becomes more streamlined and adult-like in form. Head size remains relatively constant, while the child's trunk (body) and extremities (arms and legs) continue to grow. The head gradually appears to separate from the trunk as the neck lengthens. Legs grow longer and at a faster rate than the arms, adding extra inches to the child's height. The toddler's characteristic chubby body shape becomes more streamlined as muscle tone and strength increase and results in the preschoolers' flatter abdomen and straighter posture.

Gains in weight and height are relatively slow but steady throughout this period. By 3 years of age, children weigh approximately five times their birth weight. Ideally, preschoolers should gain no more than 4 to 5 pounds (1.8–2.3 kg) per year. They begin to grow taller during this period and gain an average of 2 to 2.5 inches (5.1–6.4 cm) in height per year. By 6 years, children have nearly doubled their original birth length (from approximately 20 inches to 40 inches [50.8–101.6 cm]). By age 7, girls are approximately 42 to 46 inches (106.7–116.8 cm) tall and weigh 38 to 47 pounds (17.2–21.3 kg); boys are 44 to 47 inches (111.8–119.4 cm) tall and weigh 42 to 49 pounds (19.1–22.2 kg). This combination of rapid growth and muscle development causes children to appear longer, thinner, and more adult-like.

It is important that preschool-age children continue to consume a nutritious diet. High activity levels replace the rapid growth of earlier years as the primary demand for calories. A general rule for estimating a child's daily caloric needs is to begin with a base of 1,000 calories and add an additional 100 calories per birthday. (For example, a 7-year-old would need approximately 1,700 calories). Adults should carefully monitor children's food intake and encourage healthy eating habits because decreased appetite, inconsistent eating habits, and considerable media influence are often evident during the preschool years.

Adequate sleep continues to be essential for children's optimal growth and development. When days are long and tiring or unusually stressful, children's need for sleep may be even greater. Most preschool and school-aged children require 8 to 12 hours of uninterrupted nighttime sleep in addition to daytime rest periods, although bedtime and after-noon naps often become a source of adult-child conflict. Pre-school children often become so involved in play activities that they are reluctant to stop for sleep. Nevertheless, young children benefit from brief rest breaks during their normal daytime rou-tine. Planned quiet times, with books, puzzles, quiet music, or a small toy, may be an adequate substitute for older children.

By the time children reach school-age, they begin to enjoy one of the healthiest periods of their lives. They gen-erally experience fewer colds and upper respiratory infec-tions. Children's visual acuity continues to improve, they grow taller at a fairly rapid rate, their muscle mass increases, hair becomes darker, and permanent teeth begin to erupt.

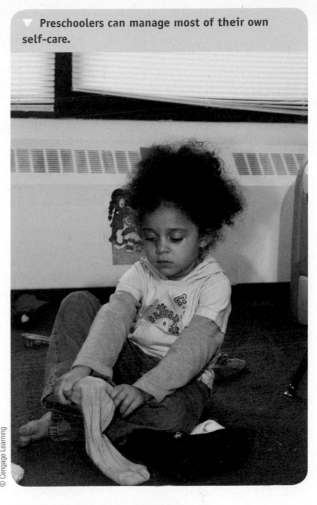

▼ Preschoolers can manage most of their own self-care.

© Cengage Learning

1-3b Development

In the span of 1 year, remarkable changes take place in the infant's **development**. The child progresses from a stage of complete dependency on adults to one marked by the acquisition of lan-guage and the formation of rather complex thought patterns. Infants also become more social and outgoing near the end of the first year, and seemingly enjoy and imitate the adults around them.

The toddler and preschool periods reflect a continued refinement of language, perceptual, motor, cognitive, and social achievements. Improved motor and verbal skills enable the toddler to explore, test, and interact with the environment for the purpose of determining personal identity, or autonomy.

Preschool-age children are becoming more self-sufficient and able to perform self-care and fine motor tasks with improved strength, speed, accuracy, control, and ease. Friends and friendships are increasingly important as preschool children expand their sphere of acquaintances beyond family members. Children are now able to participate in the socialization process as they begin to develop a con-science and learn emotional control.

A strong desire to achieve motivates 6-, 7-, and 8-year-olds. Participation in sports and other vigorous activities provides opportunities for children to practice and improve their motor skills. Adult approval and rewards continue to serve an important role in helping children build self-confidence and self-esteem. During this stage, children also begin to establish gender identity through meaningful social interactions.

A summary of major developmental achievements is presented in Table 1–3. It should be remembered that such a list represents accomplishments that a majority of children can perform at a given age. It should also be noted that not every child achieves all of these tasks. Many factors, including nutritional adequacy, opportunities for learning, access to appropriate medical and den-tal care, a nurturing environment, cultural expectations, and family support, exert a strong influ-ence on children's skill acquisition.

Early Brain Development An infant's brain begins to form during the earliest weeks of a preg-nancy. Its genetic composition is affected by various maternal practices (e.g., diet, sleep, pre-natal care, physical activity, weight gain, smoking, alcohol or drug use, stress) prior to and during this period (O'Leary et al., 2013; Foltran et al., 2011). At birth, an infant's brain weighs approximately 25 percent of what their adult brain will eventually weigh and contains more

development – *commonly refers to the process of intellectual growth and change.*

TABLE 1–3   Major Developmental Achievements

Age	Achievements
2 months	• lifts head up when placed on stomach • follows moving person or object with eyes • imitates or responds to smiling person with occasional smiles • turns toward source of sound • begins to make simple sounds and noises • grasps objects with entire hand; not strong enough to hold on • enjoys being held and cuddled
4 months	• has good control of head • reaches for and grasps objects with both hands • laughs out loud; vocalizes with coos and giggles • waves arms about • holds head erect when supported in a sitting position • rolls over from side to back to stomach • recognizes familiar objects (e.g., bottle, toy)
6 months	• grasps objects with entire hand; transfers objects from one hand to the other and from hand to mouth • sits alone with minimal support • deliberately reaches for, grasps, and holds objects (e.g., rattles, bottle) • plays games and imitates (e.g., peek-a-boo) • shows signs of teeth beginning to erupt • prefers primary caregiver to strangers • babbles using different sounds • raises up and supports weight of upper body on arms
9 months	• sits alone; able to maintain balance while changing positions; picks up objects (e.g., bits of cracker, peas) with pincer grasp (first finger and thumb) • begins to crawl • attempts to say words such as "mama" and "dada" • hesitates when unfamiliar persons approach • explores new objects by chewing or placing them in mouth
12 months	• pulls up to a standing position • may "walk" by holding on to objects • stacks several objects one on top of the other • responds to simple commands and own name • babbles using jargon in sentence-like form • uses hands, eyes, and mouth to investigate new objects • can hold own eating utensils (e.g., cup, spoon)
18 months	• crawls up and down the stairs one at a time • walks unassisted; has difficulty avoiding obstacles in pathway • is less fearful of strangers • enjoys being read to; likes toys for pushing and pulling • has a vocabulary consisting of approximately 5–50 words, can name familiar objects • helps feed self; manages spoon and cup
2 years	• runs, walks with ease; can kick and throw a ball; jumps in place • speaks in two- to three-word sentences (e.g., "dada", "bye-bye"); asks simple questions; knows about 200 words • displays parallel play • achieves daytime toilet training • voices displeasure
3 years	• climbs stairs by using alternating feet • hops and balances on one foot • feeds self • helps dress and undress self; washes own hands and brushes teeth with help • is usually toilet trained • asks and answers questions; is quite curious • enjoys drawing, cutting with scissors, painting, clay, and make-believe

TABLE 1-3   Major Developmental Achievements (*continued*)

Age	Achievements
	• throws and bounces a ball
	• states name; recognizes self in pictures
4 years	• dresses and undresses self; helps with bathing; manages own tooth brushing
	• enjoys creative activities: paints, draws with detail, models with clay, builds imaginative structures with blocks
	• rides a tricycle with confidence, turns corners, maintains balance
	• climbs, runs, and hops with skill and vigor
	• enjoys friendships and playing with small groups of children
	• enjoys and seeks adult approval
	• understands simple concepts (e.g., shortest, longest, same)
5 years	• expresses ideas and questions clearly and with fluency
	• has vocabulary consisting of approximately 2,500–3,000 words
	• substitutes verbal for physical expressions of displeasure
	• dresses without supervision
	• seeks reassurance and recognition for achievements
	• engages in active and energetic play, especially outdoors
	• throws and catches a ball with relative accuracy
	• cuts with scissors along a straight line; draws in detail
6 years	• plays with enthusiasm and vigor
	• develops increasing interest in books and reading
	• displays greater independence from adults; makes fewer requests for help
	• forms close friendships with several peers
	• exhibits improved motor skills; can jump rope, hop and skip, ride a bicycle
	• enjoys conversation
	• sorts simple objects by color and shape
7 and 8 years	• enjoys friends; seeks their approval
	• shows increased curiosity and interest in exploration
	• develops greater clarity of gender identity
	• is motivated by a sense of achievement
	• begins to reveal a moral consciousness
9–12 years	• uses logic to reason and problem-solve
	• energetic; enjoys team activities, as well as individual projects
	• likes school and academic challenge, especially math
	• learns social customs and moral values
	• is able to think in abstract terms
	• enjoys eating any time of the day

Adapted from Marotz, L. R., & Allen, K. E., (2013). *Developmental profiles: Pre-birth through adolescence* (7th ed.). Belmont, CA: Wadsworth Cengage Learning.

than 100 billion brain cells or **neurons**. At this point, the brain is relatively unorganized and dysfunctional because few meaningful pathways have been established. This explains why young infants are not able to walk, talk, or care for themselves. Complex electrical connections begin to form between neurons in response to positive and negative experiences. Each time the same experience is repeated, the neural pathway becomes stronger (Figure 1–4). Connections and pathways that are seldom used undergo a process called pruning and gradually fade away. This process of adding and deleting neural connections reaches peak activity between the ages of 3 and 16 years and transforms the brain's architecture from an otherwise disorganized system into one capable of profound thought, emotions, and learning.

The majority of brain development occurs during the first 2 to 5 years of a child's life, when the brain's **plasticity** makes it more receptive to shaping and change. Note how quickly young children learn to speak another language and how adults often struggle to do the same, and you

neurons – *specialized cells that transmit electrical impulses or signals.*
plasticity – *the brain's ability to organize and reorganize neural pathways.*

FIGURE 1–4 **Everyday experiences cause new neural connections to be formed and strengthened.**

1 Month 2 Years Adult

Did You Get It?

That most brain development occurs between ages 2 and 5 is most apparent when you observe the contrast between a young child and an adult attempting to master which task?

a. mathematics
b. inference and reasoning
c. learning a foreign language
d. reading skills

Take the full quiz on CourseMate.

will understand how this concept works. Researchers have also identified what they believe to be sensitive periods, or "windows of opportunity," during which neural connections in certain regions of the brain form more readily than they will later on. For example, vision and hearing connections peak between 2 and 4 months, whereas those governing emotional regulation begin to form months later. Sensory and learning pathways established during these sensitive periods are critical to the normal development of more advanced skills (Twardosz, 2012). For example, the visual system must be fully developed and functional before children are able to read or to play softball. An infant raised in a darkened room with few visual opportunities (e.g., mobiles, pictures, toys) will not form the network connections in the brain's sensory region that are conducive to the same quality of learning.

Neuroscientists have contributed significantly to our understanding of brain development and the practices that optimize its performance. Nutrition, especially during a mother's pregnancy and the first two years of a child's life, is of critical importance. Healthy brain and central nervous system development require specific proteins, minerals, and fats supplied in breast milk and formula. Malnutrition during infancy and toddlerhood can cause an irreversible decrease in brain cell production (and intelligence) and interfere with normal nervous system development. Poor nutrition also increases children's vulnerability to lead poisoning and affects brain function, behavior, and learning.

Although the brain's genetic foundation is in place at birth, it is the ongoing experiences in a child's environment that shape and determine how well the brain will ultimately perform. Safe, responsive caregiving helps infants to form strong attachments and neural connections that are important for learning and emotional regulation later on. Children's environments and the quality of available learning opportunities also exert a direct influence on brain development. When children are surrounded with language, encouraged to explore, play, and be creative, presented with varied and enriching experiences, and reinforced for their efforts, they are building strong neural pathways that are linked directly to cognitive development, self-esteem, and school success.

1-4 Promoting a Healthy Lifestyle

Today, concern for children's health and welfare is a shared vision. Changes in current lifestyles, family structures, cultural diversity, philosophies, and expectations have necessitated the collaborative efforts of families, teachers, and service providers to address children's well-being. Communities are also valued members of this partnership and must assume a proactive role in creating environments that are safe, enriching, and healthy places for children to live.

How can families and teachers determine whether or not children are healthy? What qualities or indicators are commonly associated with being a healthy or a **well child**? Growth and developmental norms always serve as a starting point. Again, it must be remembered that norms simply represent an average, not exact, age when most children are likely to achieve a given skill. Healthy children are more likely to exhibit characteristic behaviors and developmental skills appropriate for their age. They tend to be well-nourished, have energy to play, experience continued growth,

well child – *a child who enjoys a positive state of physical, mental, social, and emotional health.*

and have fewer illnesses. Developmental norms are also useful for anticipating and addressing children's special health needs, including injury prevention, body mechanics and physical activity, oral health, and mental well-being.

1-4a Injury Prevention

Unintentional injuries, especially those involving motor vehicles, pose the greatest threat to the lives of young children (Stewart de Ramirez et al., 2012). They are responsible for more than one-half of all deaths among children under 14 years of age in the United States. Each year an additional one million children sustain injuries that require medical attention, and many are left with permanent disabilities (Judy, 2011).

An understanding of normal growth and development is essential when planning for children's safety. Many characteristics that make children delightful to work with are the same qualities that make them prone to injury. Children's skills are seldom as well developed as their determination, and in their zealous approach to life, they often fail to recognize inherent dangers (Morrongiello et al., 2012). Their inability to judge time, distance, and speed accurately contributes to many injuries, especially those resulting from falls, as a pedestrian, or while riding a bike. Limited problem-solving abilities make it difficult for children to anticipate the consequences of their actions. This becomes an even greater challenge when infants or children with developmental disabilities are present. Adults have an obligation to provide continuous supervision and to maintain safe environments for all children at all times. Safety considerations and protective measures will be discussed in greater detail in Chapter 7.

▼ **Adults must supervise children closely to ensure their safety.**

© Cengage Learning

1-4b Body Mechanics and Physical Activity

Correct posture, balance, and proper body alignment are necessary for many physical activities that children engage in, such as walking, jumping, running, skipping, standing, and sitting. Teaching and modeling appropriate body mechanics can help children avoid problems related to poor posture that may develop later in life. The early recognition and treatment of ear infections is also important to address because they can affect children's balance and coordination.

Orthopedic problems (those relating to skeletal and muscular systems) are not common among young children. However, there are several conditions that warrant early diagnosis and treatment:

- birth injuries, such as hip dislocation, fractured collarbone
- abnormal or unusual walking patterns, such as limping or walking pigeon-toed
- bowed legs
- knock-knees
- flat feet
- unusual curvature of the spine
- unequal length of extremities (arms and legs)

Some irregularities of posture disappear spontaneously as young children mature. For example, it is not uncommon for infants and toddlers to have bowed legs or to walk slightly pigeon-toed. However, by age 3 or 4, these problems should correct themselves. If they do persist beyond the age of 4, children should be evaluated by a health professional to prevent permanent deformities.

Children's posture and body mechanics serve as excellent topics for classroom discussions, demonstrations, rhythm and movement activities, games, and art projects. Sharing this information in newsletters or posting it on bulletin boards or a website enables families to reinforce

▼ **Children should be discouraged from sitting in the "W" position.**

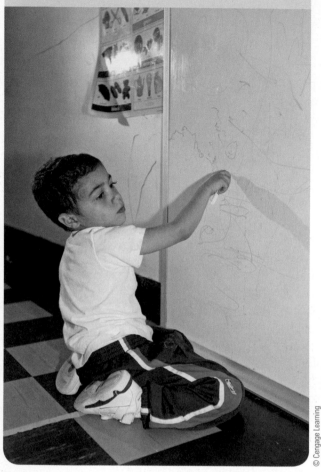

© Cengage Learning

correct practices at home. Children can begin to learn basic body mechanics, including:

▶ Sitting squarely in a chair, resting the back firmly against the chair back and with both feet flat on the floor.

▶ Sitting on the floor with legs crossed (in front) or with both legs extended straight ahead. Children should be discouraged from kneeling or sitting in a "W" position because this can place additional stress on developing joints. Have children sit in a chair with feet planted firmly on the ground or provide them with a small stool that can be straddled (one leg on each side); this eliminates adult nagging and forces children to sit in a correct position. Alternative seating supports may be required for children who have muscular or neurological disabilities.

▶ Standing with the shoulders square, the chin up, and the chest out. Body weight should be distributed evenly over both feet to avoid placing stress on one or the other hip joints.

▶ Lifting and carrying heavy objects by using the stronger muscles of the arms and legs rather than weaker back muscles. Standing close to an object that is to be lifted with feet spread slightly apart provides a wider support base. Stooping down to lift (with your legs); bending over at the waist when lifting places strain on back muscles and increases the risk of injury.

Correct posture and body mechanics are also important skills for parents and teachers to practice (Teacher Checklist 1-1). Because they perform many bending and lifting activities throughout the day, using proper technique can reduce chronic fatigue and work-related injury. Exercising regularly also improves muscle strength and makes demanding physical tasks easier to complete.

Vigorous physical activity should be an essential part of every child's day. It has a positive effect on children's growth, mental health, weight management, and behavior by relieving excess energy, stress, and boredom (Singh et al., 2012). Introducing children to a variety of sports, games, and other forms of physical activity also provides them with early opportunities

---

  TEACHER CHECKLIST 1-1

Proper Body Mechanics for Adults

- Use correct technique when lifting children; flex the knees and lift using leg muscles; avoid lifting with back muscles, which are weaker.
- Adjust the height of children's cribs and changing tables to avoid bending over.
- Provide children with step stools so they can reach water fountains and faucets without having to be lifted.
- Bend down by flexing the knees rather than bending over at the waist; this reduces strain on weaker back muscles and decreases the risk of possible injury.
- Sit in adult-sized furniture with feet resting comfortably on the floor to lessen strain on the back and knees.
- Transport children in strollers or wagons rather than carrying them.
- Exercise regularly to improve muscle strength, especially back muscles, and to relieve mental stress.
- Lift objects by keeping arms close to the body versus extended; this also reduces potential for back strain.

TeachSource Digital Download Download from CourseMate.

to discover those they enjoy and are likely to continue. Teachers should review classroom schedules and always look for ways to incorporate more physical activity into daily routines. Current guidelines recommend that children get a daily minimum of 180 cumulative minutes of aerobic activity (of any intensity), including at least 60 minutes that is of moderate intensity (CDC, 2011). It is important that families and teachers serve as positive role models for children by also participating in a variety of physical activities daily.

1-4c Oral Health

Children's oral health continues to be a major goal in the *Healthy People 2020* objectives. Yet, there are many children who seldom visit a dentist because their families cannot afford dental insurance or costly preventive care. Children from low-income and minority groups are twice as likely to experience tooth decay and to lack dental treatment (da Fonseca, 2012). Neglected dental care can result in painful cavities and infected teeth, interfere with concentration and academic performance, and affect children's behavior and self-esteem (Jackson et al., 2011). There are many adults who erroneously believe that "baby teeth," or deciduous teeth, do not require treatment because they will eventually fall out (Figure 1–5). This is an unfortunate assumption because children's temporary teeth are necessary for:

▶ chewing
▶ proper spacing for permanent teeth
▶ shaping the jaw bone
▶ speech development

Advancements in pediatric dentistry and educational efforts have resulted in significant improvements in children's dental health. Practices, such as consuming a nutritious diet during pregnancy, scheduling regular dental visits, the use of sealants, adding fluoride to drinking water supplies and toothpastes, and applying fluoride directly to teeth have collectively reduced the incidence of children's dental caries and gum disease.

Diet has an unquestionable effect on children's dental health. Proper tooth formation depends on an adequate intake of protein and minerals, particularly calcium and fluoride. Highly refined and sticky carbohydrates should be consumed in moderation to limit their negative effect on healthy teeth. They are commonly found in cakes, cookies, candies, gum, soft drinks, sweetened cereals, and dried fruits (e.g., raisins, dates, prunes). Replacing sweets in children's diet with fresh fruits and vegetables reduces the risk of dental caries and also promotes healthier eating habits. Children's medications and chewable vitamins are often sweetened with sugars so it is important that tooth brushing follow their ingestion.

Dietary practices also play an important role in the prevention of baby bottle tooth decay (BBTD). Extensive cavity development can occur when sugars in formula, breast milk, juices, and/or sweetened drinks come in frequent or extended contact with teeth. Practices that place a child at high risk for developing BBTD include putting an infant to bed with a bottle, lengthy breastfeeding at night, and allowing toddlers to carry around a sippy cup containing fruit juice, soda, or other sweetened drink.

Oral hygiene practices implemented early in children's lives also contribute to healthy tooth development. Food particles can be removed from an infant's gums and teeth by wiping them with a small, wet washcloth after feedings. A small, soft brush and water can be used for cleaning an older infant's teeth.

Most toddlers can begin to brush their own teeth with a soft brush and water at around 15 months of age (Teacher Checklist 1-2). However,

FIGURE 1–5 Approximate age when teeth erupt and are lost.

Primary teeth		Appears	Lost
Upper teeth	Central incisor	8–12 mos.	6–7 yrs.
	Lateral incisor	9–13 mos.	7–8 yrs.
	Canine (cuspid)	16–22 mos.	10–12 yrs.
	First molar	13–19 mos.	9–11 yrs.
	Second molar	25–33 mos.	10–12 yrs.
Lower teeth	Second molar	23–31 mos.	10–12 yrs.
	First molar	14–18 mos.	9–11 yrs.
	Canine (cuspid)	17–23 mos.	9–12 yrs.
	Lateral incisor	10–16 mos.	7–8 yrs.
	Central incisor	6–10 mos.	6–7 yrs.

TEACHER CHECKLIST 1-2

Promoting Children's Tooth Brushing

Make tooth brushing appealing and fun for children by:

- letting children pick out their favorite tooth brush (color and/or character) and label it with their name
- placing tooth brushes where they are accessible to children
- providing a footstool or chair so children can comfortably reach the sink
- demonstrating the correct tooth-brushing procedure and having children imitate; set a timer and brush your teeth together on occasions

 CAUTION

Supervise children closely to prevent them from slipping or falling.

- recording a favorite song (e.g., "London Bridge," "Itsy Bitsy Spider," or "Wheels on the Bus") and play it while each child brushes his or her teeth. (Check the Internet for free downloads). This can make tooth brushing fun for children.
- making a habit of having children wash their hands and brush their teeth following a meal/snack
- designing a chart where children can place a check mark or sticker each time they brush.

TeachSource Digital Download   Download from CourseMate.

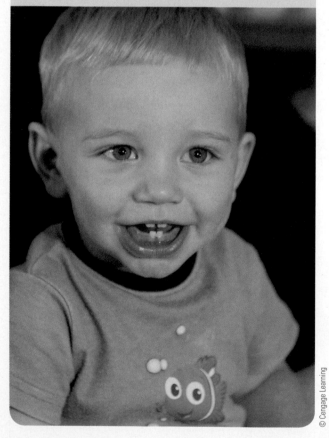

▼ **Improving children's oral health is a major goal of Healthy People 2020.**

© Cengage Learning

the use of toothpaste is not recommended before age 2; most toddlers do not like its taste and are unable to spit it out after brushing. When a child is first learning tooth brushing skills, an adult should brush over the teeth after at least one of the brushings each day to be sure all areas are clean. Teeth can also be kept clean between brushings by rinsing with water after meals and eating raw foods, such as apples, pears, and celery, that provide a natural cleansing action.

Preschool children are generally able to brush their teeth with minimal supervision, but it may still be advisable for an adult to provide a quick follow-up brushing. Although children's technique may not always be perfect, they are beginning to establish a lifelong tooth brushing habit. Proper brushing technique and fluoride-based toothpastes (pea-size application) have proven to be effective in reducing dental cavities. However, children must be supervised closely so they do not swallow the toothpaste. Ingesting too much fluoride over time can result in dental **fluorosis**, which causes white or brown spots to form on developing teeth (Kobayashi et al., 2011). The question of whether young children should learn to floss their teeth is best answered by the child's dentist. Although the practice is regarded as beneficial, much depends on the child's maturity and fine motor skills. Flossing is usually recommended once the permanent teeth begin to erupt and spaces between teeth disappear. Parents should assist children who are too young to manage this procedure by themselves.

fluorosis – *white or brown spots that form on children's teeth due to excessive fluoride intake.*

Routine dental checkups are also an important component of preventive health care, but they are not a substitute for daily oral hygiene practices and a healthful diet. Children's first visit to the dentist should be scheduled at around 12 to 15 months of age and every 6 to 12 months thereafter. Initial visits should be pleasant experiences that acquaint a child with the dentist, routine examinations, and cleanings without undergoing painful dental work. Children are more likely to maintain a favorable attitude toward dental care and to approach visits with less fear and anxiety if early experiences are positive.

During routine visits, dentists clean, apply a fluoride varnish, and inspect the child's teeth for potential problems. They also review the child's tooth brushing technique, diet, and personal habits, such as thumb sucking or grinding that may affect the teeth. The fluoridation of municipal water supplies and use of sealants (a plastic-like material applied to permanent molar groves) have also made significant contributions to a decline in childhood tooth decay.

1-4d Mental Health and Social-Emotional Competence

The wellness model recognizes a close relationship between a child's emotional and physical well-being. This association is receiving greater attention due to the increase in behavior problems, school dropout rates, substance abuse, violence, gang membership, depression, and child suicide. Approximately one in five children in the United States experiences mental health problems, and one in ten have disorders that seriously interfere with learning (Healthy People 2020, 2012). Children who live in dysfunctional or economically challenged families, or who have a disability, are at highest risk for developing mental health problems (Cushona et al., 2011).

A strong positive relationship exists between a child's mental health status and **self-concept**. Young children typically view themselves solely in terms of physical qualities, such as having brown hair, blue eyes, or being tall. By age 5 or 6, children begin to include social comparisons with peers as part of their self-definition; they can run faster than Tyshan, build higher towers than Mei, or draw flowers better than Abetzi. Nine- and 10-year-olds exhibit a higher order of self-evaluation that is more analytical: "I like to play baseball, but I don't field or hit the ball as well as Tori, so I probably won't be asked to play on a team."

A child's self-image and mental health are continuously being shaped and reshaped by complex interactions among biological (e.g., personality traits, physical well-being, illness, disability) and environmental factors (e.g., family structure, ethnicity, culture, poverty, household conditions). Each experience yields information that has a positive or negative influence on a child's outlook and behavior. For example, a child who has cerebral palsy and is teased because he doesn't walk like other children may withdraw from group activities and become depressed. In contrast, a child who is athletically talented and frequently befriended is likely to be confident and to have a positive self-concept.

Promoting Children's Social and Emotional Development Families and teachers play a major role in promoting children's social-emotional development. They improve children's chances for achieving positive outcomes by providing learning opportunities that build on individual strengths and interests. Children are more likely to experience success, take pride in their accomplishments, and feel good about themselves when adults set realistic goals and expectations. However, children's efforts should be acknowledged even when they have been unsuccessful. Failures and mistakes must be accepted as part of the learning process and should be viewed as occasions for offering guidance and positive support. In doing so, children begin to learn important lifelong lessons about initiative, risk-taking, problem-solving, and handling adversity. However, caution must be exercised never to judge children solely on their accomplishments (or failures) or to make comparisons with other children, but to recognize each child as a unique and valued individual.

Teachers occupy a strategic position for reinforcing children's development of social-emotional competence. They are able to create opportunities for children to acquire and practice effective communication, self-control, problem-solving, and decision-making skills in a supportive

self-concept – *a person's belief of who they are, how they are perceived by others, and how they fit into society.*

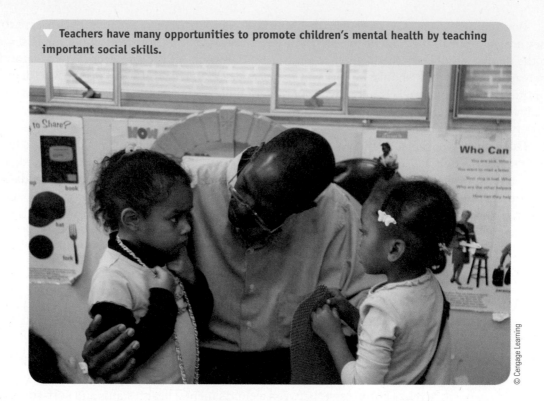

▼ **Teachers have many opportunities to promote children's mental health by teaching important social skills.**

© Cengage Learning

environment (Willis & Schiller, 2011). Teachers also foster children's social-emotional competence by creating safe and respectful classrooms that convey positive attitudes, address children's individual needs, provide constructive feedback, and are conducive to learning. In addition, they play an integral role in:

◗ modeling positive mental health behaviors.
◗ implementing sound mental health principles by being accepting, responsive, and supportive.
◗ preventing emotional problems by teaching children effective social, communication, anger management, and problem-solving skills.
◗ identifying and referring children who may exhibit signs of emotional problems, such as excessive or uncontrollable frustration, aggressive behavior, or difficulty making and keeping friends.
◗ working collaboratively with families to locate community resources.
◗ advocating for community mental health services.

When children develop positive self-esteem and confidence in their own abilities, they are more likely to experience a trajectory of personal and academic success.

Teachers as Role Models   Adults must never overlook their importance as role models for young children. Their personal behaviors and response styles exert a powerful and direct influence on children's social-emotional development.

Teachers must carefully examine their own emotional state if they are to be successful in helping children achieve positive **self-esteem**. They, too, must have a strong sense of self-worth and confidence in what they are doing. They should be aware of personal biases and prejudices, be able to accept constructive criticism, and recognize their strengths and limitations. They must have effective communication skills and be able to work collaboratively with families of diverse backgrounds, community service providers, health care professionals, and other members of the child's educational team.

self-esteem – *an individual's sense of value or confidence in himself or herself.*

If teachers are to serve as positive role models, they must also exercise the same control over their emotions that they expect of children. Personal problems and stressors must remain at home so that full attention can be focused on the children. Teachers must respect children as individuals—who they are, and not what they are able or not able to do—because every child has qualities that are endearing and worthy of recognition. Teachers must also be impartial in their treatment of children; favoritism cannot be tolerated.

Working with young children can be rewarding, but it can also be stressful and demanding in terms of the patience, energy, and stamina required. Noise, children's continuous requests, long hours, staff shortages, mediocre wages, and occasional conflicts with families or co-workers are everyday challenges. Physical demands and unresolved stress can gradually take their toll on teachers' health, commitment, and daily performance. Eventually, this can lead to job burnout and negative interactions with colleagues and children (Klassen & Chiu, 2012). For these reasons, it is important that teachers identify sources of stress in their jobs and take steps to address, reduce, or eliminate them to the extent possible (Marotz & Lawson, 2007). (See Teacher Checklist 1-3.)

Emotional Climate   A classroom's emotional climate—the positive or negative feelings one senses—can have a significant impact on children's social-emotional development. Consider the following situations and decide which classroom you would find most inviting:

> Kate enters the classroom excited and eager to tell her teacher about the tooth she lost last night and the quarter she found under her pillow from the "tooth fairy." Without any greeting, the teacher hurries to check Kate in and informs her that she is too busy to talk right now, but maybe later. When the teacher is finished checking Kate she instructs her "to find something to do without getting into trouble." Kate quietly walks away to her cubbie.
>
> Ted arrives and seems reluctant to leave his mother for some reason this morning. The home provider immediately senses his distress and walks over to greet Ted and his mother. "Ted, I am so glad that you came today. We're going to learn about farm animals and build a farm with the wooden blocks. I know that blocks are one of your favorite activities. Perhaps you'd like to build something small for your mother before it's time for her to go home." Ted eagerly builds a barn with several "animals" in the yard around it and proudly looks to his mother for approval. When Ted's mother is ready to leave, he waves good-bye.

Clearly, the teacher's actions in the two examples created a classroom atmosphere that had a different effect on each child's behavior. Children are generally more receptive and responsive to teachers who are warm, nurturing, and sensitive to their needs. Exposure to negative adult responses, such as ridicule, sarcasm, or threats is harmful to children's emotional development and simply teaches inappropriate behaviors. However, an emotional climate that fosters mutual

---

✓✓ TEACHER CHECKLIST 1-3

Strategies for Managing Teacher Stress

- Seek out training opportunities where you can learn new skills and improve your work effectiveness.
- Learn and practice time management techniques.
- Develop program policies and procedures that improve efficiency and reduce sources of tension and conflict.
- Join professional organizations; expand your contacts with other teachers, acquire new ideas, and advocate for young children.
- Take steps to improve your personal well-being—get plenty of sleep, eat a nutritious diet, and participate in some form of physical activity (outside of work) each day.
- Develop new interests, hobbies, and other outlets for releasing tension.
- Practice progressive relaxation techniques. Periodically, concentrate on making yourself relax and think about something pleasing.
- Plan time for yourself each day—read a good book, watch a movie or favorite TV program, go for a long walk, paint, go shopping, play golf, or participate in some activity that you enjoy.

cooperation, respect, trust, acceptance, and independence will promote children's social-emotional skill development.

A teacher's communication style and understanding of cultural differences also affect the emotional climate of a classroom. Treating all children as if they were the same is insensitive and can encourage failure, especially if a teacher's expectations are inconsistent or incompatible with the child's cultural background. For example, knowing that children in some Hispanic cultures are taught primarily through non-verbal instruction (modeling) may explain why a child who is only given verbal directives may not respond to this approach (Martins-Shannon & White, 2012). Some children are reluctant to participate in group activities or to answer a teacher's question because this is counter to the way they have been raised. Unless the teacher understands these cultural differences, such behaviors could easily be misinterpreted as defiance or inattention. When teachers make an effort to learn about individual children and their families, they are able to create a climate that supports learning and healthy social-emotional development.

The way in which the curriculum is planned and implemented also contributes to the emotional climate. Children's chances for achieving success are improved when learning activities are developmentally appropriate and matched to children's individual needs and interests.

Stress All children experience a host of stressful situations as they learn to master new skills, understand social convention, and/or encounter conflict. Developmental stress is a natural part of children's lives and can be healthy when it is used as a learning experience. It provides children with opportunities to acquire valuable coping and problem-solving skills if stress is experienced in a safe, secure, and supportive environment.

Scientists have increased their understanding of stress and its effects on children's physical and mental development. For example, it is now known that children's early exposure to intense, frequent, and/or chronic stress can actually damage genetic makeup (DNA) (Price et al., 2013).

▼ **The classroom atmosphere has a direct effect on children's behavior and development.**

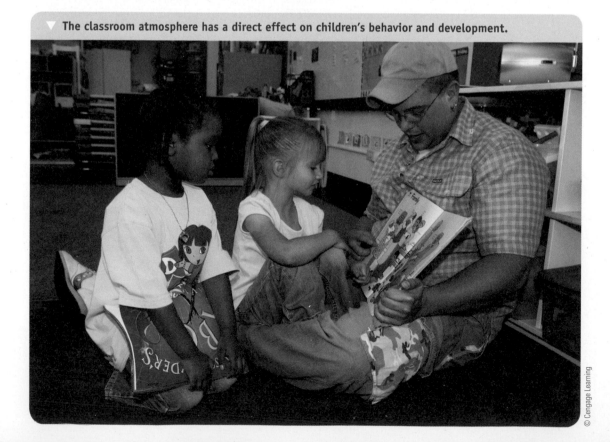

© Cengage Learning

The term **toxic stress** has been used to describe situations that increase children's risk of serious physical and mental health disorders (Shonkoff & Garner, 2012). Toxic stressors include abusive treatment, neglect, poverty, chronic illness, violence, and war. Chronic food insecurity, maternal depression, and parental substance abuse have also been associated with children's long-term psychological problems (Church, Jaggers, & Taylor, 2012).

Some children feel overwhelmed and experience undue anxiety in response to everyday events, such as:

- separation from their families
- new experiences—for example, moving, enrolling in a new school, having a mother return to work, being left with a sitter, or the birth of a sibling
- chronic illness and hospitalization
- divorce of parents
- death of a pet, family member, or close friend
- conflict of ideas; confrontations with family, friends, or teachers
- overstimulation due to hectic schedules, participation in too many extracurricular activities
- learning problems

Children's immature brain development, limited experience and coping skills, and differences in temperament influence their ability to manage stress in a healthy manner. Sudden behavior changes are often an early indication that a child is experiencing significant tension or inner turmoil. Observable signs can range from less serious behaviors—nail biting, hair twisting, excessive fear, crying, prolonged sadness, and anxiety—to those that are of significant concern—repeated aggressiveness, destructiveness, withdrawal, depression, nightmares, psychosomatic illnesses, or poor performance in school. Brief episodes of these behaviors are usually not cause for concern, but children should be referred for professional evaluation if they persist.

Teachers can help children who are experiencing acute or chronic stress by showing additional patience, understanding, and support. Children also find comfort in knowing they are safe, secure, and able to count on teachers and parents to be accepting, even at times when their emotional control may fail. Additional coping strategies are outlined in Table 1–4.

Bullying   Most school-age children report that they have been subjected to occasional verbal or physical bullying by their peers. Bullying differs from occasional name-calling and social rejection in that it is usually intentional, repetitive, and ongoing. Girls are more likely to engage in verbal taunting directed toward another girl whereas boys tend to use physical aggression to intimidate other males.

Researchers have identified two types of bullies: those who are self-assured, impulsive, lacking empathy, angry, and controlling; and those who are passive and willing to join in once another

TABLE 1–4 Stress Management for Children

1. Encourage children to talk about what is causing them to feel tense or upset.
2. Empower children by helping them to identify and express feelings appropriately.
3. Nurture positive thinking and an "I know I can do this" attitude.
4. Prepare children for stressful events (e.g., doctor's visit, moving, flying for the first time, attending a new school) by role-playing or rehearsing what to expect. Practice "what if's": "What should you do if you get lost?", "What can you do if you're afraid?"
5. Maintain predictable schedules, including mealtimes and bedtimes as much as possible.
6. Make sure children are receiving a nutritious diet and engaging in brief periods of vigorous physical activity (an effective stress reliever).
7. Schedule unstructured play time when children are free to do what they want.

toxic stress – *stress over which children have no control or adult support; it is intense, frequent, and often prolonged.*

CONNECTING TO EVERYDAY PRACTICE

Children and Cyber-Bullying

Maddie was in tears when she finally decided to show her mother the message a friend's mother had posted on her Facebook page. The mother blamed Maddie for the low grade her daughter recently received on a group science project, and accused her of "not working as hard as the other team members" and "turning in sloppy work." Maddie was reluctant to let her mother see the posting despite the fact that it had been bothering her for several days. She fears that her mother will contact school authorities or the friend's mother now that she knows and worries about the repercussions.

School-age children have been quick to adopt cyber-bullying as a preferred method for harassing their peers. Access to cell phones, tablets, and computers has made it increasingly easy for children to reach their victims and to engage in non-confrontational bullying. They consider cyber-bullying to be reasonably anonymous, transparent, and unlikely to result in after-school detention. Although victims are spared physical injury, they often suffer significant humiliation, emotional trauma, and find it difficult to avoid unless they turn off all cell phones and computers.

Many administrators believe cyber-bullying is reaching crisis levels in their schools. School boards are establishing disciplinary policies in an effort to curb malicious postings and online harassment. State legislators have also begun to introduce bills that hold children and their parents, in some instances, responsible for engaging in cyber-bullying.

Think About This:

▶ Why do some children feel the need to bully others?

▶ What behavioral changes might a parent observe if their child was being harassed?

▶ Why not just tell children to turn off their cell phones and computers to avoid being bullied?

▶ Should children who engage in bullying be expelled from school? Why might this not be the best option?

▶ Should parents be held responsible when children engage in cyber-bullying? What are the pros and cons?

child initiates the bullying (Hong & Espelage, 2012). Children who bully are often from homes where poverty, domestic violence, inconsistent supervision, and lack of social support or parental concern are common. As a result, they have had limited opportunities to develop effective interpersonal skills, impulse control, and problem-solving abilities.

Children who are targeted by bullies may be singled out because they are perceived to be socially withdrawn or loners, passive and lacking in self-confidence, having a disability or special needs, not likely to stand up for themselves, and easily hurt (emotionally). They are more often from economically disadvantaged families, smaller in physical size than their peers, and seen as having fewer friends. Warning signs that a child is being victimized may include frequent complaints of health problems, change in eating and/or sleeping habits, reluctance to attend school, and declining academic performance.

Prevention programs have been implemented in many schools to reduce bullying behavior and to create environments where children feel safe. Educational efforts address both the victims and perpetrators and are designed to teach mutual respect, reinforce effective social and communication skills, reduce harassment, and improve children's self-esteem (Strohmeier & Noam, 2012). Children who are being bullied learn how to respond in these

cyber-bullying – *sending embarrassing or threatening messages to an individual via the Internet, electronic media, or cell phone.*

situations by avoiding bullies, walking away, practicing conflict resolution, and always informing a trusted adult.

Childhood Depression Some children are unsuccessful or unable to cope with acute anxiety or chronic stress. They may develop a sense of persistent sadness and hopelessness that begins to affect the way they think, feel, and act. These may be early signs of childhood depression and can include:

- apathy or disinterest in activities or friends
- loss of appetite
- difficulty sleeping
- complaints of physical discomforts, such as headaches, stomachaches, vomiting, diarrhea, ulcers, repetitive tics (twitches), or difficulty breathing
- lack of energy or enthusiasm
- indecision
- poor self-esteem
- uncontrollable anger

Children who have learning and behavior disorders or a family history of mental health conditions are at an increased risk for developing depression. Children as young as 3 may begin showing early signs of depression particularly when their mothers also suffer from this condition (Hughes et al., 2013).

The onset of childhood depression may occur abruptly following a traumatic event, such as parental divorce, death of a close family member or friend, abusive treatment, or chronic illness. However, it can also develop slowly over time, making the early signs more difficult to notice. In either case, teachers must be knowledgeable about the behaviors commonly associated with childhood depression so children can be identified and referred for professional care. Depression requires early identification and treatment to avoid serious and debilitating effects on children's social, emotional, and cognitive development and to prevent long-term mental health disorders.

Childhood Fears Most childhood fears and nightmares are a normal part of the developmental process and are eventually outgrown as children mature. Basic fears are relatively consistent across generations and cultures, although they vary somewhat from one developmental stage to the next. For example, a 3-month-old infant seldom displays any fear, whereas 3-year-olds often are fearful of "monsters under the bed." Fears that reflect real-life events, such as fire, kidnapping, thunderstorms, or homelessness, are more common among 5- and 6-year-olds, whereas 10- and 11-year-olds may express fears related to appearance and social rejection (Marotz & Allen, 2013). Some fears are unique to an individual child and may stem from personal experiences, such as witnessing a shooting, vicious dog attack, or being involved in a car accident.

Fears and nightmares are often accentuated during the preschool years, a time when children have a heightened imagination and are attempting to make sense of their world. Children's literal interpretation of the things they see and hear can also contribute to misunderstanding and fear. For example, children are likely to believe that an adult who says, "I'm going to give you away if you misbehave one more time" will actually do so.

It is important for adults to acknowledge children's fears and to accept that they are truly real to the child. Children need consistent adult reassurance and trust to overcome their fears, even though it may be difficult to remain patient and supportive when a child repeatedly awakens at 2:00 every morning! Children also find comfort in talking about things that frighten them and rehearsing what they might do, for example, if they were to become lost at the supermarket or if it began to thunder.

Poverty and Homelessness Approximately 21.9 percent of all U.S. children currently live in families that fall below the national poverty level (U.S. Census Bureau, 2012). The adults in many of these families are either unemployed, working in low-wage jobs, recent immigrants, classified as minorities (especially Hispanic, Native American, and African American), or a single parent, usually a mother. Living in a single- versus a two-parent family places children at the highest economic risk for poverty. Children residing in rural areas also experience a high poverty rate, but they comprise an often overlooked group. Economic problems and high unemployment have forced many rural families into bankruptcy (Curtis, Voss, & Long, 2012). Collectively, these developments have caused families with young children to become the new majority of today's homeless population.

Poverty places additional burdens on the already challenging demands of parenting. Struggles to provide children with basic food, clothing, shelter, health care, and nurturing are often compromised by increased stress, fear, and conflict. Ultimately, these pressures can contribute to family tension, domestic violence, child maltreatment, and an inability to provide the love and support that children require.

The impact of poverty on children's growth and development has both immediate and long-term consequences. Children born into poverty experience a higher rate of birth defects, early death, and chronic illnesses, such as anemia, asthma, and lead poisoning (Reichman & Teitler, 2013). In addition, the quality of their diet, access to health and dental care, and mental health status are often compromised. Children living in poverty are also more likely to experience abuse or neglect, learning and behavior problems, teen pregnancy, substance abuse, high dropout rates, and reduced earning potential as adults. Ultimately, the cumulative effects of poverty can threaten children's chances of growing up to become healthy, educated, and productive adults.

Violence Children today live in a world where daily exposure to violence is not uncommon. The incidence of crime, substance abuse, gang activity, and access to guns tends to be greater in neighborhoods where poverty exists and can result in unhealthy urban environments where children's personal safety is at risk. Children living in these settings are also more likely to become victims of child abuse or to witness domestic violence. Their families exhibit a higher rate of dysfunctional parenting skills, are often less responsive and nurturing, and use discipline that is either lacking, inconsistent, or punitive and harsh (Burke et al., 2011). Parents in these situations are also less likely to be supportive of children's education or to assume an active role in their school activities. As a result, many children who grow up in poverty are at greater risk of experiencing learning problems, becoming violent adults, and developing serious mental health disorders. Teachers who understand this potential can be instrumental in helping children overcome adversity by reaching out and strengthening their resiliency skills as well as assisting families in locating supportive community resources. (See Teacher Checklist 1-4.)

Children growing up in violent and disadvantaged environments face challenges not only at home but also at school. Younger children are more likely to attend child care programs and schools that are of poorer quality than their counterparts in higher income neighborhoods (Burchinal et al., 2011). In addition, children of all ages often have fewer opportunities to engage in learning and enrichment experiences at home. Researchers have observed that children living in disadvantaged households typically have delayed language development and literacy skills due to a lower rate of parent-child interactions and lack of available reading materials (Nelson et al., 2011). This combination sets many children up for early school failure.

Media Violence Children are frequently exposed to sources of extreme violence and death in movies, video games, cartoons, on television, and on the Internet. Researchers have observed an increase in children's aggressive behaviors after they have witnessed violent media entertainment, but no direct link has been established with adult criminal activity (Gentile, Mathieson, & Crick, 2011). However, repeated exposure to media violence and death has been shown to desensitize children to their dysfunctional significance (Ferguson, 2011). Families are encouraged to limit children's media viewing to 1 or 2 hours daily, choose and monitor content carefully, and help children to understand media as a form of fantasy entertainment (AAP, 2011). Television and other media entertainment formats (e.g., CD movies, video games, smartphones, iPads) are not recommended for children under 2 years. Young children learn best through hands-on experience and have difficulty understanding abstract content viewed on an electronic screen.

TEACHER CHECKLIST 1-4

Strategies for Increasing Children's Resilient Behaviors

- Be a positive role model for children; demonstrate how you expect them to behave.
- Accept children unconditionally; avoid being judgmental.
- Help children develop and use effective communication skills.
- Listen carefully to children to show that you value their thoughts and ideas.
- Use discipline that is developmentally appropriate and based on natural or logical consequences.
- Use and enforce discipline consistently.
- Help children to understand and express their feelings; encourage them to have empathy for others.
- Avoid harsh physical punishment and angry outbursts.
- Help children establish realistic goals, set high expectations for themselves, and have a positive outlook.
- Promote problem-solving skills; help children make informed decisions.
- Reinforce children's efforts with praise and encouragement.
- Give children responsibility; assign household tasks and classroom duties.
- Involve children in activities outside of their home.
- Encourage children to believe in themselves, to feel confident rather than seeing themselves as failures or victims.

TeachSource Digital Download   Download from CourseMate.

1-4e Resilient Children

Children face many challenges as they grow up in this complex world. Stress, violence, uncertainty, and negative encounters are everywhere. What makes some children more vulnerable to the negative effects of stress and aversive treatment or more likely to develop inappropriate behaviors? Many factors, including genetic predisposition, malnutrition, prenatal exposure to drugs or alcohol, poor attachment to primary caregivers, physical and/or learning disabilities, and/or an irritable personality, have been suggested as possible explanations. Researchers have also studied home environments and parenting styles that make it difficult for some children to achieve normal developmental tasks and positive self-esteem (Alegre, 2011).

Why are other children better able to overcome the negative effects of an impoverished, traumatic, violent, or stressful childhood? This question continues to be a focus of study as researchers attempt to learn what conditions or qualities enable some children to be more **resilient** in the face of adversity. Although much remains to be understood, several important protective factors have been identified. These include having certain personal characteristics (such as above-average intelligence, positive self-esteem, and effective social and problem-solving skills), having a strong and dependable relationship with a parent or parent substitute, and having a social support network outside of one's immediate family (such as a church group, organized sports, Boys and Girls clubs, or various youth groups).

Competent parenting is, beyond a doubt, one of the most important factors necessary for helping children to cope with and overcome adversity and its potentially damaging consequences (Hardaway, McLoyd, & Wood, 2012). Children who grow up in an environment where families are caring and emotionally responsive, provide meaningful supervision and discipline that is consistent and developmentally appropriate, offer encouragement and praise, and help children learn to solve problems in a peaceful way are more likely to demonstrate resilient behavior. Teachers, likewise, can promote resiliency by establishing classrooms where children feel accepted, respected, and supported in their efforts.

Management Strategies Understandably, all children undergo occasional periods of emotional instability or undesirable behavior. Short-term or one-time occurrences are usually not cause for

resilient – *the ability to withstand or resist difficulty.*

concern. However, when a child consistently demonstrates abnormal or antisocial behaviors, an intervention program or counseling therapy may be necessary.

At times, it may be difficult for families to recognize or acknowledge abnormal behaviors in their own children. Some emotional problems develop slowly over time and may therefore be difficult to distinguish from normal behaviors. Some families find it difficult to talk about or to admit that their child has an emotional disturbance. Others, unknowingly, may be contributing to their children's problems because of dysfunctional (e.g., abusive, unrealistic, inconsistent, or absent) parenting styles.

For whatever reasons, it may be teachers who first identify children's abnormal social and emotional behaviors based on their understanding of typical development, careful observations, and documentation of inappropriate conduct. They also play an instrumental role in promoting children's emotional health by providing stable and supportive environments that foster children's self-esteem and self-confidence. They model and help children develop socially appropriate behaviors. They teach conflict resolution, problem-solving, and communication skills so children will be able to cope effectively with daily problems. In addition, teachers can use their expertise to help families acknowledge children's problems, counsel them in positive behavior management techniques, strengthen parent-child relationships, and assist them in arranging professional counseling or other needed services. Although most families welcome an opportunity to improve their parenting skills, the benefit to high-risk or dysfunctional families may be even greater.

Did You Get It?

Children living in_____ families are at increased risk for developing mental health disorders.
- **a.** minority
- **b.** dysfunctional
- **c.** dual-earner
- **d.** inner-city

Take the full quiz on CourseMate.

PARTNERING with FAMILIES

Growing Your Child's Brain

Dear Families,

Your child's brain is much like a flower or plant in your garden. It requires daily nourishment and attention, especially in the beginning, and is affected by positive and negative conditions in the environment. There are many things you can do every day to encourage your child's healthy brain growth and development:

❥ Read, sing, and talk often to your infant or young child. Encourage your child to make up silly songs, rhymes, and stories. Read your child's favorite books over and over, have them turn the pages, point to pictures, and name objects.

❥ Provide nutritious meals and snacks to build healthy brain cells.

❥ Make sure your child gets sufficient sleep.

❥ Respond to your child's needs in a consistent, caring, and constructive manner. Harsh words, physical punishment, and abusive treatment can have a damaging effect on the brain's structure over time.

❥ Encourage your child to be physically active every day. Change an infant's position frequently so she uses different muscles and sees different things in the environment.

❥ Allow children time to try and solve their own problems; intervene only if they become overly frustrated and then help guide their solution by providing choices.

(continued)

Growing Your Child's Brain   *(continued)*

▶ Encourage your child's curiosity and provide safe learning opportunities for exploring and experimenting.

▶ Help your child learn to recognize and manage his feelings. Be a positive role model and show your child how to appropriately respond to difficult situations.

▶ Most importantly, tell and show your child often that he or she is loved.

CLASSROOM CORNER

Teacher Activities

The Importance of Friendship

(**NHES** PreK–2, National Health Education Standard 4.2.1)

Concept: Having fun with friends.

Learning Objectives

▶ Children will learn that there are many activities to do with friends.

▶ Children will learn that friendship requires sharing and turn-taking.

▶ Children will learn that working together can be a lot of fun.

Supplies

▶ a variety of colors of construction paper cut into large hearts (each heart should then be cut in half in a variety of ways so that the two heart pieces can be put back together to form a large heart); glue sticks; various art supplies (glitter, feathers, puff balls, foam shapes, etc.); adhesive tape; large piece of bulletin board paper (large enough to display all of the hearts)

Learning Activities

▶ Read and discuss one of the following books:

- *What Is a Friend?* by Josie Firmin
- *A Rainbow of Friends* by P.K. Hallinan
- *Winnie the Pooh: Friendship Day* by Nancy Parent
- *Pooh: Just Be Nice . . . to Your Little Friends!* by Caroline Kenneth

▶ Explain to the children that they are going to make a friendship quilt.

- Have the children come up and pick a heart half. After they have all selected half of a heart, pair the two children together whose heart halves fit together. Provide art supplies and one glue stick per pair of children to encourage sharing and cooperation. When each pair of children has finished decorating their heart half, tape the two halves together. Label each heart set with the names of both children. Arrange the completed hearts on a large sheet of bulletin board paper to create a friendship quilt that can be hung up in your classroom.

▶ Talk about the experience, including what it means to work with a partner and to make a friendship quilt.

Evaluation

▶ Children will work together and take turns.

▶ Children will name activities they like to do with their friends.

Additional lesson plans for grades 3–5 are available on CourseMate.

Summary

▶ The concept of preventive health care:

- recognizes that health attitudes and practices are learned behaviors.
- encourages individuals to assume an active role in developing and maintaining practices that promote health.

▶ A child's health is determined by the interplay of genetic makeup and environment.

- Health is a dynamic state of physical, mental, and social well-being that is continuously changing as a result of lifestyle decisions.

▶ Children's growth and developmental potentials are determined, in part, by genetics, and the interactions of multiple health, safety, and nutrition factors.

- Health promotion begins with a sound understanding of children's growth and development.

▶ Several aspects of children's health require special adult attention: safety and injury prevention; body mechanics and physical activity promotion; oral health; and mental health, including fostering self-esteem, social-emotional competence, and resilience.

Terms to Know

preventive health *p. 3*	norms *p. 12*	plasticity *p. 17*
health *p. 8*	normal *p. 12*	well child *p. 18*
heredity *p. 9*	growth *p. 13*	fluorosis *p. 22*
predisposition *p. 9*	head circumference *p. 13*	self-concept *p. 23*
sedentary *p. 10*	attachment *p. 13*	self-esteem *p. 24*
food insecurity *p. 10*	deciduous teeth *p. 13*	toxic stress *p. 27*
nutrients *p. 11*	development *p. 15*	cyber-bullying *p. 28*
resistance *p. 11*	neurons *p. 17*	resilient *p. 31*

Chapter Review

A. By Yourself:

1. Define each of the *Terms to Know* listed at the end of this chapter.
2. Explain how genetics and environment influence the quality of a child's well-being.
3. Describe how singing, talking, and reading to an infant promote early brain development.
4. Explain why young children are at high risk for unintentional injury.
5. Identify several preventive practices that promote children's oral health.
6. Explain why children living in poverty may experience lower self-esteem.
7. Describe several ways that families can help children to build resilience.

B. As a Group:

1. Discuss how an individual's lifestyle decisions can have either a positive or negative effect on health.
2. Describe how teachers can use their knowledge of children's development for health promotion.
3. Explain why an abundant food supply does not always ensure a healthy diet.
4. Discuss why it is important to involve and include families in children's health education activities. What steps can a teacher take to be sure that children's cultural beliefs are respected?
5. Explain the benefits of physical activity for both children and teachers. Conduct several classroom observations with different age groups to identify ways that teachers can incorporate more aerobic activity into children's daily schedule. Describe how several of these activities could be modified for children who have limited vision or are in a wheelchair.

6. Define the term self-concept. Provide specific examples of things teachers might do that could have a positive and negative effect on children's self-esteem.

7. Discuss how a teacher's mental health state can potentially affect children.

Case Study

Jose, 7 years old, and his mother live alone in a one-bedroom apartment close to his school. Most afternoons Jose walks home alone, lets himself into their apartment, and watches television until his mother comes home from work. His favorite after-school snack consists of potato chips and a soda or fruit drink. For dinner, Jose's mother usually brings something home from a local fast food restaurant because she is "too tired to cook." She knows this isn't good for either one of them. Jose's mother is currently being treated for high blood pressure, and the pediatrician has expressed concern about Jose's continued weight gain. However, Jose's mother doesn't see how she can change anything given her work schedule and limited income.

1. How would you describe Jose's short- and long-term health potential?

2. What concerns would you have about Jose's safety?

3. What potential health problems is Jose likely to develop if his current behaviors do not change?

4. What environmental risk factors may be contributing to the family's health problems?

5. If you were working with this family, what suggestions would you have for improving their health?

Application Activities

1. Observe a small group of preschool-aged children for two 15-minute intervals during free-play or outdoor times. For each observation, select a different child and record the number of times that child engages in cooperative play. Repeat this observation procedure with a group of toddler or school-age children. Describe the differences.

2. Contact your local public health department. Arrange to observe several routine well-child visits. What preventive health information was given to families? Was it presented in a way that families could understand and use?

3. Select and read ten children's books from the Mental Health section in Appendix D. Prepare a brief annotation for each book, including the topic, theme, and recommendations. Describe how you would use each book to develop a learning activity that promotes children's social-emotional competence.

4. Research and read more about the national health initiatives described in this chapter. Find out if they are available in your area and what services are provided. Are the programs and services meeting the needs of children in your community? If not, what recommendations would you offer for improvement?

5. Develop a month-long series of classroom learning activities focused on children's oral health. Make arrangements to conduct several of your lessons with children in a local school and evaluate their effectiveness. What changes or improvements would you make the next time?

6. Modify the "Classroom Corner" activity on friendship to meet National Health Education Standard 4.5.3. (Demonstrate non-violent strategies to manage or resolve conflict.) Design and describe at least three classroom activities that would teach and reinforce positive resolution techniques.

Helpful Web Resources

American Institute of Stress   http://www.stress.org

Centers for Disease Control and Prevention: http://www.cdc.gov/HealthyYouth/CSHP/
    Coordinated School Health Program

Council for Exceptional Children	http://www.cec.sped.org
Centers for Disease Control and Prevention: Adolescent and School Health	http://www.cdc.gov/HealthyYouth/
U.S. Department of Health and Human Services: Indian Health Service	http://www.ihs.gov
National Association for Child Development	http://www.nacd.org
Let's Move! Child Care	http://healthykidshealthyfuture.org
National Center for Children in Poverty	http://www.nccp.org
Mental Health America	http://www.mentalhealthamerica.net/go/children

 Visit the Education CourseMate for this textbook to access the eBook, Did You Get It? quizzes, Digital Downloads, TeachSource Video Cases, flashcards, and more. Go to CengageBrain.com to log in, register, or purchase access.

References

Alegre, A. (2011). Parenting styles and children's emotional intelligence: What do we know? *The Family Journal*, 19(1), 56–62.

American Academy of Pediatrics (AAP). (2011). Media and children. Accessed on May 8, 2012 from http://www.aap .org/en-us/advocacy-and-policy/aap-health-initiatives/Pages/Media-and-Children.aspx.

American Academy of Pediatrics (AAP), American Public Health Association (APHA), & National Resource Center for Health and Safety in Child Care and Early Education (NRC). (2011). *Caring for our children: National health and safety performance standards: Guidelines for early care and education programs* (3rd ed.). Elk Grove Village, IL: American Academy of Pediatrics; Washington, DC: American Public Health Association.

Blunden, S. (2012). Behavioral sleep disorders across the developmental age span: An overview of causes, consequences, and treatment modalities, *Psychology*, 3(3), 249–256.

Burchinal, M., McCartney, K., Steinberg, L., Crosnoe, R., Friedman, S., McLoyd, V., & Pianta, R. (2011). Examining the black-white achievement gap among low-income children using the NICHD study of early child care and youth development, *Child Development*, 82(5), 1404–1420.

Burke, N., Hellman, J., Scott, B., Weems, C., & Carrion, V. (2011). The impact of adverse childhood experiences on an urban pediatric population, *Child Abuse & Neglect*, 35(6), 408–413.

Cavalari, R., & Romanczyk, R. (2012). Supervision of children with an autism spectrum disorder in the context of unintentional injury, *Research in Autism Spectrum Disorders,* 6(2), 618–627.

CDC. (2011). Physical activity for everyone. Accessed on April 28, 2012 from http://www.cdc.gov/physicalactivity/ everyone/guidelines/children.html.

Centers for Disease Control & Prevention (CDC). (2012). Child injury. Accessed on April 15, 2012 from http://www .cdc.gov/vitalsigns/ChildInjury/index.html.

Centers for Medicare & Medicaid Coverage. (2013). Children's Health Insurance Program (CHIP). Accessed on April 5, 2013 from http://www.medicaid.gov.

Church, W., Jaggers, J., & Taylor, J. (2012). Neighborhood, poverty, and negative behavior: An examination of differential association and social control theory, *Children & Youth Services Review*, 34(5), 1035–1041.

Colby, M., Lipson, D., & Turchin, S. (2012). Value for the money spent? Exploring the relationship between expenditures, insurance adequacy, and access to care for publicly insured children, *Maternal & Child Health Journal*, 16(Suppl. 1), 51–60. DOI: 10.1007/s10995-012-0994-y.

Curtis, K., Voss, P., & Long, D. (2012). Spatial variation in poverty-generating processes: Child poverty in the U.S., *Social Science Research*, 41(1), 146–159.

Cushona, J., Vu, L., Janzen, B., & Muhajarine, N. (2011). Neighborhood poverty impacts children's physical health and well-being over time: Evidence from the Early Development Instrument, *Early Education & Development*, 22(2), 183–205.

da Fonseca, M. (2012). The effects of poverty on children's development and oral health, *Pediatric Dentistry*, 34(1), 32–38.

Daniels, S., Pratt, C., & Hayman, L. (2011). Reduction of risk for cardiovascular disease in children and adolescents, *Circulation*,124, 1673–1686.

Ferguson, C. (2011). Video games and youth violence: A prospective analysis in adolescents, *Journal of Youth & Adolescents*, 40(4), 377–391.

Foltran, F., Gregori, D., Franchin, L., Verduci, E., & Giovannini, M. (2011). Effect of alcohol consumption in prenatal life, childhood, and adolescence on child development, *Nutrition Reviews*, 69(11), 642–659.

Gentile, D., Mathieson, L., & Crick, N. (2011). Media violence associations with the form and function of aggression among elementary school children, *Social Development*, 20(2), 213–232.

Hardaway, C., McLoyd, V., & Wood, D. (2012). Exposure to violence and socioemotional adjustment in low-income youth: An examination of protective factors, *American Journal of Community Psychology*, 49(1–2), 112–126.

Healthy People 2020. (2012). Mental health. Accessed on April 5, 2013 from http://www.healthypeople.gov/2020/LHI/mentalHealth.aspx.

Hong, J., & Espelage, D. (2012). A review of research on bullying and peer victimization in school: An ecological system analysis, *Aggression & Violent Behavior*, 17(4), 311–322.

Hughes, C., Roman, G., Hart, M., & Ensor, R. (2013). Does maternal depression predict young children's executive function?—A 4-year longitudinal study, *Journal of Child Psychology & Psychiatry*, 54(2), 169–177.

Jackson, S., Vann, W., Kotch, J., Pahel, B., & Lee, J. (2011). Impact of poor oral health on children's school attendance and performance, *American Journal of Public Health*, 101(10), 1900–1906.

Judy, K. (2011). Unintentional injuries in pediatrics, *Pediatrics in Review*, 32(10), 431–439.

Klassen, R., & Chiu, M. (2012). The occupational commitment and intention to quit of practicing and pre-service teachers: Influence of self-efficacy, job stress, and teaching context, *Contemporary Educational Psychology*, 36(2), 114–129.

Kobayashi, C., Belini, M., Italiani, F., Pauleto, A., Julianelli de Araújo, J., Tessarolli, V., Grizzo, L., Pessan, J., Machado, M., & Buzalaf, M. (2011). Factors influencing fluoride ingestion from dentifrice by children, *Community Dentistry & Oral Epidemiology*, 39(5), 426–432.

Liu J., & Raine, A. (2011). Malnutrition and externalizing behavior. In D. Benton (ed.), *Lifetime nutritional influences on cognition, behavior, and psychiatric illness*. Cambridge, UK: Woodhead Publishing.

Marotz, L.R., & Allen, K.E. (2013). *Developmental profiles: Pre-birth through adolescence* (7th ed.). Belmont, CA: Wadsworth Cengage Learning.

Marotz, L., & Lawson, A. (2007). *Motivational leadership*. Clifton Park, NY: Thomson Delmar Learning.

Martins-Shannon, J., & White, M. (2012). Support culturally responsive teaching!, *Kappa Delta Pi Record*, 48(1), 4–6.

Maxwell, M., Lemacks, J., Coccia, C., Ralston, P., & Ilich, J. (2012). A student-led pilot project to improve calcium intake and health lifestyle in African American communities, *Topics in Clinical Nutrition*, 27(1), 54–66.

McCormick, M., Litt, J., Smith, V., & Zupancic, J. (2011). Prematurity: An overview and public health implications, *Annual Review of Public Health*, 32, 367–379.

Morrongiello, B., Kane, A., McArthur, B., & Bell, M. (2012). Physical risk taking in elementary-school children: Measurement and emotion regulation issues, *Personality & Individual Differences*, 52(4), 492–496.

National Association for the Education of Young Children (NAEYC). (2012). NAEYC accreditation criteria. Accessed on April 15, 2012 from http://www.naeyc.org/files/academy/file/NewGuidanceOnNAEYCAccreditationCriteriaEffectiveApril2012.pdf.

Nelson, K., Welsh, J., Trup, E., & Greenberg, M. (2011). Language delays of impoverished preschool children in relation to early academic and emotion recognition skills, *First Language*, 31(2), 164–194.

Okechukwu, C., El Ayadi, A., Tamers, S., Sabbath, E., & Berkman, L. (2012). Household food insufficiency, financial strain, work–family spillover, and depressive symptoms in the working class: The Work, Family, and Health Network Study, *American Journal of Public Health*, 102(1), 126–133.

O'Leary, C., Jacoby, P., Bartu, A., D'Antoine, H., & Bower, C. (2013). Maternal alcohol use and sudden infant death syndrome and infant mortality excluding SIDS, *Pediatrics*, 131(3), e770–e778.

Price, L., Hung-The, K., Burgers, D., Carpenter, L., & Tyrka, A. (2013). Telomeres and early-life stress: An overview, *Biological Psychiatry*, 73(1), 15–23.

Reichman, N., & Teitler, J. (2013). Lifecourse exposures and socioeconomic disparities in child health, *National Symposium on Family Issues*, 3, 107–134.

Safe Kids Canada. (2012). Safety information. Accessed on April 15, 2012, from http://www.safekidscanada.ca.

Shonkoff, J., & Garner, A.; Committee on Psychosocial Aspects of Child and Family Health; Committee on Early Childhood, Adoption, and Dependent Care; Section on Developmental and Behavioral Pediatrics. (2012). The lifelong effects of early childhood adversity and toxic stress, *Pediatrics*, 129(1), e232–246.

Singh, A., Uijtdewilligen, L., Twisk, J., van Mechelen, W., & Chinapaw, M. (2012). Physical activity and performance at school, *Archives of Pediatrics & Adolescent Medicine*, 166(1), 49–55.

Stewart de Ramirez, S., Hyder, A., Herbert, H., & Stevens, K. (2012). Unintentional injuries: Magnitude, prevention, and control, *Annual Review of Public Health*, 33, 175–191.

Strohmeier, D., & Noam, G. (2012). Bullying in schools: What is the problem, and how can educators solve it?, *New Directions for Youth Development*, 2012(133), 7–13.

Su, W., & Aurelia, D. (2012). Preschool children's perceptions of overweight peers, *Journal of Early Childhood Research*, 10(1), 19–31.

Twardosz, S. (2012). Effects of experience on the brain: The role of neuroscience in early development and education, *Early Education & Development*, 23(1), 96–119.

U.S. Census Bureau. (2012). Poverty. Accessed on September 17, 2012 from http://www.census.gov/hhes/www/poverty/about/overview.

Weill, J. (2012). Food insecurity in America: A call to action, *Journal of Applied Research on Children*, 3(1). Informing policy for children at risk, Article 1. Available at http://digitalcommons.library.tmc.edu/childrenatrisk/vol3/iss1/1/.

Willis, C.A., & Schiller, P. (2011). Preschoolers' social skills steer life success, *Young Children*, 66 (1), 50–54.

Daily Health Observations

naeyc Standards Chapter Links

◗ **#1 a and b:** Promoting child development and learning
◗ **#2 a, b, and c:** Building family and community relationships
◗ **#3 a, b, c, and d:** Observing, documenting, and assessing to support young children and families
◗ **#6 b:** Becoming a professional
◗ Field Experience

Learning Objectives

After studying this chapter, you should be able to:

LO 2-1 Discuss several ways that teachers and programs can promote children's health.
LO 2-2 Explain why it is important to conduct daily health observations.
LO 2-3 Perform a daily health check.
LO 2-4 Discuss how teachers can involve children's families in the health appraisal process.
LO 2-5 Describe ways that teachers can incorporate health education into daily health checks.

The *Healthy People 2020* national initiative reinforces the important relationship that exists between children's health and their ability to learn (HHS, 2012). It also recognizes that not all children have equal access to medical and dental care or to environments that promote a healthy lifestyle. It underscores the collaborative effort necessary for ensuring children's health and educational success, and challenges professionals and communities to address these problems. Teachers and health care providers also play a critical role in implementing the *Healthy People 2020* goals to help children achieve their optimal health and development.

Only when children are healthy and well-nourished are they able to fully benefit from learning experiences. Acute and chronic illnesses, undetected health **impairments**, inadequate diet, maltreatment, and mental health problems can interfere with a child's level of interest, involvement, and performance in school. For example, a mild hearing loss may distort a child's perception of letter sounds, pronunciations, and responsiveness. If left undetected, it can have a profound and long-term effect on a child's language development and ability to learn. However, health problems do not have to be obvious or complex to have a negative effect. Even a simple cold, toothache, allergic reaction, or chronic tonsillitis will disrupt a child's energy level, cooperation, attention span, and learning enjoyment. Teachers are in an ideal position to monitor children's health, note early signs of problems that can hinder learning, and work with families to obtain the care children need to be successful.

impairments – *a condition or malfunction of a body part that interferes with optimal functioning.*

CONNECTING TO EVERYDAY PRACTICE

The Impact of Health on Learning

High drop-out rates among school-age children continue to attract national attention. According to several recent studies, many of these children have undiagnosed health problems, such as vision and hearing impairments, allergies, asthma, and anemia, which interfere with their ability to learn and to succeed in school. After years of struggle and failure, some children simply choose to abandon the source of their frustration.

The visionary founders of Head Start clearly understood the importance of early identification and treatment of health problems to ensure that children were ready and able to learn upon entering school. The same preventive philosophy is evident in the *Healthy People 2020* goals and reinforces the valuable role teachers play in assessing and promoting children's well-being.

Think About This:

▶ Should inservice and teacher education programs include more training about children's health care needs? Explain.

▶ In what ways do state child-care licensing regulations encourage teachers to be proactive in protecting children's health and safety?

▶ What right does a teacher have to insist that children receive treatment for their health problems? Explain.

▶ What health care options exist for children whose families cannot afford needed treatments?

Did You Get It?

Health impairments can have a profound effect on a student's ability to concentrate and learn successfully. The most critical step to overcoming these prospective barriers is
   a. accommodation.
   b. counseling.
   c. medical or behavioral intervention.
   d. detection.

Take the full quiz on CourseMate.

2-1 Promoting Children's Health

Schools and early childhood programs make significant contributions to children's wellness by providing on-site health care, educational programs, safe learning environments, and nutritious meals. High-quality programs also conduct teacher observations and daily health checks to monitor children's health and identify potential health problems. It is important that this process be ongoing because children's health status changes continuously, as illustrated in the following example:

> Braden, age 3, ran ahead of his mother so he could reach the classroom before she did. He greeted his friends with the usual, "Hey guys" and seemed fine when the teacher checked him in. However, later that morning she noted that Braden had refused snack and was lying in the book area with his blanket. When she touched his arm it felt warm and was covered with red, raised bumps. She immediately recognized the symptoms as a likely case of chickenpox and called Braden's mother to come and take him home.

When teachers remain alert to changes in children's appearance and behavior, they are often able to identify an impending illness or undiagnosed health condition when it is still in the early stages. This can be especially important for limiting the spread of a contagious disease or the negative impact of a disorder on a child's growth and development.

2-1a Gathering Information

Information about children's overall health can be obtained from a variety of resources, including:

- dietary assessment
- health histories
- results of medical examinations
- teacher observations and daily health checks
- dental examinations
- family interviews
- vision and hearing screenings
- speech evaluations
- psychological testing
- developmental evaluations

Several of these assessment tools can be administered by teachers or volunteers, whereas others require the skills of specially trained health professionals. Often, the process of identifying a specific health impairment requires the cooperative efforts of specialists from several different fields:

- pediatric medicine
- nursing
- speech
- dietetics
- dentistry
- psychology
- education
- ophthalmology
- social work
- audiology

Information about a child's health should always be collected from multiple sources before any final conclusions are reached. A single **health assessment** may present a biased and unreliable picture of the child's condition (Allen & Cowdery, 2012). Children may also behave or respond in **atypical** ways when faced with new surroundings or an unfamiliar adult examiner. However, the nature of a child's health problem and its impact on development and learning become more apparent when information is obtained from several evaluation procedures. For example, the need to refer a child to a hearing specialist may be confirmed when testing results are combined with teacher and family observations.

▼ **Changes in children's appearance and behavior may be early signs of an illness.**

© Cengage Learning

Did You Get It?

What describes the teacher's role in using health assessment screening tools?

a. Teachers can use some screening tools.

b. Teachers are forbidden by law to use screening tools.

c. Teachers can use some screening tools, but they should not use them.

d. Teachers can use all screening tools.

Take the full quiz on CourseMate.

2-2 Observation as a Screening Tool

Teachers are valuable members of a child's comprehensive health team. Their interactions with children in the classroom and knowledge of developmental patterns place them in an ideal position to note the early signs of health problems. They can use information obtained from daily **observations** to establish a baseline of typical behavior and appearance for each child. When this information is combined with an understanding of normal growth and development, teachers can be effective in detecting early changes and deviations.

. . . .

health assessment – *the process of gathering and evaluating information about an individual's state of health.*
atypical – *unusual; different from what might commonly be expected.*
observation – *to inspect and take note of the appearance and behavior of other individuals.*

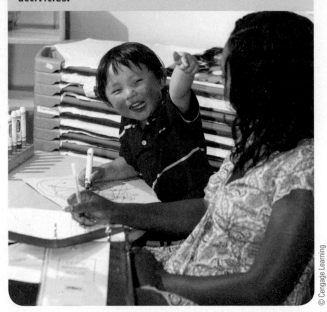

▼ **Teachers can observe and note children's health problems while they are engaged in daily classroom activities.**

© Cengage Learning

Health observations provide a simple and effective screening tool that is readily available to teachers. Many skills necessary for making objective health observations are already at their disposal. Sight, for example, is one of the most important senses; much can be learned about children's health by merely watching them in action. A simple touch can detect a fever or enlarged lymph glands. Odors may indicate lack of cleanliness or an infection. Careful listening may reveal breathing difficulties or changes in voice quality. Problems with peer relationships, eating habits, self-esteem, or abuse in the child's home may be detected during a conversation. Utilizing one's senses to the fullest—seeing children as they really are, hearing what they really have to say, and responding to their needs—is a skill that requires time, patience, and practice to perfect.

Conclusions drawn from teacher observations, as with any form of evaluation, should be made with caution. It must always be remembered that a wide range of normal behavior and skill attainment exists at each developmental stage. Norms merely represent the average age at which most children are able to perform a given skill. For example, many 3-year-olds can reproduce the shape of a circle, name and match primary colors, and walk across a balance beam. However, there will also be some 3-year-olds who will not be able to perform these tasks. This does not imply that they are not "normal." Some children simply take longer than others to master a particular skill. Developmental norms are useful for identifying children who may be experiencing health problems, as well as those who may simply require additional time and support in acquiring these skills. However, an abrupt change or prolonged delay in a child's developmental progress should be noted and prompt further evaluation.

Did You Get It?

The first step a teacher should take when using observation to monitor a child's health and development is to:

  a. note any and all changes
  b. note changes that have the potential to affect learning
  c. identify attainable goals
  d. establish a baseline for each child

Take the full quiz on CourseMate.

2-3 Daily Health Checks

Valuable information about health status and readiness to learn can be obtained by assessing children daily. Health checks require only a minute or two to complete and they enable teachers to detect the early signs and symptoms of common illnesses and health impairments. Daily health checks also help teachers to become familiar with each child's usual appearance and behavior so that changes are easily recognized. This is especially important in classrooms where children who have chronic conditions or other special health needs are present because their disorders can make them more susceptible to infectious illnesses (Forrest et al., 2011; Grier & Bradley-Klug, 2011). Teachers can minimize children's exposure by conducting daily health checks and identifying and removing any child who appears ill.

Parents should be encouraged to remain with their child until the health check has been completed. Children often find comfort in having a family member nearby. Families are also able to provide information about conditions or behaviors the teacher may observe. In addition, parents may feel less apprehensive if they have an opportunity to witness health checks firsthand and to ask their own questions. However, if a parent is unavailable, it may be advisable to have a second teacher witness the procedure to avoid any potential allegations of misconduct.

2-3a Method

A quiet area set aside in the classroom is ideal for performing health checks. A teacher may choose simply to sit on the floor with the children or provide a more structured setting with a table and chairs. Conducting health checks in the same designated area each day also helps children become familiar with the routine.

Performing health checks in a systematic manner improves the teacher's efficiency and ensures that the process will be consistent and thorough each time. Teacher Checklist 2-1 illustrates a simple observation tool that can be used for this purpose. It is organized so that observations are conducted from head to foot, first looking at the child's front and then back. However, this procedure can easily be modified to meet a program's unique needs in terms of the setting and children being served. For example, teachers who work with school-age children may prefer to use the information while simply observing children rather than for conducting a hands-on health check.

A teacher should begin daily health checks by observing children as they first enter the classroom. Clues about a child's well-being, such as personal cleanliness, weight change, signs of illness, facial expressions, posture, skin color, balance, and coordination can be noted at this time. The nature of parent-child interactions and their relationship with one another can also be observed and may help to explain why some children exhibit certain behaviors. For example, does the parent have a tendency to do everything for the child—take off boots, hang up clothing, pick up items the child has dropped—or is the child encouraged to be independent? Is the child allowed to answer questions or does the parent always respond?

A flashlight is used to inspect the inside of the child's mouth and throat for unusual redness, swollen or infected tonsils, dental cavities, sores, or breath odors. The child's hair and face, including the eyes, ears, and nose, should also be closely observed for clues about general hygiene and signs of communicable illness.

Next, the child's clothing can be lifted and any rashes, unusual scratches, bumps or bruises, and skin color on the chest, abdomen, and arms noted. These areas should be carefully inspected as many rashes associated with communicable disease often first appear on the warmer areas of the body. Blue-gray discolorations, called **Mongolian spots**, may be visible on the lower back of children who are of Asian, Native American, and Middle Eastern ethnicities. These spots appear similar to bruises, but do not undergo the color changes typical of an injury. They also tend to gradually fade as children approach 8 or 9 years of age.

Finally, the child is asked to turn around so the head, hair, and back areas can be inspected. Teachers should continue to observe the child following the health check. For example, balance,

© 2015 Cengage Learning

▶❚❚ TeachSource Video Connections

Infants and Toddlers: Daily Health Checks

Children's ability to learn is affected by their state of well-being. Because young children are highly susceptible and prone to infectious illnesses, it is important that teachers conduct daily health checks. As you watch the learning video, *Infants and Toddlers: Daily Health Checks*, consider the following questions:

1. Why should health checks be conducted daily?
2. Why is it important that teachers spend time interacting with parents as part of their daily health checks?
3. What are the best times of the day to perform a daily health check on an infant or toddler?
4. What conditions should the teacher note during the health check?

Watch on CourseMate.

Mongolian spots – *patches of blue-gray skin located on the lower back; more common among children of Asian, Native American, and Middle Eastern ethnicities.*

TEACHER CHECKLIST 2-1

Health Observation Checklist

General appearance—note changes in weight (gain or loss), signs of fatigue or unusual excitability, skin tone (pallor or flushed), and size for age group.

Scalp—observe for signs of itching, head lice, sores, hair loss, and cleanliness.

Face—notice general expression (e.g., fear, anger, happiness, anxiety), skin tone, or any scratches, bruises, or rashes.

Eyes—look for redness, tearing, puffiness, sensitivity to light, frequent rubbing, sties, sores, drainage, or uncoordinated eye movements.

Ears—check for drainage, redness, and appropriate responses to sounds or verbal requests.

Nose—note any deformity, frequent rubbing, congestion, sneezing, or drainage.

Mouth—look inside and at the teeth; note cavities (brown or black spots), sores, red or swollen gums, mouth-breathing, or unusual breath odor.

Throat—observe for enlarged or red tonsils, red throat, drainage, or white patches on throat or tonsils.

Neck—feel for enlarged glands.

Chest—listen to the child's breathing and note any wheezing, rattles, shortness of breath, or coughing (with or without other symptoms).

Skin—observe the chest and back areas for color (pallor or redness), rashes, scratches, bumps, bruises, scars, or unusual warmth and perspiration.

Speech—listen for clarity, stuttering, nasality, mispronunciations, monotone voice, and appropriateness for age.

Extremities—observe posture, coordination; note conditions such as bowed legs, toeing-in, arms and legs of unequal length, or unusual gait.

Behavior and temperament—note any changes in activity level, alertness, cooperation, appetite, sleep patterns, toileting habits, irritability, or uncharacteristic restlessness.

TeachSource Digital Download Download from CourseMate.

coordination, and posture can easily be noted as an infant crawls away or an older child walks over to join his or her friends. A child's aggressive tendencies or inability to play cooperatively with other children during outdoor play may provide important clues about social-emotional development and mental health. (See Teacher Checklist 2-2.)

TEACHER CHECKLIST 2-2

Warning Signs of Potential Mental Health Problems

Occasional responses to stress and change are to be expected. However, children who experience excessive or frequent episodes of the following behaviors may need to be referred for professional evaluation and treatment:

- *tearfulness or sadness*—cries easily; seldom appears happy
- *preference for being alone*—is withdrawn; reluctant to play with others
- *hostility or excessive anger*—overreacts to situations; has frequent tantrums
- *difficulty concentrating*—has trouble staying focused, remembering, or making decisions
- *aggressiveness*—initiates fights, hurts animals or others, destroys property
- *irritability*—seems anxious, restless, or overly worried; is continuously fidgeting
- *unexplained change in eating and/or sleeping habits*—refuses to eat or eats compulsively; has persistent nightmares and/or difficulty sleeping
- *excessive fear*—exhibits fear that is excessive or unwarranted
- *feelings of worthlessness*—is often self-critical; has undue fear of failure; is unwilling to try new things
- *refusal to go to school*—fails repeatedly to complete work; performs poorly in school
- *complains of physical ailments*—experiences frequent stomachaches, headaches, joint aches, or fatigue without any reasonable cause
- *engages in substance abuse (for older children)*—uses drugs and/or alcohol
- *talks about suicide*—is overly curious about death and suicide

TeachSource Digital Download Download from CourseMate.

Teachers become skilled in conducting daily health checks and making insightful observations with practice. They are able to recognize the early signs and **symptoms** of various communicable illnesses and health conditions and know when it is necessary to refer a child for further evaluation.

▼ Valuable clues about children's health can be noted during teacher observations.

© Cengage Learning

2-3b Recording Observation Results

Information obtained during daily health checks should be recorded immediately following the procedure to ensure its accuracy. Checklists are ideal to use for this purpose because they enable teachers to conduct and record information systematically. Attendance records or a similar form developed for this purpose can also be used to record **anecdotal** information. These records should be placed in each child's permanent health file (electronic or hard copy) or a designated notebook. Any changes noted in a child's condition throughout the day, such as a seizure, uncontrollable coughing, or diarrhea, should also be documented on this form and reported to the family.

Observational information is only meaningful and useful to other teachers, administrators, and health care providers when it is recorded in clear, accurate, and precise terms. To say that a child "looks sick" is vague and open to individual interpretation. However, stating that a child is flushed, has a fever of 101°F (38.3°C), and is covered with a fine red rash on his torso is definitive and provides a functional description that can be shared with the child's family and physician (Weist et al., 2012).

Did You Know...

that each year U.S. schools provide services for approximately 5.8 million children, 6 to 21 years, who have special health and disability needs?

2-3c Confidentiality of Health Information

Information obtained from daily health checks and teacher observations must be treated with utmost confidentiality. It should not be shared or made accessible to other families, staff, or service personnel. Additionally, this information must never be released to another individual or organization without first obtaining written permission

▼ Information in children's health records is confidential and should be shared only with certain school personnel.

© Cengage Learning

Did You Know...

that the Family Education Rights and Privacy Act (Buckley Amendment) prohibits schools from releasing any information about a child under 18 years without written parental permission?

---

symptoms – *changes in the body or its functions that are experienced by the affected individual.*
anecdotal – *brief notes describing a person's observations.*

▶❚❚ TeachSource Video Connections

Communicating with Parents about Health in Early Childhood: A Parent-Teacher Meeting

Children ultimately benefit when schools establish meaningful partnerships with their families. Parents also gain from their involvement in children's educational programs. They may become more confident, have an improved understanding of what teachers are trying to accomplish, and develop a greater interest in children's learning. As you watch the learning video, *Communicating with Parents about Health in Early Childhood: A Parent-Teacher Meeting*, consider the following questions:

1. Why do you think it is important to schedule a parent-teacher meeting before a child begins to attend classes?

2. What did the teacher do to put the parent at ease and begin to establish a trusting partnership?

3. What communication skills (e.g., body language, checking for understanding, listening) did the teacher demonstrate during the meeting?

4. Was the teacher successful in communicating the program's health information to the parent? What suggestions would you offer to this teacher for improvement?

Watch on CourseMate.

from the child's parent or legal guardian (Johnson & Guthrie, 2012). Anecdotal records and health checklists should be kept in a notebook or folder to protect children's identity until the information can be transferred to their personal files. However, federal law guarantees families the right to access information in their child's health file at any time and to request the correction of any perceived errors (U.S. Department of Education, 2011).

2-3d Benefits of Health Observations

On-going monitoring of children's health status offers several distinct advantages. Teachers are able to fulfill their professional and moral obligations to protect the health of all children in a group setting. For example, a teacher may note changes in a child's appearance or behavior that signal the onset of a communicable illness. This information can then be used to determine if a child is too ill to remain in the classroom based on the program's exclusion policies. Sending a sick child home reduces the risk of exposing other children to an illness and often hastens the recuperation time.

Information gathered during daily observations is also useful to health care providers for diagnosing and treating a child's condition. Teachers are able to provide unique information that explains how a health problem, such as a hearing loss or allergies, is affecting the child's behavior and ability to perform in school. Their insights can hasten the diagnostic process and, thus, limit the negative effects an undetermined condition may otherwise have on a child's development.

> **CAUTION**
>
> *Responsibility for interpreting signs and symptoms of an illness or health condition and establishing a final **diagnosis** always belongs to trained health care professionals.*

Daily health checks offer several additional benefits. They provide an opportunity for teachers to give children individualized attention and talk with them about a variety of health-related topics, such as why it is important to brush teeth, drink water, wash hands, or play outdoors. These one-on-one occasions convey a powerful message of caring and can empower children to begin developing a personal interest in their own well-being.

Patterns of illness or significant changes in a child's behavior may also be noted when daily health check information is examined. For example, knowing that several children have been exposed to chicken pox or that an outbreak of head lice has occurred in another classroom should alert teachers to be even more vigilant in the coming weeks.

diagnosis – *the process of identifying a disease, illness, or injury from its symptoms.*

2-4 Family Involvement

Health checks provide an ideal opportunity for involving families in children's health promotion. Teachers can create an atmosphere where families feel comfortable voicing concerns, asking questions, or seeking information about their child's health needs, behavior, or adjustment to school (Griffin, 2011). It is unrealistic to think that teachers will always be able to answer parents' question. However, they can begin to build a culturally responsive and trusting relationship with families by showing interest, encouraging their questions, and offering assistance in locating information and services (Edwards & Da Fonte, 2012; Grant & Ray, 2009).

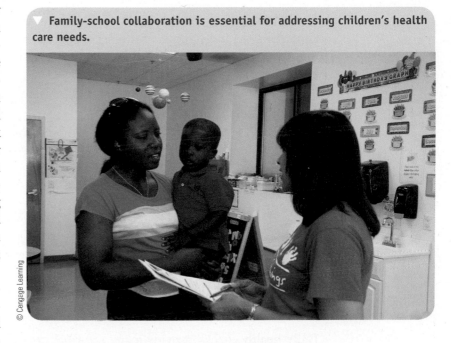
Family-school collaboration is essential for addressing children's health care needs.

© Cengage Learning

Teachers can also foster family involvement by sharing information about outbreaks of communicable illness, signs and symptoms to watch for, and effective preventive measures such as hand washing and good nutrition that can be taken. Parents may also be able to provide simple explanations for problems the teacher observes. For example, a child's fatigue or aggressiveness may be the result of a new puppy, a grandmother's visit, a new baby in the home, or a seizure the night before. Allergies or a red vitamin taken at breakfast may explain a questionable red throat. Without this direct sharing of information, such symptoms might otherwise be cause for concern.

2-4a The Family's Responsibility

Primary responsibility for a child's health care *always* belongs to the family. They are ultimately responsible for maintaining their child's well-being, following through with recommendations, and obtaining any necessary evaluations and medical treatments.

Often families are the first to sense that something is wrong with their child (Marotz & Allen, 2013). However, they may delay seeking professional advice, either denying that a problem exists or hoping the child will eventually outgrow it. Cultural differences in developmental expectations and the way children are raised may also explain why some families fail to take action. For example, a toddler's delayed walking may not be cause for concern in cultures where early walking is not encouraged. Parents may not understand that health problems can have negative consequences on children's development and learning potential or they may not know where to go for appropriate diagnosis and treatment. Some families fail to see the need for routine health care when a child appears to be healthy. Others simply cannot afford preventive care. However, cost must not discourage families from obtaining needed medical attention. In the United States, every state currently makes low-cost health insurance available to income-eligible children through the national Children's Health Insurance Program (CHIP). In addition, most communities offer a variety of free or low-cost health services for children through:

▶ Head Start
▶ Child Find screening programs
▶ Medicaid assistance
▶ Well-child clinics
▶ University-affiliated training centers and clinics
▶ Public health immunization centers
▶ Community centers
▶ Interagency coordinating councils

These agencies can generally be located in the telephone directory, on the Internet, or by contacting the local public health department. Teachers should also become familiar with community resources and assist families in securing appropriate health care services for children in need (Allen & Cowdery, 2012).

Did You Get It?

Although a variety of people and organizations are often involved in supporting children's well-being, the primary responsibility for a child's health and health care _____ lies with his or her family.

a. sometimes
b. always
c. ideally
d. most often

Take the full quiz on CourseMate.

2-5 Health Education

Daily health checks provide many informal opportunities for teaching children about health, safety, and nutrition. Teachers can encourage children's awareness and provide information about a range of healthy lifestyle practices, including oral hygiene, nutrition, physical activity, mental health, and sleep. For example:

▶ "Sandy, did you brush your teeth this morning? Brushing helps to keep teeth healthy and chases away the mean germs that cause cavities."
▶ "Mario, have you had a drink of water yet today? Bodies need water to grow and to stay healthy just like the plants in our classroom."
▶ "Harrison, what should you do if a stranger asks you to come with him or her?"

School-age children can be engaged in discussions that are more advanced. For example:

▶ "Yolanda, how many different fruits and vegetables have you eaten today? What vitamins and minerals does our body get from fruits and vegetables?"
▶ "Raja, did you put on sunscreen before playing outdoors? Why is this important? What else can we do to protect ourselves from the sun's harmful rays?"
▶ "Keiko, if someone teases or says hurtful things to you, who should you tell?"

When health education is linked to everyday situations, children are better able to comprehend its importance and application to their personal lives. They are also more likely to follow through and to implement what they have learned.

Including families in children's health education is also essential and improves the consistency of information and practices between school and the child's home. Teachers can utilize time during daily health checks to interact with families and to raise their awareness about a variety of children's health issues:

- new safety alerts and equipment recalls
- the importance of eating breakfast
- nutritious snack ideas
- ideas for increasing children's physical activity
- hand washing
- sun protection
- oral hygiene
- new vaccines
- home fire drills

Families are also more likely to support a school's health education goals when genuine efforts are made to reach out and to engage them in children's learning experiences.

Did You Get It?

Learning becomes more meaningful for children when it:
- **a.** is presented in the context of everyday experiences.
- **b.** addresses novel information.
- **c.** is provided during formal lessons.
- **d.** challenges children's curiosity.

Take the full quiz on CourseMate.

PARTNERING with FAMILIES

Children's Oral Health

Dear Families,

Oral health and a bright smile are important components of children's well-being. Teeth are essential for chewing, speech, maintaining proper space for permanent teeth, and appearance. Decay and infection can cause discomfort and make it difficult for children to focus on school. Unfortunately, tooth decay continues to affect many young children today despite increased public education and improved dental treatments. Practices that you can implement at home to promote children's oral health include:

- Keep an infant's gums clean by wiping them with a damp washcloth after each feeding.

- Dampen a soft toothbrush and use it twice daily to clean an infant's first teeth.

- Don't put infants to bed with a bottle containing juice, formula, or breast milk. These solutions can pool around gums and teeth and lead to early decay. Offer water if your infant takes a bottle to bed. Also, stop breastfeeding once he or she falls asleep.

- Apply a pea-sized dab of toothpaste to a soft brush and encourage toddlers to begin brushing their own teeth. Follow up their efforts by "going once around the block."

- Use fluoride toothpaste and drink fluoridated water (provided in most city water supplies) to reduce dental decay. Your child's dentist may prescribe fluoride drops or tablets if local water does not contain adequate fluoride.

- Continue to supervise preschool children's twice-daily tooth brushing. Discourage children from swallowing fluoride toothpaste because it can cause white or brown spots to form on permanent teeth.

- Monitor school-age children to make sure they brush and floss daily.

- Schedule your child's first routine dental check between 1 and 2 years of age. Older children should visit the dentist every six months. If you can't afford dental care, contact

(continued)

PARTNERING with FAMILIES

Children's Oral Health   *(continued)*

local public health personnel for information about free or low-cost options in your community. Reduced-cost dental insurance is also available to eligible families in some states.

❱ Serve nutritious meals and snacks. Include fresh fruits and vegetables, dairy products, whole-grain breads, crackers and cereals, and limit sugary foods and drinks.

❱ Offer children water when they are thirsty. Limit their consumption of carbonated beverages, fruit drinks, and sport drinks, which tend to be high in sugars.

CLASSROOM CORNER

Teacher Activities

Hear with My Ears . . .

(**NHES** PreK–2; National Health Education Standard 1.2.1)

Concept: You use your ears to hear sounds.

Learning Objectives

❱ Children will learn that ears are used for hearing sounds.

❱ Children will learn that there are many sounds all around.

Supplies

❱ various musical instruments (need two of each); a divider or a barrier

Learning Activities

❱ Read and discuss one of the following books:
  - *You Hear with Your Ears* by Melvin and Gilda Berger
  - *The Ear Book* by Al Perkins
  - *Hearing* (*The Five Senses*) by Maria Ruis, J. M. Parramon, & J. J. Puig
  - *The Listening Walk* by Paul Showers

❱ Explain to the children that their ears are for hearing sounds. Ask them some of the sounds that they hear each day.

❱ Place the musical instruments where the children can see them and play each one so they can become familiar with the sound each instrument makes.

❱ Next, place one of each instrument in front of the barrier/divider and one of each behind the barrier/divider.

❱ Call up one child to go behind the divider and pick an instrument to play. While that child is playing the instrument, call on another child to come up and pick the instrument that makes the matching sound to the instrument the child is playing behind the barrier.

❱ Continue until each child has had a turn, and then have the children play all the instruments at once.

❱ Talk about why it is important to take good care of our ears so we can hear.

Evaluation

❱ Children can name which body part is used for hearing.

❱ Children will name several different sounds in their environment.

❱ Children can match sounds.

Additional lesson plans for grades 3–5 are available on CourseMate.

Summary

▶ High-quality programs and schools understand that good health is essential to children's growth, development, and ability to learn.

- They promote wellness by monitoring and assessing children's health, making referrals, maintaining safe learning environments, providing health education, involving families, and serving nutritious food.

▶ Teachers' observations and health checks are an essential component of a school's health promotion efforts.

- They yield information that is useful for identifying changes in children's health status (physical, mental, social-emotional) and developmental problems.

▶ Daily health checks provide an efficient, effective, and cost-free method for monitoring children's health and development.

- Checklists can be used to ensure that observations are thorough and findings are recorded in meaningful terms.
- Information obtained from these sources must be treated with confidentiality and recorded immediately to retain its accuracy.

▶ Family involvement is essential for promoting children's wellness. Children benefit when there is mutual sharing of information between teachers and families. Teachers can make recommendations, but families are ultimately responsible for obtaining health care for children.

▶ Daily health checks provide teachers with valuable opportunities for educating children and their families about a variety of health-related topics.

Terms to Know

impairment *p. 39*　　　　observation *p. 41*　　　　anecdotal *p. 45*
health assessment *p. 41*　Mongolian spots *p. 43*　diagnosis *p. 46*
atypical *p. 41*　　　　　 symptoms *p. 45*

Chapter Review

A. **By Yourself:**

1. Define each of the *Terms to Know* listed at the end of this chapter.
2. Explain how health status affects a child's ability to learn.
3. List the reasons why teachers should conduct daily health checks.
4. Describe how an elementary teacher might modify the health check procedure to use with school-age children.
5. Examine and describe your feelings about conducting daily health checks in a reflective journal entry. Do you think all beginning teachers have similar feelings? Outline several steps you might take to improve your observational skills and gain confidence in identifying children's health problems.

B. **As a Group:**

1. Describe the resources available to teachers for gathering information about a child's health.
2. Describe the health check routine. What common health problems/conditions should teachers look for?

3. Discuss how you might respond to a parent who objects to the daily health checks conducted by her child's teacher.

4. What benefits do daily health checks provide for children?

5. What suggestions would you have for a preschool teacher who says he is too busy to conduct daily health checks?

6. What are some things teachers can do to get families more involved in their child's preventive health care?

Case Study

Chris, the head teacher in the Sunflower classroom, has recently had some concerns about Lynette's vision. He has noticed that during group story time, Lynette quickly loses interest, often leaves her place in the circle, and crawls closer to him in an apparent effort to see the pictures in books he is holding up. Chris has also observed that when Lynette is working on puzzles, manipulatives, or an art project, she typically lowers her head close to the objects. Lynette's parents have also expressed concern about her clumsiness at home.

The results of two vision screening tests, administered by the school nurse on different days, suggest that Lynette's vision is not within normal limits. The nurse shared these findings during a conference with Lynette's parents, and encouraged them to arrange for a follow-up evaluation with an eye specialist. However, because Lynette's father was recently laid off from his job, they no longer have health insurance and cannot afford a doctor's visit at this time. The nurse continued to work closely with the family and helped them locate two reduced-fee health clinics in their community that provided the type of services Lynette required.

1. What behaviors did Lynette exhibit that made her teacher suspect some type of vision disorder?

2. Identify the sources from which information concerning Lynette's vision problem was obtained before she was referred to an eye specialist.

3. If the teacher suspected a vision problem, why didn't he just go ahead and recommend that Lynette get glasses?

4. What responsibilities do teachers have when they believe a child has a health impairment?

5. If you were the nurse advising Lynette's parents, what free or low-cost health service options could you recommend in your community?

Application Activities

1. Develop a health observation checklist. With another student, role-play the daily health check procedure. Use the checklist to record your findings, and discuss your reactions to the experience. What suggestions would you have for the "teacher" who conducted the observation?

2. Invite a public health nurse from a well-child clinic or a local pediatrician to speak to the class about preventive health care recommendations for children birth to 12 years.

3. Visit several early childhood programs in your community. Note whether health checks are conducted as children arrive. Describe the method you observed at each center. Also, briefly discuss how this information was recorded.

4. Develop a list of available resources in your state and local community for children who have vision or hearing impairments, speech problems, cerebral palsy, autism, and learning disabilities. Be

creative in your search; consider child care options, schools, special equipment needs, availability of special therapists, transportation requirements, family financial assistance, and so on.

5. Modify the "Classroom Corner" feature activity in this chapter so a child who is severely hearing impaired could participate.

Helpful Web Resources

Canadian Paediatric Society	http://www.caringforkids.cps.ca
Child Development Institute	http://childdevelopmentinfo.com
Early Head Start National Resource Center	http://www.ehsnrc.org
U.S. Department of Health & Human Services: Administration for Children & Families	http://www.acf.hhs.gov
Tufts University: Children and Family Web Guide	http://www.cfw.tufts.edu
National Center for Infants, Toddlers, and Families: Zero to Three	http://www.zerotothree.org

 Visit the Education CourseMate for this textbook to access the eBook, Did You Get It? quizzes, Digital Downloads, TeachSource Video Cases, flashcards, and more. Go to CengageBrain.com to log in, register, or purchase access.

References

Allen, K. E., & Cowdery, G. (2012). *The exceptional child: Inclusion in early childhood education* (7th ed.). Belmont, CA: Wadsworth Cengage Learning.

Edwards, C., & Da Fonte, A. (2012). The 5-point plan: Fostering successful partnerships with families of students with disabilities, *Teaching Exceptional Children*, 44(3), 6–13.

Forrest, C., Bevans, K., Riley, A., Crespo, R., & Louis, T. (2011). School outcomes of children with special health care needs, *Pediatrics*, 128(2), 303–312.

Grant, K., & Ray, J. (2009). *Home, school, and community collaboration: Culturally responsive family involvement.* Thousand Oaks, CA: Sage Publications.

Grier, B., & Bradley-Klug, K. (2011). Collaborative consultation to support children with pediatric health issues: A review of the biopsychoeducational model, *Journal of Educational & Psychological Consultation*, 21(2), 88–105.

Griffin, D. (2011). Parent involvement with African American families in expanded school mental health practice, *Advances in School Mental Health Promotion*, 4(2), 16–26.

Johnson, K., & Guthrie, S. (2012). Harnessing the power of student health data, *NASN School Nurse*, 27(1), 26–33.

Marotz, L. R., & Allen, K. E. (2013). *Developmental profiles: Pre-birth through adolescence.* (7th ed.). Belmont, CA: Wadsworth Cengage Learning.

U.S. Department of Education. (2011). Family Educational Rights and Privacy Act (FERPA). *Federal Register*, 76(232). Accessed on March 30, 2012 from http://www.gpo.gov/fdsys/pkg/FR-2011-12-02/pdf/2011-30683.pdf.

U.S. Department of Health & Human Services (HHS). (2012). *Healthy People 2020.* Accessed April 2, 2012 from http://www.healthypeople.gov.

Weist, M., Mellin, E., Chambers, K., Lever, N., Haber, D., & Blaber, C. (2012). Challenges to collaboration in school mental health and strategies for overcoming them, *Journal of School Health*, 82(2), 97–105.

chapter 3

Assessing Children's Health

- **#1 a and b:** Promoting child development and learning
- **#2 a, b, and c:** Building family and community relationships
- **#3 a, b, c, and d:** Observing, documenting, and assessing to support young children and families
- **#4 a, b, and c:** Using developmentally effective approaches to connect with children and families
- **#5 b:** Using content knowledge to build meaningful curriculum
- **#6 b:** Becoming a professional
- Field Experience

Learning Objectives

After studying this chapter, you should be able to:

LO 3-1 Discuss how teachers can use information in health records to promote children's development and well-being.

LO 3-2 Describe five screening procedures and the common disorders they can be used to detect.

LO 3-3 Explain why it is important to follow up with families after making an initial referral.

Teachers understand that health problems can interfere with a child's ability to learn and that early detection improves the success of many interventions. They have access to screening tools for identifying children who may require further evaluation. When information is collected in an objective manner and from a combination of observations and screening procedures, it yields (1) reliable data for health promotion, (2) clues that aid in the early detection of conditions affecting children's growth and development, and (3) an opportunity to modify learning environments to meet a child's unique needs.

3-1 Health Records

Careful recordkeeping is not always a priority in many early childhood programs. However, when information in children's files is current and sufficiently detailed, it can be used to promote developmental progress and well-being (Table 3–1). The types of records schools are required to maintain are usually mandated by state departments of education. Child care licensing divisions in each state issue similar requirements for licensed centers and home-based programs. However, because these regulations typically reflect only minimal standards, programs may want to consider keeping additional types of documentation. Unlicensed programs are not obligated to maintain any records.

Forms and records should be designed to gather information that is consistent with a program's goals and philosophy and protects the legal rights of the children and staff. This information serves many purposes, including:

- determining children's health status
- identifying patterns and potential problem areas

TABLE 3–1   Children's Health Records

Children's permanent health records should include:
- child/family health history
- copy of a recent medical assessment (physical examination)
- immunization records
- emergency contact information
- record of dental examinations
- attendance data
- school-related injuries
- documentation of family conferences concerning the child's health
- screening results, e.g., vision, hearing, speech, developmental
- medications administered while the child is at school

⏵ developing **intervention** programs
⏵ evaluating the outcome of special services, e.g., speech therapy, occupational therapy
⏵ coordinating services
⏵ making referrals
⏵ monitoring a child's progress
⏵ research

Health records contain confidential information about children and their families. This information should be shared only with personnel who must know something specific about a child in order to work effectively with him or her. Personal details about a child or family must never serve as topics of conversation outside of the classroom. No portion of a child's health record should ever be released to another agency, school, health professional, or clinician until written permission has been obtained from the child's parent or legal guardian. A special release form, such as the one shown in Figure 3–1, can be used for this purpose. The form should clearly indicate the nature of information to be released and the agency or person to whom it is to be transferred. It must also be dated and signed by the parent or legal guardian, and a copy retained in the child's folder.

Recordkeeping is most efficient when one person is responsible for maintaining all health-related records. However, input from all members of the teaching team is important for determining how health problems may be affecting a child and for tracking children's progress. Health records are considered legal documents and should be retained for at least 5 years.

3-1a Child Health Histories

The nature of information requested on health history forms varies from program to program. Unless a standardized form is required by a licensing agency or school district, programs may wish to develop their own. Sample forms can often be obtained from other programs or state agencies and modified to meet a program's specific needs. Health history questionnaires should be designed to gather basic information about:

⏵ circumstances related to the child's birth
⏵ family structure, such as siblings and their ages, family members, predominant language spoken, and legal custody issues
⏵ major developmental milestones
⏵ previous injuries, illnesses, surgeries, or hospitalizations
⏵ daily habits, such as toileting, eating habits, and napping
⏵ family concerns about the child, such as behavior problems, social development, and speech delays
⏵ any special health conditions, such as allergies, asthma, seizures, diabetes, vision or hearing disorders, and prescribed medications

intervention – *practices or procedures implemented to modify or change a specific behavior or condition.*

FIGURE 3–1 **Sample information release form.**

INFORMATION RELEASE FORM

I understand the confidentiality of any personally identifiable information concerning my child shall be maintained in accordance with the Family Education Rights and Privacy Act (P.L.93–380), federal and state regulations, and used only for the educational benefit of my child. Personally identifiable information about my child will be released only with my written consent. With this information, I hereby grant the

_____

(Name of program, agency, or person)

permission to release the following types of information:

Medical information   _____

Assessment reports   _____

Child histories   _____

Progress reports   _____

Clinical reports   _____

(Other)   _____

to:_____

(Name of agency or person to whom information is to be sent)

regarding _____ _____ _____

(Child's Name)   (Birthdate)   (Gender)

_____

Signature of Parent or Guardian

_____

Relationship of Representative

_____

Date

Families can complete a written health history form and provide a copy of the child's current immunization record at the time of enrollment. Alternatively, families may be asked to supply this information during a home visit or meeting with the program administrator. Information obtained from health history questionnaires enables teachers to better understand each child's uniqueness, including their family background, daily routines and preferences, health status, and developmental strengths and limitations. This information can be used to accommodate children's special needs, such as dietary restrictions, hearing loss, or mobility limitations and to establish developmentally appropriate learning goals. However, caution must be exercised not to base expectations for children on this information alone. A child's potential for learning must never be discounted until an impairment is confirmed and known to restrict performance. When goals are set too low, children may lack incentive and perform only to the level of adult expectations. In contrast, expectations that are unrealistic and beyond a child's capabilities may cause repeated failure and loss of motivation.

Child health histories also provide an indication of the medical supervision a child typically receives and the value a family places on preventive health care. This information can be especially beneficial for planning children's health education and making future referrals.

3-1b Medical and Dental Examinations

Most states require children to have a complete health assessment and current immunizations before they attend school or an early childhood program. Some states require an annual physical examination whereas others request it only at the time of admission. Health care providers recommend well-child checkups every 2 to 3 months for infants, every 6 months for 2- and 3-year-olds, and annually for children 4 and older. More frequent medical supervision may be necessary if children have existing health problems or new conditions develop.

Information about a child and his or her family is updated at each visit. Families may also be asked to complete a brief developmental questionnaire to better help medical personnel assess all aspects of the child's health. The child's immunization record is reviewed and additional doses are administered as indicated. The child's heart, lungs, eyes, ears, **skeletal** and **neurological** development, and gastrointestinal function (stomach and intestines) are also carefully examined. Head circumference is routinely measured on all infants and children until 3 years of age to be certain that head size continues to increase at an acceptable rate. Height, weight, and blood pressure readings (after age 3) are also recorded and compared to prior measurements to determine if a child's growth is progressing satisfactorily. Growth failure, especially in height, may be an indication of other health problems that need to be investigated. Specialized tests, such as blood tests for anemia, sickle cell disease, or lead poisoning, may be ordered to identify or rule out any of these conditions. Urinalysis, tuberculin testing, vision screening, and hearing evaluation may also be obtained.

Although dental examinations are seldom required for admission purposes, their benefits are unquestionable. Families should be encouraged to arrange routine dental checks and preventive care for children, including visual inspection of the teeth, cleaning, and fluoride applications, every 6 to 12 months.

Did You Get It?

The release of the health records for a child moving to a new school:

a. must be accompanied by a release form signed by the child's parent or legal guardian

b. can be processed after verbal permission has been obtained

c. can be done without consent if the child is moving to a school in the same state

d. can only be transferred with the consent of a court

Take the full quiz on CourseMate.

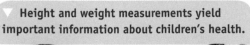

▼ Height and weight measurements yield important information about children's health.

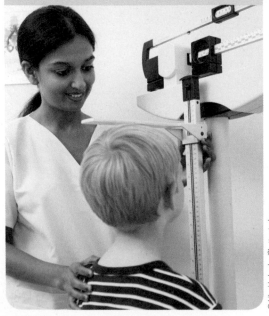

© bikeriderlondon/Shutterstock.com

3-2 Screening Procedures

Screening tests are also an essential component of the comprehensive health assessment process. They support the preventive care philosophy through the early detection of health problems and impairments that could otherwise interfere with a child's ability to learn.

Most screening procedures are relatively quick, inexpensive, and efficient to administer to groups of young children. Some tests can be conducted by teachers whereas others require the services of professional clinicians. Screening tests are designed only to identify children who may have a condition that requires professional evaluation, *never* to diagnose or confirm a specific impairment. Test results simply provide additional information about a child that can be used in combination with family and teacher observations, assessments of growth and development, and daily health-check findings.

3-2a Height and Weight

The first 5 years of life are an important period of rapid growth. Increases in height and weight are most dramatic during infancy, and continue at a slower, but steady, rate throughout the preschool

skeletal – *pertaining to the bony framework that supports the body.*
neurological – *pertaining to the nervous system, which consists of the nerves, brain, and spinal column.*

and school-age years (Marotz & Allen, 2013). Height is the most reliable indicator of a child's general health and nutritional status. Because weight can fluctuate in response to recent illness, infection, emotional stress, or over- or undereating, it is not considered a dependable reflection of long-term health.

Teachers and families must understand that a child's growth potential is ultimately governed by genetics. This is especially important to remember when working with children from different cultures and ethnic backgrounds. The Centers for Disease Control and Prevention (CDC) has updated its standard growth charts to more accurately represent the diverse child population in the United States, although they still may not be appropriate for all ethnicities. The World Health Organization (WHO) has also published international Child Growth Standards for children birth to 19 years (www.who.int/childgrowth/en). Their charts include developmental milestones (Windows of Achievement) based on an extensive study of children birth to age 5 from around the world and may more accurately reflect the growth and developmental patterns typical of today's children.

Ideally, children's height and weight should be measured at 4- to 6-month intervals and recorded in their permanent health file. A single measurement is unlikely to identify the child who is experiencing a growth disturbance related to physical illness, dysfunctional parenting, or an eating disorder. Rather, what is most important is the pattern of change that occurs over time. Measurements recorded on standardized growth charts allow comparisons to be made with previous data and can be useful for determining if a child's growth is progressing satisfactorily. Growth charts are available from the Centers for Disease Control & Prevention (CDC) (http://www.cdc.gov/growthcharts).

3-2b Body Mass Index

The body mass index (BMI) is a relatively new screening tool that provides a height-for-weight ratio. It is appropriately used with children 2 years and older to determine their risk of being **underweight**, normal weight, **overweight**, or **obese**. Gender-specific charts for plotting children's BMI-for-age (2–20 years) can be accessed from the CDC (www.cdc.gov/healthyweight/assessing/BMI/index.html). Children who are underweight, overweight, or obese should be referred to a health care provider for further evaluation.

3-2c Vision

Most of what children learn during the early years is acquired through their senses, particularly vision and hearing (Basch, 2011). For this reason, it is important that these systems function properly to avoid disruptions in children's learning and development. Vision impairments affect approximately one in twenty preschoolers and one in four school-age children (Prevent Blindness America, 2010). Some conditions, such as cataracts or blindness, may be present at birth. Others can develop as the result of a head injury or infectious illness, such as meningitis. Vision problems are also more common in children who have other disabilities, such as cerebral palsy, Down syndrome, autism, or fetal alcohol syndrome (FAS) (Jackson, Krishnaswami, & McPheeters, 2011).

Early detection improves the success of medical treatments and a child's readiness for school (Morale et al., 2012). Permanent vision loss can often be avoided by examining an infant's eyes for abnormalities and muscle imbalance during routine well-child checkups. It is also recommended that all young children have a professional eye evaluation performed by an **ophthalmologist** or **optometrist** by age 2 years or

Did You Know...
that infants have extremely poor vision and are unable to see detail, such as facial features, until 3–4 months of age?

underweight – *a BMI of less than 18.5.*
overweight – *a BMI greater than 25.*
obese – *a BMI over 30.*
ophthalmologist – *a physician who specializes in diseases and abnormalities of the eye.*
optometrist – *a specialist (nonphysician) trained to examine eyes and prescribe glasses and eye exercises.*

▼ **Often it is the teacher who first notices signs of a child's vision problem.**

© Cengage Learning

at least before entering kindergarten. Undiagnosed vision problems may cause children to be inappropriately labeled as learning disabled or intellectually challenged when, in fact, they simply cannot see well enough to learn (Marotz & Allen, 2013). The following case study illustrates the point:

In many ways, Tina is a typical 4-year-old, although the teachers have been puzzled by some of her recent behaviors. Tina seems easily frustrated and unable to complete many of the pre-academic tasks that her peers enjoy, such as puzzles, tracing, threading beads, and simple object labeling. She trips over toys, runs into children, and is often reluctant to join her classmates in outdoor games. Tina's teachers are concerned that she may have a learning disability and have begun developmental testing. They also arranged with the school health consultant to have Tina's vision checked and were surprised to learn that it was only 20/100. Tina's mother was encouraged to make an appointment with an eye specialist and, after further testing, it was determined that Tina needed corrective glasses. The teachers are amazed by the changes that Tina's improved ability to see have made in her behavior, social interaction, and academic progress.

Assessment Methods Observing children carefully for specific behavioral indicators is an important first step in the early identification of vision problems (Teacher Checklist 3-1). For example, an infant's vision can be tested informally by holding an object, such as a rattle, 10 to 12 inches away and observing the infant's ability to focus on (fixation) and track (follow) the object as it is moved in a 180-degree arc around the child's head. The infant's eyes should also be observed for any uncoordinated movements as the object is brought closer to (convergence) and farther away from the face. In addition, the blink reflex (sweep hand quickly in front of the eyes; observe for blinking), and pupil response (shine a penlight, held 4 to 6 inches away, into the eye; pupil should become smaller) should also be checked. Infants exhibiting any abnormal responses should be referred for professional evaluation.

Teachers may be the first to notice clues in children's behavior that suggest a vision disorder. Young children are seldom aware or able to communicate to an adult that they are not seeing well, especially if their vision has never been normal. Some vision problems are also difficult to detect because they have no visible signs or symptoms. However, vision problems often become more

 TEACHER CHECKLIST 3-1

Early Signs of Visual Abnormalities in Infants and Toddlers

Observe the infant closely for:
- roving eye movements that are suggestive of blindness
- jerky or fluttering eye movements
- eyes that wander in opposite directions or are crossed (after age 3 months)
- inability to focus or follow a moving object (after age 3 months)
- pupil of one eye larger than the other
- absence of a blink reflex
- drooping of one or both lids
- cloudiness on the eyeball
- chronic tearing

TeachSource Digital Download Download from CourseMate.

TABLE 3–2 Examples of Acuity Tests for Preschool Children

- Denver Eye Screening Test (DEST)
- HOTV Symbols Visual Acuity Test
- Screening Test for Young Children and Retardates (STYCAR) (This test can be used with children who have developmental delays.)
- Snellen "Tumbling" E chart
- Allen Card Test
- Teller Acuity Cards
- Cover-Uncover Test
- Lea Symbols Visual Acuity Test
- Random Dot E Stereoacuity Test

apparent during the school years when children must complete academic work with greater detail and accuracy. Screening tests may confirm a teacher's observations and should be discussed with the child's family. It is also important to help families understand that children's vision problems are not outgrown, nor do they usually improve without treatment.

Teachers and volunteers can be trained by health professionals to administer many of the standardized visual acuity tests (Table 3–2). Printable versions of the Eye Tests for Children (HOTV charts for near and distance vision) can also be downloaded from the Prevent Blindness America website (www.preventblindness.org). Children's eyes should also be checked for:

- convergence
- depth perception (Titmus Fly test)
- binocular fusion (Worth 4-Dot test; Random Dot E)
- deviations in pupil position (Test by holding a penlight 12 inches from the child's face, direct light at the bridge of the nose; the light reflection should appear in the same position on both pupils; any discrepancy requires professional evaluation.)

Photoscreening is a relatively new screening tool that is increasingly being used with young children, especially those who are preverbal, nonverbal, or have developmental delays or disabilities that would make it difficult for them to complete conventional screening procedures (Longmuir et al., 2013). A special camera records a small beam of light as it reflects on the eyeball, and is an especially useful test for the early detection of amblyopia and strabismus. Although it is an efficient and effective screening technology, the equipment is relatively expensive and the test requires special training to administer.

▼ **Early detection and treatment of vision problems improves children's learning success.**

It is important that children understand the instructions and expected response method before any screening test is administered or the results may be invalid. Children who fail an initial screening should be retested within 2 weeks. If a second screening is failed, testing results should be shared with the child's family and a referral made to a professional eye specialist for a comprehensive evaluation.

The early detection and treatment of vision impairments in children has been targeted as a major goal in the *Healthy People 2020* initiative. Efforts to increase public awareness and to reach children in medically underserved areas are aimed at combating unnecessary and irreversible vision loss. Information about the symptoms of common visual impairments, testing procedures, and treatments is available on many professional organization websites, including Prevent Blindness America (http://www.preventblindness.org), American Academy of Ophthalmology (http://www.aao.org), American Academy of Pediatrics (http://www.aap.org), and the American Association of Pediatric Ophthalmology and Strabismus (http://www.aapos.org).

TEACHER CHECKLIST 3-2

Signs of Visual Acuity Problems in Older Children

- rubs eyes frequently
- attempts to brush away blurs
- is irritable with close work
- is inattentive to distant tasks, e.g., watching a movie, catching a ball
- strains to see distant objects, squints, or screws up face
- blinks often when reading, holds books too close or far away
- is inattentive with close work, quits after a short time
- closes or covers one eye to see better
- tilts head to one side
- appears cross-eyed at times
- reverses letters, words
- stumbles over objects, runs into things
- complains of repeated headaches or double vision
- exhibits poor eye-hand coordination
- experiences repeated sties, redness, or watery eyes

TeachSource Digital Download Download from CourseMate.

▶❚❚ **TeachSource** Video Connections

© 2015 Cengage Learning

0–2 Years: Sensation and Perception, Vision in Infants and Toddlers

Although infants see poorly at birth, their visual system matures rapidly in the months that follow. Improvements in the infant's ability to see are critical to learning and developments in other sensory systems. As you watch the learning video, *0–2 Years: Sensation and Perception, Vision in Infants and Toddlers*, consider the following questions:

1. Explain the term "tracking."
2. What does the infant's ability to track an object indicate?
3. What purpose does depth perception serve the infant?

Watch on CourseMate.

Common Disorders Vision screening programs are designed to detect three common disorders in young children, including:

- amblyopia
- strabismus
- myopia

Amblyopia, or "lazy eye," affects approximately 2 percent of all children younger than 10 years. Children born to mothers who smoke seem to be at higher risk for developing this and other vision disorders (Borchert et al., 2011). Amblyopia is caused by a muscle imbalance or childhood cataracts that result in blurred or double vision. The child's brain is confused by the distortion and begins to acknowledge only images received from the stronger eye while ignoring (suppressing) those from the weaker or "lazy" eye. Consequently, sight is gradually lost in the weaker eye as a result of disuse. This condition also causes a loss of depth perception, which requires comparable sight in both eyes.

Early identification and treatment of amblyopia is critical for preventing permanent vision loss. However, this condition is often overlooked and treatment delayed because there are no visible signs or abnormalities and children are seldom aware that anything is wrong with their vision. For these reasons, it is important that young children have periodic routine screenings and comprehensive eye examinations. A significant portion of the child's eyesight can often be restored if amblyopia is diagnosed before the age of 6 or 7. Even greater improvements

amblyopia – *a condition of the eye commonly referred to as "lazy eye"; vision gradually becomes blurred or distorted due to unequal balance of the eye muscles. There are no observable abnormalities of the eyes when a child has amblyopia.*

may be achieved when this condition is diagnosed and treated before the age of 2 years. However, research suggests that children as old as 12 may regain some lost sight with treatment (Gunton, 2013).

Several methods are used to treat amblyopia. One of the more common treatments involves patching the child's stronger (unaffected) eye for several hours each day until muscles in the weaker (affected) eye gradually become stronger. Other treatment methods include corrective glasses, eye drops, special eye exercises, and surgery. Teachers may be asked to administer treatments while children are in school. They must understand the importance of maintaining a child's treatment schedule and be supportive when children resist or are embarrassed by having to wear special glasses or a patch. Added safety precautions, such as clearing obstacles from pathways and guiding children through unfamiliar spaces, may need to be taken to avoid injury during treatments. Teachers can use these opportunities to help all children develop greater respect and acceptance of individuals who have special needs.

Strabismus, commonly referred to as crossed eyes, affects approximately 3 to 5 percent of young children (Optometrists Network, 2012). Strabismus causes an observable misalignment of the child's eyes (for example, both eyes may turn inward or one eye may turn inward or outward) that occurs intermittently or consistently. Because the eyes are not able to work together as one unit, children may experience symptoms similar to those of amblyopia, including

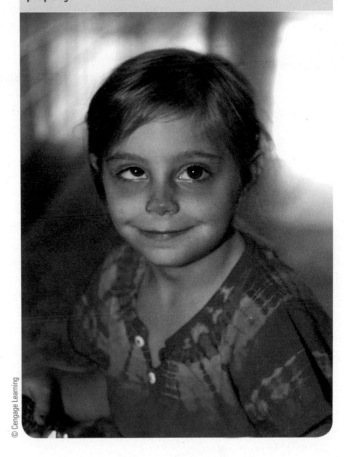

▼ **Strabismus interferes with children's ability to see properly.**

© Cengage Learning

double or blurred vision, images from the weaker eye being ignored by the brain, and gradual vision loss.

Early recognition and treatment of strabismus is essential for restoring normal vision. Today, even infants are being treated aggressively for this condition. Although uncoordinated eye movements are common in very young infants, their eyes should begin moving together as a unit by 4 months of age. Treatments for strabismus include surgical correction, patching of the unaffected eye, and eye exercises.

Myopia, or nearsightedness, can affect young children, but is more common in school-aged children. A child who is nearsighted sees near objects clearly, but has poor distant vision. This condition is especially problematic for young children because they move about quickly and engage in play that involves running, jumping, and climbing. As a result, children who have myopia may appear clumsy, and repeatedly stumble or run into objects. Squinting is also common as children attempt to bring distant objects into focus. Teachers can be instrumental in noting these behaviors and referring children for comprehensive screening.

Farsightedness, or **hyperopia**, is thought to be a normal occurrence in children under the age of 5 due to a shortness of their eyeball (Tarczy-Hornoch, 2012). This condition often corrects itself as children mature and the eyeball enlarges and changes shape. Children who are farsighted see distant objects clearly but have difficulty focusing on near objects. Older children

---

strabismus – *a condition of the eyes in which one or both eyes appear to be turned inward (crossed) or outward (walleye).*
myopia – *nearsightedness; an individual has good near vision but poor distant vision.*
hyperopia – *farsightedness; a condition of the eyes in which an individual can see distant objects clearly but has poor close vision.*

may struggle academically, read poorly, have a short attention span, and complain of headaches, tired eyes, or blurred vision following periods of close work. Because hyperopia can be difficult to detect with most routinely administered screening procedures, teacher and parent observations may provide the best initial clues to this disorder. A child who exhibits signs of hyperopia should be referred to a professional eye specialist for evaluation.

Color blindness affects a small percentage of children and is generally limited to males. Females are carriers of this hereditary defect but are rarely affected. The most common form of color blindness involves the inability to discriminate between red and green. Testing young children for color blindness is difficult and often omitted because learning is not seriously affected and there is no corrective treatment.

Management When a vision problem is suspected, the child's family should be counseled and encouraged to arrange for professional evaluation. Teachers can assist families in locating services and reinforce the importance of following through with treatment recommendations. Vision testing can often be arranged through pediatricians' offices, "well-child" clinics, public health departments, professional eye doctors, and public schools. Local service organizations, such as the Lions Clubs, may assist qualified families with the costs of professional eye examinations and glasses.

Children who do not pass an initial vision screening should be retested. Failure to pass a second screening necessitates referral to a professional eye specialist for comprehensive evaluation and diagnosis. Results obtained from routine vision screening tests should be viewed with caution because they do not guarantee that a problem does or does not exist. Also, most routine screening procedures are not designed to detect all types of vision impairments. For these reasons, there will always be some over-referral of children who do not have a vision disorder, while other children may be missed. It is for this reason that teachers' and families' observations are extremely important. Children's visual acuity can also change over time, so it is important that adults be continuously vigilant of children's visual performance.

3-2d Hearing

Each year approximately 12,000 infants in the United States are born with a hearing loss (March of Dimes, 2011). Undetected hearing losses can have a profound effect on children's language acquisition, social interactions, emotional development, and learning abilities (Laws et al., 2012). When children do not hear properly, they may respond and behave in seemingly unacceptable ways. This can lead to incorrect labels such as slow learner, cognitively challenged, or behavior problem. The early diagnosis of hearing impairments or severe loss is, therefore, extremely critical.

Assessment Methods Inappropriate responses and behaviors may be the first indication that a child is not hearing properly. Signs of hearing loss can range from obvious problems to those that are subtle and difficult to identify (Teacher Checklist 3-3).

Hospitals in most states now comply with Universal Infant Hearing Screening recommendations (Deem, Diaz-Ordaz, & Shiner, 2012). Trained hospital personnel test infants' hearing shortly after birth to detect deafness so that early intervention services can be initiated. An interactive map listing state-by-state testing sites and services is available at the National Center for Hearing Assessment and Management (NCHAM) website (http://www.infanthearing.org/states/index.html).

An infant's hearing development should continue to be monitored by checking behavioral responses such as eye blinking or attempts to locate sounds (e.g., stop crying, turn head, interrupt sucking) (Teacher Checklist 3-4). Older infants and toddlers can be

Did You Know...

that over 5 million children and adolescents have permanent hearing loss caused by exposure to excessive noise levels?

?

TEACHER CHECKLIST 3-3

Behavioral Indicators of Children's Hearing Loss

Families and teachers may observe behaviors that suggest a possible hearing loss, such as:
- frequent mouth breathing
- failure to turn toward the direction of a sound
- delays in acquiring language; development of poor speech patterns
- difficulty understanding and following directions
- asking to have statements repeated
- rubbing or pulling at ears
- mumbling, shouting, or talking loudly
- reluctance to interact with others; quiet or withdrawn
- using gestures rather than words
- excelling in activities that do not depend on hearing
- imitating others at play
- responding to questions inappropriately
- mispronouncing many word sounds
- having an unusual voice quality—one that is extremely high, low, hoarse, or monotone
- failing to respond to normal sounds and voices

TeachSource Digital Download   Download from CourseMate.

assessed by observing as they search for sounds (often emitted through speakers in formal testing procedures), as well as by the appropriateness of their responses and language development. Although these procedures can be useful for identifying some children with hearing disorders, they are not effective for detecting all forms of hearing loss.

Children's hearing should be formally tested by a trained specialist, such as a nurse or **audiologist**, at least once during the preschool and school-age years and more often if a hearing problem is suspected. Hearing tests evaluate a child's ability to hear the normal range of tones used in everyday conversation.

Most children are able to complete routine hearing screenings with minimal instruction. However, an unfamiliar situation involving new people, instruments and equipment, a novel task, a lack of understanding, or failure to cooperate may occasionally interfere with a child's performance and yield unreliable test results. These factors must be taken into consideration if an initial screening is failed, and arrangements made to have the child retested at a later date to confirm or rule out the initial findings. Children who pass a hearing test yet continue to exhibit behaviors suggestive of a hearing loss should continue to be monitored.

TEACHER CHECKLIST 3-4

Early Signs of Hearing Loss in Infants and Toddlers

Observe the infant closely for:
- absence of a startle response to a loud noise
- failure to stop crying briefly when adult speaks to baby (3 months)
- failure to turn head in the direction of sound, such as a doorbell or a dog barking (4 months)
- absence of babbling or interest in imitating simple speech sounds (6–8 months)
- no response to adult commands, such as "no" or "come"

TeachSource Digital Download   Download from CourseMate.

audiologist – *a specially prepared clinician who uses nonmedical techniques to diagnose hearing impairments.*

▼ **Hearing screenings are conducted by an audiologist or specially trained personnel.**

© Brian Eichhorn/Shutterstock.com

Teachers and families should always prepare young children for hearing screenings so they know in advance what to expect. Play activities that require children to practice listening skills and wearing headphones (e.g., disk jockey, airplane pilot, musician) will help increase their comfort level with screening procedures. Teachers should also make an effort to determine what response method (such as raising one hand, pressing a button, pointing to pictures, or dropping a wooden block into an empty can) children will be expected to use during the screening and practice this activity in advance. If a special room is to be used for testing purposes, children should be given an opportunity to visit the facilities and equipment beforehand. This will help to reduce their anxiety and increase the reliability of test results.

Common Disorders   Children who are born with any physical disability have an increased risk of also experiencing hearing problems (Marotz & Allen, 2013). Temporary and permanent hearing losses can affect one or both ears and are commonly associated with:

▶ a family history of hearing problems
▶ prenatal exposure to maternal infections, such as herpes, German measles, or cytomegalovirus
▶ prematurity, low birthweight
▶ bacterial meningitis, measles, mumps
▶ allergies
▶ frequent colds and ear infections (otitis media)
▶ birth defects, such as Down syndrome, fetal alcohol syndrome (FAS), cleft lip/cleft palate, cerebral palsy
▶ head injuries
▶ exposure to excessive or prolonged noise

Any parent who expresses concern about a child's hearing should always be acknowledged and encouraged to seek professional advice. The most common forms of childhood hearing loss are:

Did You Know...

that ears are important for maintaining balance and allow you to hear even when you are asleep?

?

▶ **Conductive loss** affects the volume of word tones. For example, this child will be able to hear loud, but not soft, sounds. Conductive hearing loss occurs when sound waves are not transmitted properly from the external ear to structures in the middle ear (Figure 3–2). Foreign objects, excess wax, and fluid accumulation in the child's middle ear following an infection are common causes of conductive hearing loss.
▶ **Sensorineural loss** results when the structures of the inner ear (cochlea) or the auditory nerve (which connects to the brain) have been damaged or do not function properly. This type of hearing loss is permanent and affects a child's ability to understand speech and to hear sounds. Children who have a sensorineural loss are considered to have a learning disability that requires special educational management.
▶ **Mixed hearing loss** refers to a disorder that involves a combination of conductive and sensorineural hearing losses. Structures in both the outer or middle ear and the inner ear or auditory nerve have either been damaged or are no longer functional.

conductive loss – *affects the volume of word tones heard, so that loud sounds are more likely to be heard than soft sounds.*
sensorineural loss – *a type of loss that occurs when sound impulses cannot reach the brain due to damage of the auditory nerve, or cannot be interpreted because of prior brain damage.*
mixed hearing loss – *a disorder that involves a combination of conductive and sensorineural hearing losses.*

Management A child who experiences a sudden or gradual hearing loss should be referred to a health care provider for a medical diagnosis or to an audiologist for a comprehensive hearing evaluation. Families can arrange for this testing through the child's physician, a speech and hearing clinic, public health department, public school, or an audiologist.

Hearing loss can often be successfully treated if it is identified in the early stages. Treatment methods depend on the underlying cause and range from prescription ear drops and antibiotic therapy to surgery (Elloy & Marshall, 2012). Some children who experience permanent hearing loss benefit from hearing aids, whereas others may receive cochlear implants or eventually learn sign language.

Teachers who understand how various impairments affect children's ability to hear can take appropriate steps to improve communication and modify learning environments (Teacher Checklist 3-5). Additional information about hearing impairments, testing procedures, and resources for families can be accessed on the American Association of Speech-Language-Hearing Association website (http://www.asha.org).

FIGURE 3–2   Diagram of the ear.

Outer Ear, Middle Ear, Inner Ear, Auditory Nerve, Ear Canal, Cochlea, Ear Drum

3-2e Speech and Language

Throughout the early years, children make impressive gains in the number of words they understand (receptive vocabulary) and use to express themselves (expressive vocabulary) (Table 3–3). Children's receptive vocabulary develops earlier and is usually more extensive than their expressive vocabulary. For example, most toddlers understand and can follow simple directions long before they use words to verbalize their wants or needs. Children's language becomes increasingly fluent and complex with maturation and practice.

Although many factors influence children's **speech** and language development, the ability to hear is especially important during the early years when children are learning to imitate sounds,

TEACHER CHECKLIST 3-5
Strategies for Communicating with Children Who Are Hearing-Impaired

- Reduce background noises, such as musical tapes, radio, motors, or fans that can interfere with a child's limited ability to hear.
- Provide individualized versus group instructions.
- Face and stand near the child when speaking.
- Bend down to the child's level; this makes it easier for the child to hear and understand what is being said.
- Speak slowly and clearly.
- Use gestures or pictures to illustrate what is being said; for example, point to the door when it is time to go outside.
- Demonstrate what the child is expected to do; for example, pick up a bead and thread it on a shoestring.

TeachSource Digital Download Download from CourseMate.

speech – *the process of using words to express one's thoughts and ideas.*

TABLE 3–3   Speech and Language Developmental Milestones

Infants	
birth–4 months	• turns to locate the source of sound • begins to coo and make babbling sounds: *baa, aah, ooh* • imitates own voice and sounds
4–8 months	• repeats syllables in a series: *ba, ba, ba* • "talks" to self • responds to simple commands: *no, come*
8–12 months	• recognizes labels for common objects: shoe, blanket, cup • "talks" in one word sentences to convey ideas or requests: *cookie* (meaning, "I want a cookie")

Toddlers	
12–24 months	• follows simple directions • knows and uses 10–30 words • points to pictures and body parts on request and asks frequently, "What's that?" "Why?" • enjoys being read to • understands 200–300 words • speaks in 2–3 word sentences • has speech that is 65–70 percent understandable
24–36 months	• refers to self as "me": "Me do it myself." • uses language to get desired attention or object • understands simple concepts when asked: "Find the small ball." • follows simple directions: "It's time to get dressed." • understands and uses 50–300 new words • has speech that is 70–80 percent understandable

Preschoolers	
3–6 years	• answers simple questions appropriately • describes objects, events, and experiences in fairly detailed terms • sings simple songs and recites nursery rhymes • carries on detailed telephone conversations • makes up and tells stories; acquires a vocabulary of approximately 10,000–14,000 words by age 6 • uses verb tenses and word order correctly

School-age	
6–8 years	• enjoys talking and conversing with adults • uses language, in place of physical aggression, to express feelings • tells jokes and riddles • understands complex statements and performs multistep requests • finds pleasure in writing stories, letters, and e-mail messages • expresses self fluently and in elaborate detail
9-12 years	• talks nonstop • understands grammatical sequences and uses them appropriately • speaks in longer, complex sentences • uses and understands irony and sarcasm • achieves mastery of language development • becomes a thoughtful listener

Adapted from Marotz L. R., & Allen, K. E. (2013). *Developmental profiles: Pre-birth through adolescence* (7th ed.). Belmont, CA: Wadsworth Cengage Learning.

words, and word patterns. Hearing disorders can jeopardize the normal acquisition of speech and language development and lead to long-term speech impairments. Whenever there is concern about the progress of a child's language development, a comprehensive hearing evaluation is always recommended.

It is also important to consider a child's home environment when evaluating language development. Families support children's language skills by reading aloud, engaging children in frequent conversation, and providing literacy-rich opportunities (e.g., books, singing, playing). Homes where these opportunities are lacking may limit children's ability to develop language, acquire vocabulary, and practice communication skills.

Young children also acquire early speech and language skills by imitating speech that is heard in their homes (Venuti et al., 2012). For example, children who have a parent with an unusual voice inflection or speech impairment are likely to exhibit similar qualities. Children who live in bilingual homes may take longer to acquire language skills because they must learn to think and speak in multiple languages (Dixon, Wu, & Daraghmeh, 2012). Cultural values and variations also exert a strong influence on children's language usage, style, and speech patterns.

Assessment Methods Families are often aware of children's speech problems but may not know if action needs to be taken or where to go for help. Many adults also believe erroneously that children will eventually outgrow these disorders, so they take no action. Indeed, some children have developmentally appropriate **misarticulations** that will improve with time. For example, many 3-year-olds mispronounce "r" as "w" as in "wabbit" (rabbit) or "s" as "th" as in "thong" (song); by age 4 or 5 they are able to correctly pronounce these letter sounds. Nevertheless, children who demonstrate speech or speech patterns that are not developmentally appropriate should be referred to a speech therapist for evaluation (McQuiston & Kloczko, 2011). A hearing test should be included in this evaluation to rule out the possibility of a hearing loss that could be affecting the child's speech. Speech and hearing clinics are often affiliated with colleges and universities, medical centers, child development centers, public health departments, public schools, and Head Start programs. Certified speech and hearing specialists can also be located in telephone directories or Internet listings or by contacting local school districts or the American Speech, Language, and Hearing Association.

Common Disorders The term *speech impairment* has many different meanings to persons working with children. For some, the term implies obvious problems, such as stuttering, lisping, or unintelligent speech patterns. For others, any deviation may be cause for concern, such as a monotone voice, nasality, improper pitch of the voice, a voice tone that is too high or too low, misarticulations, or omissions of certain letter sounds.

Delayed language development or abnormal speech patterns that persist for more than a few months should be evaluated and include:

- no speech by 2 years of age
- stuttering
- substitution of word sounds
- rate of speech that is too fast or unusually slow
- monotone voice
- no improvement in speech development
- speech by age 3 that is difficult to understand
- inattentive behavior or ignoring others

Management Families and teachers serve as important role models and promote children's speech and language skills through frequent communication opportunities and experiences. Teachers can be instrumental in identifying and referring children who have speech and language patterns that are developmentally inappropriate or that interfere with effective communication. Significant improvements can often be achieved when these disorders are identified and treated in their earliest stages.

misarticulations – *improper pronunciations of words and word sounds.*

3-2f Nutritional Status

The quality of children's diets has an unquestionable effect on brain development, behavior, and health. However, rising costs and economic struggles have forced many families to sacrifice the quantity and nutritional value of foods they purchase and serve to children. Television advertising, fast food consumption, and increasing reliance on prepackaged and convenience foods have contributed to a further decline in children's nutrient intake at a time when obesity rates are climbing.

Valuable clues about a child's nutritional status can be obtained during daily health observations. Signs such as facial **pallor**, dry skin, bleeding gums, **lethargy**, or frequent illness may reflect poor eating habits. In contrast, a healthy, well-nourished child has:

- height appropriate for age
- weight appropriate for height
- bright, clear eyes—no puffiness, crusting, or paleness of inner lids
- clear skin—good color; no pallor or scaliness
- teeth—appropriate number for age; no caries or **mottling**
- gums—pink and firm; not puffy, dark red, or bleeding
- lips—soft, moist; no cracking at corner of mouth
- tongue—pink; no cracks, white patches, or bright red color

Assessment Methods   Selecting an appropriate method for evaluating children's nutritional status depends upon the child's age, reason for concern, type of information desired, and available resources. Common methods include:

- dietary assessment—used to determine nutrient adequacy and areas of nutrient deficiencies in the child's eating patterns. Food intake is recorded for a specified time period (24 hours, 3 days, 1 week) (Figure 3–3). The data is then analyzed by using one of several methods, such as nutrient analysis software, Reference Daily Intakes (RDIs), or MyPlate. (See Chapter 12.)
- anthropometric assessment—based on height, weight, BMI, and head circumference measurements that are compared to standardized norms. **Skinfold** thickness and mid-arm circumference measurements may also be taken to estimate body fat percentage.
- clinical assessment—involves observing a child for signs of nutritional deficiency (Table 3–4). This is not considered a reliable method because of its subjective nature and the fact that physical symptoms typically do not appear until a deficiency is severe.
- biochemical assessment—involves laboratory testing of various body tissues and fluids, such as urinalysis or hemoglobin (testing for iron level) to validate concerns related to over- or underconsumption of nutrients. These tests must be ordered by a health care provider and performed by trained laboratory technicians.

Common Disorders—Malnutrition and Obesity   Teachers and families should be alert to several nutritional problems that can have a significant effect on children's health and development. Malnutrition, for example, occurs when children's diets lack essential nutrients, especially protein, vitamins A and C, iron, and calcium for prolonged periods. Misinformation or inadequate nutrition knowledge, poverty, and food insufficiencies may leave children malnourished simply because they do not get enough to eat or are consuming unhealthy foods (Franklin et al., 2012). Long-term use of certain medications such as steroids, aspirin, antibiotics, and laxatives or the lack of exposure to sunshine can interfere with nutrient absorption and deplete children of essential vitamins and minerals. Malnourished children often fail to reach typical growth and developmental standards and are at greater risk for behavior and learning problems, communicable

---

pallor – *paleness.*
lethargy – *a state of inaction or indifference.*
mottling – *marked with spots of dense white or brown coloring.*
skinfold – *a measurement of the amount of fat under the skin; also referred to as fat-fold measurements.*

FIGURE 3–3 Sample questionnaire for obtaining information about a child's eating habits.

DIETARY ASSESSMENT

Dear Parent:

Nutrition is a very important part of our program. In order to plan appropriate nutrition-education activities and menus, we would like to know more about your child's eating patterns. Please take the time to fill out the questionnaire carefully.

CHILD'S NAME _____ AGE _____ DATE _____

1. How many days a week does your child eat the following meals or snacks?
   a morning meal _____   a midafternoon snack _____
   a lunch or midday meal _____   an evening snack _____
   an evening meal _____   snack during the night _____
   a midmorning snack _____

2. When is your child most hungry?
   morning _____
   noon _____
   evening _____

3. What are some of your child's favorite foods? _____

4. What foods does your child dislike?
   _____

5. Is your child on a special diet? Yes _____   No _____
   If yes, why? _____ _____
   Describe diet _____
   Diet prescribed by whom? _____

6. Does your child eat things not usually considered food, e.g., paste, dirt, paper? _____
   If yes, what is eaten? _____
   How often? _____

7. Is your child taking a vitamin or mineral supplement?
   Yes _____   No _____   If yes, what kind? _____

8. Does your child have any dental problems that might create a problem when eating certain foods? _____

9. Does your child see a dentist regularly? _____

10. Does your child have any diet-related health problems?
    Diabetes _____ Allergies _____ Lactose Intolerance _____ Other _____

11. Is your child taking any medication for a diet-related health problem?
    _____

12. How much water does your child typically drink throughout the day?
    _____

13. Please list any foods that should be included or avoided for cultural or religious reasons.
    _____

14. Please list as accurately as possible what your child eats and drinks on a typical day. If yesterday was a typical day, you may use those foods and drinks.

TIME	PLACE	FOOD	AMOUNT

TABLE 3–4   Physical Signs of Malnutrition

Tissue	Sign	Cause
Face	Pallor	Niacin, iron deficiency
	Scaling of skin around nostrils	Riboflavin, B6 deficiency
Eyes	Hardening of cornea and lining: pale lining	Iron deficiency
	Foamy spots in cornea	Vitamin A deficiency
Lips	Redness; swelling of mouth and lips; cracking at corners of mouth	Riboflavin deficiency
Teeth	Decayed or missing	Excess sugar (or poor dental hygiene)
	Mottled enamel	Excess fluoride
Tongue	Red, raw, cracked, swollen	Niacin deficiency
	Magenta color	Riboflavin deficiency
	Pale	Iron deficiency
Gums	Spongy, red, bleeding	Vitamin C deficiency
Skin	Dry, flaking	Vitamin A deficiency
	Small underskin hemorrhages	Vitamin C deficiency
Nails	Brittle, ridged	Iron deficiency

illness, infection, chronic irritability, anemia, and fatigue. However, not all malnourished children are thin and emaciated. Some overweight children are also malnourished because their diets lack the proteins, vitamins, and minerals essential for healthy growth and development.

Obesity also presents a serious challenge to children's health. Approximately 33 percent of all children in the United States are considered obese or overweight for their age (AHA, 2012). Although the causes of childhood obesity are multiple and complex, the primary factors point to inactivity and unhealthy eating behaviors (Shi et al., 2013). Because these patterns are well-established during the early years and often persist throughout adulthood, it is important that corrective measures be taken while children are young. Children who are overweight or obese are at significantly greater risk for developing life-threatening health problems including heart disease, stroke, sleep apnea, asthma, and diabetes. They also experience a higher rate of bullying, psychological problems, and academic failure.

▼ **Increasing children's physical activity is an effective weight management strategy.**

© Cengage Learning

Management Obesity in young children cannot be ignored. Although prevention is always ideal, steps can be taken to help children of any age implement healthy eating and activity behaviors (Brotman et al., 2012). For maximum success, weight management approaches must include the collaborative efforts of the child, family, teachers, and health care personnel, and target:

- meal planning and establishing healthy eating habits
- strategies for increasing children's daily activity level (For example, children can be asked to run errands, walk a pet, help with daily household chores, or ride their bike to school.)
- acquainting children with new outside interests, hobbies, or activities, such as hiking, swimming, dancing, roller skating, neighborhood baseball, soccer, or learning to ride a bike (Involvement in fun activities can divert children's attention away from food.)
- finding ways to help children experience success and develop a positive self-image (For example, acknowledging children's efforts can boost self-esteem. For many children, positive adult attention replaces food as an important source of personal gratification.)

CONNECTING TO EVERYDAY PRACTICE

Children and Poverty

The U.S. Census Bureau redefined the term poverty so that it more accurately reflects today's economic standards (U.S. Census Bureau, 2011). However, current guidelines continue to exclude many families whose income is often not adequate to meet even minimal requirements for food, clothing, shelter, and health care. Race, ethnicity, immigrant status, and single-parenting place many children and their families at the highest risk for living in poverty (National Kids Count, 2012). Although a majority of adults in these families are employed, they often work in minimum wage jobs. Health care and insurance are luxuries that many cannot afford. Changes in eligibility guidelines for various government assistance programs (food, cash, medical care, housing, child care, and job training) have further reduced some families' access to resources that affect children's health. It is estimated that 1 in 4 children under 18 years (32 million) in the United States live in low-income or poverty families; children under 6 years account for nearly half of this number. Increased poverty has contributed to more homelessness and food insecurity (including obesity), especially among families with children—currently the fastest growing segment of the homeless population (NCTSN, 2011).

Think About This:

▶ Why is it important that teachers be aware of changes in national fiscal policy and federal programs?

▶ What effects would you expect poverty to have on children's early brain development?

▶ What physical and mental health problems might you anticipate if you were working with children who are economically disadvantaged?

▶ What steps can classroom teachers take to meet the special developmental and educational needs of children living in economically disadvantaged families?

▶ What resources are available in your community to assist low-income families with children?

Childhood obesity will be discussed throughout the book because of its current importance, complexity, and serious health consequences.

Long-term weight management is achieved by attending to all aspects of a child's well-being—physical, emotional, spiritual, and social. Placing children on weight reduction plans is not advisable unless they are under a doctor's or dietitian's supervision. Careful attention must be given to planning weight reduction programs that meet children's critical nutrient needs for sustained growth and development. Adults who model healthy eating and an active lifestyle are also in a position to have a positive influence on children's preferences and weight management behaviors. Additional ideas for healthy eating and physical activities will be addressed throughout the book and are also available on numerous websites, including the President's Council on Fitness, Sports & Nutrition (http://www.fitness.gov), the USDA's MyPlate for Kids (http://www.choosemyplate.gov), the CDC's Division of Adolescent and School Health (http://www.cdc.gov/healthyyouth/npao/index.htm), and the National Center for Physical Development and Outdoor Play (http://www.aahperd.org/headstartbodystart).

Did You Get It?

When working with children of varying _____, educators must be aware of the role that genetics plays in physical growth potential.

   a. cultures

   b. cultures, races, and ethnicities

   c. ethnicities

   d. socioeconomic backgrounds

Take the full quiz on CourseMate.

▶❚❚ TeachSource Video Connections

Students with Special Needs: The Referral and Evaluation Process

Teachers play a central role in the early identification of children who may be experiencing developmental or academic challenges. They often initiate the evaluation process and meet with colleagues and families to discuss the child's special needs. As you watch the learning video, *Students with Special Needs: The Referral and Evaluation Process,* consider the following questions:

1. Why is it important to conduct a careful assessment before contacting the child's family?

2. What are the advantages of using a team approach for assessment?

3. Are there disadvantages to a team approach? Explain.

4. Why would it be important to include a vision and hearing screening in this assessment?

Watch on CourseMate.

© 2015 Cengage Learning

3-3 Referrals

A **referral** is made by sharing observation and screening test results with a child's family and assisting them in identifying appropriate follow-up resources. Referrals are most successful when teachers have established cooperative and trusting partnerships with children's families. Knowing something about their beliefs, customs, values, and community resources improves a teacher's ability to make effective referrals. For example, mistrust of the medical profession, poverty, job conflicts, religious beliefs, a lack of transportation, or limited education may affect a family's ability and willingness to follow through with any recommendation.

Meeting with the child's family, or calling them on the telephone, is often the most effective method for making referrals:

Teacher: "I am concerned about Ryan's vision. On several occasions, I have noticed that his right eye turns inward more than the left eye and that he holds his head close to materials when he is working. Have you observed any of these behaviors at home?"

Parent: "Yes, but we didn't think it was anything to worry about. We thought he was just tired or trying to be funny."

Teacher: "I can't be sure that anything is wrong with Ryan's eyesight, but the behaviors I have observed may indicate a vision problem and should be evaluated by an eye specialist. I will provide a written copy of my observations that you can take along. Please let me know if I can be of assistance in locating a doctor, and the outcome of Ryan's evaluation."

Although a face-to-face meeting with the child's family is always preferable, a well-written letter may be the only way to reach some families. Copies of all screening test results should be given to families so they can be shared with the child's doctor. When medical personnel have access to this information, they are better able to understand how the child's behavior is being affected. Teachers can also alleviate some of the family's frustration by offering information about local resources, such as hospitals, clinics, health departments, medical specialists, public and private agencies, volunteer organizations, and funding sources where services can be obtained.

A follow-up contact should always be made after several days to determine if families have been successful in securing a professional evaluation. The occasion can also be used to learn about the child's diagnosis, treatment plan, and any instructional or environmental modifications that a teacher may need to make. It is also an ideal time to acknowledge the family's efforts in following through with recommendations and to convey the teacher's genuine interest in the child's well-being.

----

referral – *directing an individual to other sources, usually for additional evaluation or treatment.*

Did You Get It?

A face-to-face meeting with parents or guardians is _____ for the referral process.

a. a legal requirement
b. a legal and ethical requirement
c. ideal but not always possible
d. unnecessary

Take the full quiz on CourseMate.

PARTNERING with FAMILIES

Children's Eye Safety

Dear Families,

Each year, thousands of children sustain eye injuries as the result of hazardous conditions at home or school. The majority of these injuries are preventable through proper supervision, careful selection of toys and equipment, and use of appropriate eye protection. You play an important role in identifying potentially dangerous situations and taking steps to protect children from unnecessary exposure or risk. It is also important that you take similar precautions to protect your own eye safety and serve as a positive role model for children.

▶ Never shake an infant! Vigorous shaking can cause serious eye damage and blindness.

▶ Insist that children wear sunglasses whenever they play outdoors to limit exposure to ultraviolet (UV) light. Over time, UV exposure increases the risk of developing a number of serious eye conditions, including macular degeneration and cataracts. Purchase sunglasses that fit closely, wrap around the entire eye area, and provide UV-A and UV-B protection.

▶ Keep children indoors whenever mowing or edging the lawn. Stones, sticks, and small debris can become dangerous projectiles.

▶ Select toys and play equipment based on your child's age and abilities. Avoid toys with projectile parts, such as darts, slingshots, pellet guns, and missile-launching devices.

▶ Monitor children's access to items, such as stones, rubber bands, balls, wire coat hangers, and fish hooks that pose a serious eye danger.

▶ Supervise children closely whenever they are using a sharp item, such as a fork, pencil, toothpicks, wire, paperclips, scissors, or small wooden dowels.

▶ Keep children away from fireworks. Do not allow them to light fireworks or to be near anyone while they are doing so.

▶ Lock up household cleaners, sprays, paints, paint thinners, and chemicals such as garden fertilizers and pesticides that could injure children's eyes.

▶ Make sure children wear appropriate protective eyewear, such as goggles or a helmet with a face guard, when participating in sports.

▶ Don't allow children to shine a laser pointer or aim a squirt gun or spray nozzle toward anyone's eyes.

▶ Remind children to avoid touching their eyes with unwashed hands.

CLASSROOM CORNER

Teacher Activities

My Five Senses...

(NHES PreK–2; National Health Education Standard 1.2.2)

Concept: Seeing, hearing, tasting, touching, and smelling are your five senses.

Learning Objectives

‣ Children will learn to name all five senses.

‣ Children will learn which body parts go with which senses: see with eyes, hear with ears, taste with tongue, touch with fingers and skin, and smell with nose.

Supplies

‣ Small blanket; various objects (items that children can label—plastic foods, animals, people, and so on); small paper cups; tin foil; various scents or foods (vanilla, orange peel, ketchup, peppermint, chocolate, ranch dressing, green pepper, etc.); tape recording of children's and teachers' voices; feely box; various items with shapes that children can recognize (ball, pine cone, banana, block, plate, cup, and so on); salty (crackers), sweet (mandarin orange), sour (lemon), and bitter (unsweetened chocolate) items; hand wipes; plates; forks

Learning Activities

‣ Read and discuss the following books:

- *Your Five Senses* by Bobbi Katz
- *The Sense of Hearing* by Elaine Landau
- *You Smell with Your Nose* by Melvin Berger
- *You Touch with Your Fingers* by Melvin & Gilda Berger

‣ Each day discuss one of the senses and have the children participate in an activity.

‣ Seeing—Tell the children that you are going to play a game called "What's Missing?" This is a game that uses their sense of seeing. Place four to five objects out on the floor in front of the children. Name each item, and then line the items up in a way so that all the children can see them. Place the towel over the items. Remove one of the items and wrap it in the towel. Ask children to guess which item is missing. Call on children one at a time; if they name the missing item, they can come up and hide the next item. Continue until all children have had a turn. Vary the toys to keep children interested.

‣ Smelling—Tell the children that you are going to do an activity to learn about their sense of smell. Make "smelling cups": for liquid scents, put a few drops on a cotton ball and place it in the cup. Cover the cup with foil in which holes have been poked. Pass the cups around. Have children smell each cup and try to guess what the smell is. After each child has had a chance to smell each cup, remove the foil so they can see if they were correct.

‣ Hearing—Make a recording of the teachers and children while they are playing. On another day, tell the children that they will use their sense of hearing for this activity. Play the recording and see if the children can guess whose voices they are hearing on the tape.

‣ Feeling—Tell the children that this activity will involve using their sense of touch. Place various items in a feely box. Have each child reach in and use their sense of touch to determine what the object is.

(continued)

CLASSROOM CORNER

Teacher Activities *(continued)*

▶ Tasting—Tell the children you are going to have them taste some different items to see if they are sweet, sour, salty, or bitter. Tell them that their tongue has little things called taste buds on it that help them know what a food tastes like. Next, have all the children wash their hands with a wipe. Place a cracker, a mandarin orange, a small piece of lemon, and bit of unsweetened chocolate on each plate, and set a plate in front of each child. Have the children taste one item at a time and talk about the different tastes.

Evaluation

▶ Children will name each of the five senses.

▶ Children will name which body parts are associated with each sense.

Additional lesson plans for grades 3–5 are available on CourseMate.

Summary

▶ Teachers play an important role in the monitoring and assessing children's health

- Information about children's physical and mental health status can be obtained from a variety of sources, including teacher observations, health records, screening procedures, daily health checks, and interactions with families.
- Assessment information is used to identify children who require professional evaluation, make referrals, and modify children's learning environments to accommodate any special needs.

▶ Screening tools provide a relatively quick and inexpensive way to evaluate groups of children for a variety of conditions, including height/weight, BMI, vision and hearing disorders, speech and language problems, and nutritional status.

- The results of screening procedures are not diagnostic by themselves; they do not confirm that a child does or does not have an impairment. They do help to identify children who may have a potential problem that requires further evaluation.

▶ Teachers can initiate the referral process after gathering and evaluating information about a child's health from multiple sources.

- A follow-up contact should always be made with the child's family to learn about assessment outcomes, treatment recommendations, and any classroom modifications that may be needed.

Terms to Know

intervention *p. 56*
skeletal *p. 58*
neurological *p. 58*
underweight *p. 59*
overweight *p. 59*
obese *p. 59*
ophthalmologist *p. 59*
optometrist *p. 59*

amblyopia *p. 62*
strabismus *p. 63*
myopia *p. 63*
hyperopia *p. 63*
language *p.*
audiologist *p. 65*
conductive loss *p. 66*
sensorineural loss *p. 66*

mixed hearing loss *p. 66*
speech *p. 67*
misarticulations *p. 69*
pallor *p. 70*
lethargy *p. 70*
mottling *p. 70*
skinfold *p. 70*
referrals *p. 74*

Chapter Review

A. By Yourself:

1. Define each of the *Terms to Know* listed at the end of this chapter.

2. Select the screening test that is recommended for children with the following behaviors, signs, or symptoms. Place the appropriate code letter in each space for questions 1–15.

H	Hearing screening
V	Vision screening
D	Developmental screening
HW	Height and weight
Dt	Dental screening
S	Speech evaluation
N	Nutrition evaluation

_____   1. blinks frequently; often closes one eye when reading

_____   2. stutters whenever tense and in a hurry to speak

_____   3. appears listless and very small for her chronological age

_____   4. stumbles over objects in the classroom; frequently walks into play equipment in the play yard

_____   5. has overlapping and missing teeth that make speech difficult to understand

_____   6. ignores the teacher's requests; pushes and shouts at the other children to get their attention

_____   7. is obese and experiences shortness of breath when running and playing

_____   8. has trouble catching a ball, pedaling a bicycle, and cutting with scissors

_____   9. appears to focus on objects with one eye while the other eye looks off in another direction

_____ 10. a toddler who has multiple cavities and refuses to chew solid foods

_____ 11. is extremely shy and withdrawn; spends the majority of his time playing alone and imitating other children's actions

_____ 12. seems extremely hungry at snack time; always asks for extra servings and takes food from other children's plates when the teacher isn't looking

_____ 13. becomes hoarse after shouting and yelling while playing outdoors

_____ 14. arrives at school each morning with potato chips, candy, or a cupcake and soda

_____ 15. a 4½-year-old who whines and has tantrums to get his own way

B. As a Group:

1. Identify and describe the vision disorders that are most common among young children. What behavioral indicators might a teacher observe? How is each typically treated?

2. Discuss how teachers might use information in health records to improve learning experiences for children with special sensory needs?

3. Discuss how the learning activities outlined in the Classroom Corner feature could be modified for a child who is blind or has low vision. How might they be adapted for a child with significant hearing loss?

4. Brainstorm ideas for ways that teachers can incorporate more physical activity into classroom routines to help children achieve the recommended 60 minutes of vigorous daily activity.

5. Debate whether or not teachers should calculate children's BMI and inform families if a child is overweight. Role-play how a teacher might share this information with an unreceptive parent and offer suggestions for improving the child's nutrition and physical activity. Critique each other's responses.

6. If a family asks you where they can get their 2-year-old's hearing tested, what resources in your community would you recommend?

Case Study

A friend encouraged Mrs. Howard to take her son to the developmental screening clinic being held this week at the community recreation center. Parker is nearly 2 years old and speaks only a few words that are understandable. He has few opportunities to play with other children his age because he spends most days with his grandmother while his mother works at a nearby hospital. On the day of the developmental screening, team members checked Parker's height, weight, vision, hearing, speech, cognitive abilities, and motor skills. The team leader also read through the child history form that Mrs. Howard had completed and noted that Parker had several food allergies, as well as frequent upper respiratory and ear infections. All of Parker's screening results proved to be within normal limits, with the exception of his hearing tests, which revealed a significant loss in one ear and a moderate loss in the other.

1. Is Parker's speech development appropriate for his age? Explain.

2. What significance might Parker's ear infections have to his hearing loss? How might his food allergies be contributing to the loss?

3. Should the screening team's recommendation for Parker include a referral to his physician? Why?

4. What behavioral signs of hearing loss might you expect Parker to exhibit?

5. What strategies might the developmental team suggest to Parker's mother and grandmother for improving his speech development and communication skills?

Application Activities

1. Locate and read instructions for administering the Snellen Tumbling E and one additional acuity screening test. Pair up with another student and practice testing each other. Alternatively, volunteer to conduct vision screening at a local early childhood program or shelter for homeless families. What advantages does each test offer? Disadvantages? Did you encounter any problems administering the test? How would you modify your instructions to a child based on this experience?

2. Devise a monitoring system that can be used in a group setting to record the daily food intakes of individual children. Be sure to address the following questions:

   a. What nutritional information do you want to collect? In what form?

   b. Who will be responsible for collecting this data?

   c. How can this information be obtained efficiently?

   d. How can teachers and families use this data to improve children's eating habits?

   e. What other ways might teachers use this information to promote children's health?

3. Collect samples of child history forms from several schools and early childhood programs in your area. Review the type of information that is most often requested. Design your own form and distribute it to several families for their comments and suggestions.

4. Attend a signing class. Learn to say "hello" and "good-bye" and 10 additional words in sign language.

5. Make arrangements with a local school or early childhood program to conduct a comparison study of children's growth. Measure and record the heights and weights of 15 children, ages

3 to 6 years, on the standard Growth Charts (download from the text's premium website). Then, determine each child's BMI and plot this information on the BMI-for-age charts. Which method provides the most accurate information about children's growth? What did you learn about the children's potential risk for becoming overweight? Learn more about the BMI measure and initiatives for preventing childhood obesity at the CDC website (http://www.cdc.gov).

6. Obtain an audiometer. Have a nurse or audiologist demonstrate the technique for testing a person's hearing. Practice administering the test with a partner. In what ways did this experience change your ideas about how to prepare children for testing?

7. Research the Internet or contact your local American Heart Association chapter to learn about their educational programs that target children's cardiovascular health. Are the materials/programs developmentally appropriate? How is improvement measured?

Helpful Web Resources

American Speech, Language, and Hearing Association (ASHA)	http://www.asha.org
National Association of Parents with Children in Special Education	http://www.napcse.org
National Institutes of Health	http://www.health.nih.gov
Prevent Blindness America	http://www.preventblindness.org
Action for Healthy Children	http://www.actionforhealthykids.org

Visit the Education CourseMate for this textbook to access the eBook, Did You Get It? quizzes, Digital Downloads, TeachSource Video Cases, flashcards, and more. Go to CengageBrain.com to log in, register, or purchase access.

References

American Heart Association (AHA). (2012). Overweight in children. Accessed on April 10, 2012 from http://www.heart.org/HEARTORG/GettingHealthy/Overweight-in-Children_UCM_304054_Article.jsp#.T4SqhNmyEhA.

Basch, C. (2011). Vision and the achievement gap among urban minority youth, *Journal of School Health*, 81(10), 599–605.

Borchert, M., Varma, R., Cotter, S., Tarczy-Hornoch, K., McKean-Cowdin, R., Lin, J., Wen, G., Azen, S., Torres, M., Tielsch, J., Friedman, D., Repka, M., Katz, J., Ibironke, J., & Giordano, L. (2011). Risk factors for hyperopia and myopia in preschool children: The multi-ethnic pediatric eye disease and Baltimore pediatric eye disease studies, *Ophthalmology*, 118(10), 1966–1973.

Brotman, L., Dawson-McClure, S., Huang, K., Theise, R., Kamboukos, D., Wang, J., Petkova, E., & Ogedegbe, G. (2012). Early childhood family intervention and long-term obesity prevention among high-risk minority youth, *Pediatrics*, 129(3), e621–e628.

Deem, K., Diaz-Ordaz, E., & Shiner, B. (2012). Identifying quality improvement opportunities in a universal newborn hearing screening program, *Pediatrics*, 12(1), e157–e164.

Dixon, L., Wu, S., & Daraghmeh, A. (2012). Profiles in bilingualism: Factors influencing kindergartners' language proficiency, *Early Childhood Education Journal*, 40(1), 25–34.

Elloy, M., & Marshall, A. (2012). The management of hearing loss in children, *Paediatrics & Child Health*, 22(1), 13–18.

Franklin, B., Jones, A., Love, D., Puckett, S., Macklin, J., & White-Means, S. (2012). Exploring mediators of food insecurity and obesity: A review of recent literature, *Journal of Community Health*, 37(1), 253–264.

Gunton, K. (2013). Advances in amblyopia: What have we learned from PEDIG trials?, *Pediatrics*, 131(3), 540–547.

Jackson, K., Krishnaswami, S., & McPheeters, M. (2011). Unmet health care needs in children with cerebral palsy: A cross-sectional study, *Research in Developmental Disabilities*, 32(6), 2714–2723.

Laws, G., Bates, G., Feuerstein, M., Mason-Apps, E., & White, C. (2012). Peer acceptance of children with language and communication impairments in a mainstream primary school: Associations with type of language difficulty, problem behaviours, and a change in placement organization, *Child Language Teaching and Therapy*, 28(1), 73–86.

Longmuir, S., Boese, E., Pfeifer, W., Zimmerman, B., Short, L., & Scott, W. (2013). Practical community photoscreening in very young children, *Pediatrics*, 131(3), e764–e769.

March of Dimes. (2011). Newborn screening. Accessed on April 9, 2012 from http://www.marchofdimes.com/professionals/bringinghome_screening.html.

Marotz, L. R., & Allen, K. E. (2013). *Developmental profiles: Pre-birth through adolescence.* (7th ed.). Belmont, CA: Wadsworth Cengage Learning.

McQuiston, S., & Kloczko, N. (2011). Speech and language development: Monitoring process and problems, *Pediatrics in Review*, 32(6), 230–239.

Morale, S., Hughbanks-Wheaton, D., Cheng, C., Subramanian, V., O'Connor, A., & Birch, E. (2012). Visual acuity assessment of children with special needs, *American Orthoptic Journal*, 62, 90–98.

National Child Traumatic Stress Network (NCTSN). (2011). National Homeless Youth Awareness Month (November 2012). Accessed on April 10, 2012 from http://www.nctsnet.org/resources/public-awareness/national-homeless-youth-awareness-month.

National Kids Count. (2012). The Annie E. Casey Foundation. Accessed on May 4, 2012 from http://datacenter.kidscount.org.

Optometrists Network. (2012). Strabismus. Accessed on April 8, 2012, from http://www.strabismus.org.

Prevent Blindness America. (2010). Quick facts: Children's eye problems. Accessed April 9, 2012 from http://www.preventblindness.org/sites/default/files/national/documents/fact_sheets/MK03_QuickFactsChildren.pdf.

Shi, X., Tubb, L., Fingers, S., Chen, S., & Caffrey, J. (2013). Associations of physical activity and dietary behaviors with children's health and academic problems, *Journal of School Health*, 83(1), 1–7.

Tarczy-Hornoch, K. (2012). Accommodative lag and refractive error in infants and toddlers. Accessed on April 8, 2012 from http://dx.doi.org/10.1016/j.jaapos.2011.10.015.

U.S. Census Bureau. (2011). How the Census Bureau measures poverty. Accessed on April 10, 2012 from http://www.census.gov/hhes/www/poverty/about/overview/measure.html.

Venuti, P., de Falco, S., Esposito, G., Zaninelli, M., & Bornstein, M. (2012). Maternal functional speech to children: A comparison of autism spectrum disorder, Down syndrome, and typical development, *Research in Developmental Disabilities*, 33(2), 506–517.

The Infectious Process and Environmental Control

naeyc Standards Chapter Links

▶ **#1 a, b, and c:** Promoting child development and learning
▶ **#3 a, c, and d:** Observing, documenting, and assessing to support young children and families
▶ Field Experience

Learning Objectives

After studying this chapter, you should be able to:

LO 5-1 Discuss why young children experience frequent communicable illness.
LO 5-2 Describe the components required for an illness to be communicable.
LO 5-3 Identify the four stages of a communicable illness.
LO 5-4 Name and discuss four control measures that teachers can use to reduce the transmission of communicable illnesses in the classroom.

Young children, especially those under 3 years of age, are highly susceptible to communicable illness. Frequent upper respiratory infections are common, especially during a child's first experiences in group settings.

5-1 Risk Factors

Several factors contribute to the frequency of communicable illnesses that young children typically experience. First, children have had fewer opportunities to develop protective **antibodies** due to their limited prior exposures to infectious illnesses. Physical disabilities and chronic conditions, such as diabetes, sickle cell anemia, allergies, and asthma further reduce children's resistance and leave them more susceptible to communicable conditions.

Second, the immature development of children's body structures also contributes to a higher rate of illness. For example, shorter distances between an infant's or toddler's ears, nose, and throat make it easy for organisms to enter and infect these locations.

Third, group settings, such as home- and center-based early childhood programs and elementary school classrooms, are ideal environments for the rapid spread of illness (Vermeer et al., 2012). Children spend their days in close proximity and come in frequent contact with items, such as toys and furniture, that others have touched. They are also exposed to communicable illnesses in places wherever there are groups of people, including grocery stores, shopping centers, churches, libraries, and restaurants. Many of children's habits, such as sucking on fingers, mouthing toys, carelessness with bodily secretions (runny noses, drool, urine, stool), and an abundance of physical contact also encourage the rapid spread of communicable illness. For these reasons, every attempt must be made to establish and implement policies, practices, and learning experiences that will help protect young children from unnecessary exposure.

. . . .

antibodies – *special substances produced by the body that help protect against disease.*

5-2 Communicable Illness

Communicable illnesses are infectious conditions that can be transmitted or spread from one person or animal to another. Three factors, all of which must be present at approximately the same time, are required for this process to occur (Figure 5–1).

- a pathogen
- a susceptible host
- a method of transmission

First, a **pathogen** or microorganism, such as a bacteria, virus, fungus, or parasite, must be present and available for transmission. These invisible germs are specific for each disease and are most commonly located in discharges from the respiratory (nose, throat, lungs) and intestinal tract of infected persons. They can also be found in the blood, urine, and discharges from the eyes and skin. Most pathogens require a living host (e.g., human, animal, insect) for their survival, with the exception of the organism that causes tetanus; it is able to survive in soil and dust for several years.

Second, there must be a **susceptible host** or person who is vulnerable to the disease-causing organism. Most communicable illnesses that children experience enter their new host through either a break in the skin, the **respiratory tract**, or digestive tract. The entry route is specific for each infectious disease.

Not every child who is exposed to a particular virus, bacteria, or other pathogen will become infected. Conditions must be favorable to allow an infectious organism to successfully avoid the body's defense systems, multiply, and establish itself. Children who are well rested, adequately nourished, **immunized**, and healthy are generally less susceptible to infectious organisms. Some children will have immunity as a result of having experienced a prior case of the same illness. However, the length of this protection varies with the illness and can range from several days to a lifetime. For example, a child who has had chickenpox will have permanent immunity against a recurrence of the

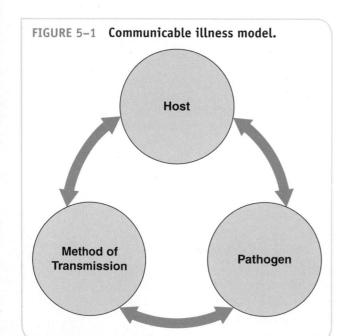

FIGURE 5–1 Communicable illness model.

Host

Method of Transmission

Pathogen

---

communicable – *capable of being spread or transmitted from one individual to another.*

pathogen – *a microorganism capable of producing illness or infection.*

susceptible host – *an individual who is capable of being infected by a pathogen.*

respiratory tract – *the nose, throat, trachea, and lungs.*

immunized – *a state of becoming resistant to a specific disease through the introduction of living or dead microorganisms into the body, which then stimulates the production of antibodies.*

disease, whereas immunity following a cold may last only a few days. Children who are carriers or who experience a mild case of some communicable diseases may also develop immunity without knowing that they have been infected.

Third, a method for transmitting the infectious agent from the original source to a new host is necessary to complete the communicable process. Infectious agents are most commonly spread via **airborne transmission** in school settings. Disease-causing pathogens are carried on tiny droplets of moisture that are expelled during coughs, sneezes, or while talking (Figure 5–2). Influenza, colds, meningitis, tuberculosis, and chickenpox are examples of infectious illnesses spread in this manner.

Fecal-oral transmission is the second-most common route by which infectious illnesses are spread in group settings, particularly when infants and toddlers in diapers are present. Teachers who fail to wash their hands properly after changing diapers or assisting children with toileting needs are often responsible for spreading disease-causing germs, especially if they also handle food. For this reason, it is advisable to assign diaper changing and food preparation responsibilities to different teachers. Children's hands should always be washed after diaper changes or after using the bathroom because their hands often end up in their mouths. Appropriate hand washing procedures should be taught and monitored closely to be sure children are washing correctly. Pinworms, hepatitis A, salmonella, and giardiasis are examples of illnesses transmitted by fecal-oral contamination.

A third common method of transmission involves **direct contact** with body fluids, such as blood or mucus, or an infected area on another person's body. The infectious organisms are transferred directly from the original source of infection to a new host. Ringworm, athlete's foot, impetigo, hepatitis B, and conjunctivitis (pinkeye) are a few of the conditions spread in this manner.

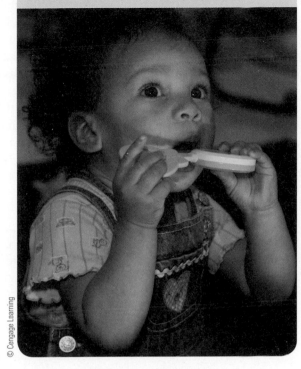

▼ Communicable illnesses can be spread when children mouth toys and other objects.

© Cengage Learning

Did You Know...

that children experience an average of 5-8 colds per year?

FIGURE 5–2   How infectious illnesses are spread.

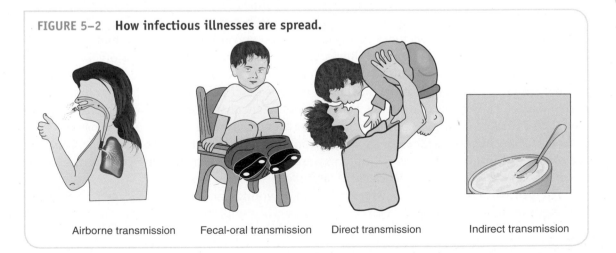

Airborne transmission   Fecal-oral transmission   Direct transmission   Indirect transmission

airborne transmission – *the process by which germs are expelled into the air through coughs and sneezes, and transmitted to another individual via tiny moisture drops.*

fecal-oral transmission – *the process in which germs are transferred to the mouth via hands contaminated with fecal material.*

direct contact – *coming in direct or immediate contact with infectious material.*

Communicable illnesses can also be transmitted through **indirect contact**. This method involves the transfer of infectious organisms from an infected individual to an intermediate object, such as water, milk, dust, food, toys, towels, eating utensils, animals, or insects, and finally to the new susceptible host. It is also possible to infect oneself with certain bacteria and viruses, such as those causing colds and influenza, simply by touching the moist linings of the eyes, nose, or mouth with contaminated hands. Several communicable illnesses, including conjunctivitis (pinkeye), cytomegalovirus (CMV), impetigo, scabies, and head lice can be transmitted through indirect and direct contact.

Eliminating any one of these factors (pathogen, host, or method of transmission) will interrupt the spread of a communicable illness. This is an important concept for families and teachers to understand when trying to control communicable illness, especially in group settings. It can also be beneficial for reducing the number of illnesses that teachers may experience or carry home to their families.

Did You Get It?

Which is not one of the three distinct factors that must be present for an illness to be transmitted from one child to another?

a. A method of transmission.

b. The child's age at the time of exposure.

c. A pathogen.

d. A host susceptible to a pathogen.

Take the full quiz on CourseMate.

5-3 Stages of Illness

Communicable illnesses generally develop in fairly predictable stages:

- incubation
- prodromal
- acute
- convalescence

The length of each stage is often different for each illness. In some cases, the stages may overlap and be difficult to identify when one begins and another ends.

The **incubation** stage includes the time between exposure to a pathogen and the appearance of the first signs or symptoms of illness. During this period, the infectious organisms enter the body and multiply rapidly in an attempt to establish themselves and overpower the body's defense systems. The length of the incubation stage is described in terms of hours or days and varies for each communicable disease. For example, the incubation period for chickenpox ranges from 2 to 3 weeks following exposure, whereas for the common cold it is thought to be only 12 to 72 hours. Many infectious illnesses are already communicable near the end of this stage. Children are often **contagious** before any symptoms appear, which can make some communicable illnesses difficult to control despite teachers' careful observations.

The **prodromal** stage begins when an infant or young child experiences the first nonspecific signs of infection and ends with the appearance of symptoms characteristic of a particular

---

indirect contact – *coming in contact with infectious material that is transmitted via surfaces, animals, or insects.*

incubation – *the interval of time between exposure to infection and the appearance of the first signs or symptoms of illness.*

contagious – *capable of being transmitted or passed from one person to another.*

prodromal – *the appearance of the first nonspecific signs of infection; this stage ends when the symptoms characteristic of a particular communicable illness begin to appear.*

communicable illness. This stage may last from several hours to several days. However, not all communicable diseases have a prodromal stage. Early symptoms commonly associated with the prodromal stage may include headache, unexplained fatigue, low-grade fever, a slight sore throat, and a general feeling of restlessness or irritability. Many complaints are so vague that they can easily go unnoticed. However, because children are highly contagious during this stage, teachers and parents must understand that these subtle changes may signal an impending illness.

During the **acute** stage there is no doubt that an infant or child is sick and highly contagious. The onset of this stage is marked by the appearance of symptoms characteristic of the illness and it ends as the child begins to recover. Early symptoms, such as fever, sore throat, cough, runny nose, rash, or enlarged lymph glands are common to many infectious diseases. However, they often develop in a characteristic pattern that can be useful for identifying the communicable illness involved.

The **convalescent** or recovery stage generally follows automatically unless complications develop. During this stage, symptoms gradually disappear and children begin to feel better.

> ### Did You Get It?
>
> A student who has been exposed to influenza, feels fine today, but will develop a high fever and stay home from school tomorrow is in the _____ stage.
> **a.** prodromal
> **b.** convalescent
> **c.** incubation
> **d.** acute
>
> **Take the full quiz on CourseMate.**

5-4 Control Measures

Teachers have an obligation and responsibility to help protect young children from communicable illnesses. Although many illnesses are simply an inconvenience, others can cause serious complications. Because classrooms are ideal settings for the rapid spread of many infectious conditions, control measures must be practiced diligently to limit their spread.

5-4a Observations

Teachers' daily health observations can be effective for identifying children in the early stages of a communicable illness. Removing children who are ill from classrooms eliminates a direct source of infection. However, it is important to remember that many illnesses are communicable before the characteristic symptoms appear, so not all spread can be avoided. For this reason it is important to continuously note changes in children's appearance and behavior patterns. This process is made easier by the fact that young children often look and behave differently when they are not feeling well. Their actions, facial expressions, skin color, sleep habits, appetite, and comments provide valuable warnings of impending illness. Additional signs may include:

- unusually pale or flushed skin
- red or sore throat
- enlarged **lymph glands**
- nausea, vomiting, or diarrhea
- rash, spots, or open lesions
- watery or red eyes
- headache or dizziness
- chills, fever, or achiness
- fatigue or loss of appetite

The appearance of these signs and symptoms does not always warrant concern in all children. For example, a teacher who knows that Tony's allergies often cause a red throat and cough

---

acute – *the stage of an illness or disease during which an individual is definitely sick and exhibits symptoms characteristic of a specific illness or disease.*

convalescent – *the stage of recovery from an illness or disease.*

lymph glands – *specialized groupings of tissue that produce and store white blood cells for protection against infection and illness.*

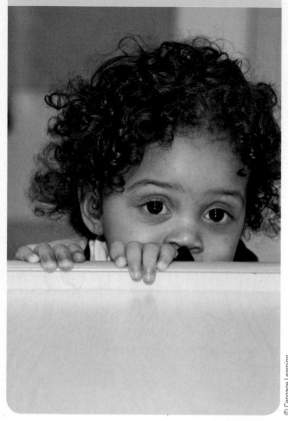

▼ **Changes in children's appearance and behavior can be early indications of an impending illness.**

© Cengage Learning

in the fall, or that Shadra's recent irritability is probably related to her mother's hospitalization, would not be alarmed by these observations. Teachers must be able to distinguish between children with potentially infectious illnesses and those with health problems that are explainable and not necessarily contagious. Knowing that some illnesses are more prevalent during certain times of the year or that a current outbreak exists in the community can also be useful for identifying children who may be infectious.

5-4b Policies

Written policies offer another important method for controlling infectious illnesses in group settings (Egger et al., 2012). Policies should be consistent with state regulations, and in place before a program begins to enroll children. They should be reviewed frequently so that staff members are familiar with the guidelines and more likely to enforce them consistently.

General health and exclusion policies should also be described in handbooks that are given to families. Collaborative partnerships are strengthened when families know in advance what to expect if their child does become ill. Exclusion and inclusion policies should establish clear guidelines for when children who are ill should be kept home, when they will be sent home due to illness, and when they are considered well enough to return (Figure 5–3).

Opinions differ on how restrictive exclusion policies should be. Some experts believe that children with mild illnesses can remain in group care, while others feel that children who exhibit symptoms should be sent home. Because many early signs of communicable illnesses are nonspecific, teachers and families may have difficulty distinguishing between conditions that warrant exclusion and medical attention and those that do not.

FIGURE 5–3   Sample exclusion policy.

EXCLUSION POLICY

Control of communicable illness among the children is a prime concern. Policies and guidelines related to outbreaks of communicable illness in this center have been developed with the help of the health department and local pediatricians. In order to protect the entire group of children, as well as your own child, we ask that families assist us by keeping children who are ill at home if they have experienced any of the following symptoms *within the past 24 hours:*

■ fever over 100°F (37.8°C) orally or 99°F (37.2°C) axillary (under the arm)

■ signs of a newly developing cold or uncontrollable coughing

■ diarrhea, vomiting, or an upset stomach

■ unusual or unexplained loss of appetite, fatigue, irritability, or headache

■ any discharge or drainage from eyes, nose, ears, or open sores

Children who become ill with any of these symptoms will be sent home. We appreciate your cooperation with this policy. If you have any questions about whether or not your child is well enough to attend school or group care that day, please call *before* bringing your child.

FIGURE 5-4   **Sample letter notifying families of their child's exposure.**

Date_____

Dear Parent:

There is a possibility that your child has been exposed to impetigo. Please observe your child's skin closely for the next 2–10 days and look for:

- itchy rash that may develop blisters
- moist sores that are more likely to appear around the face, ears, nose, or arms
- sores that increase in size or spread to other parts of the body

Impetigo is highly contagious and requires careful hand washing to prevent it from infecting others. Please contact your child's health care provider for advice about treating the condition. Children may return to school after receiving medical care and all sores have healed over.

If you have any questions, please call before bringing your child to school. We appreciate your cooperation in helping us to protect children's well-being.

Consequently, programs may decide to set exclusion policies that are fairly restrictive unless they are prepared to care for sick children.

It is also important for programs to adopt policies about notifying families when children are exposed to communicable illnesses. This measure enables parents to watch for early symptoms and to keep sick children home (Figure 5–4). Immunization requirements, as well as actions the program will take if children are not in compliance, should also be addressed in a program's policies. Local public health authorities can provide useful information and guidance to programs when they are formulating new policies or are confronted with a communicable health problem about which they are unsure.

Guidelines for Teacher Illness   Teachers are exposed to many infectious illnesses through their daily contact with young children. They often experience an increased frequency of illness—especially during the initial months of employment—that is similar to what young children experience when they enroll in a new program or school (Tak et al., 2011). However, over time, teachers gradually build up resistance to many of these illnesses. They can also take steps to minimize their risk by obtaining a pre-employment health assessment, having a tuberculin test, updating immunizations, following a healthy lifestyle, and practicing frequent hand washing. Teachers who are pregnant may want to temporarily reconsider working around young children because some communicable illnesses, such as cytomegalovirus (CMV) and German measles can affect the fetus, especially during the early months.

When teachers are ill and trying to decide whether or not they should go to work, they must follow the same exclusion guidelines that apply to sick children. Adults who do not feel well will not be able to meet the rigorous demands necessary for working with young children and also face an increased risk of sustaining personal injury. Programs should maintain a list of substitute teachers so that staff members do not feel pressured to work when they are ill.

Administration of Medication   The administration of medicine to young children is a responsibility that must always be taken seriously. (See Teacher Checklist 5-1.) Policies and procedures for administering prescription and nonprescription medications, including ointments and creams; eye, ear, and nose drops; cough syrups; pain or fever-reducing medications; inhalers; and nebulizer breathing treatments should be developed in accordance with state licensing or school district regulations to safeguard children as well as teaching staff. These policies and procedures

TEACHER CHECKLIST 5-1

Administering Medications to Children

1. Always wash your hands before handling medications and after administering them.
2. Be honest when giving children medication! Do not use force or attempt to trick children into believing that medicines are candy. Instead, use the opportunity to help children understand the relationship between taking a medication and recovering from an illness or infection. Also, acknowledge the fact that the taste of medicine may be disagreeable or a treatment may be somewhat unpleasant; offer a small sip of juice or cracker to eliminate an unpleasant taste or read a favorite story as a reward for their cooperation.
3. Designate one individual to accept medication from families and administer it to children; this could be the director or the head teacher. This step will help minimize the opportunity for errors, such as omitting a dose or giving a dose twice.
4. When medication is accepted from a family, it should be in the original container and labeled with the child's name, the drug name, and the time and dose to be administered.

 CAUTION

NEVER give medicine from a container that has been prescribed for another individual.

5. Store all medicines in a locked cabinet. If it is necessary to refrigerate a medication, place it in a locked box and store it on a top shelf in the refrigerator.
6. Concentrate on what you are doing and do not talk with anyone until you are finished.
   a. Read the label on the bottle or container three times:
      - when removing it from the locked cabinet
      - before pouring it from the container
      - after pouring it from the container
   b. Administer medication on time, and give only the amount prescribed.
   c. Be sure you have the correct child! If the child is old enough to talk, ask "What is your name?" and have the child state his or her name.
7. Record and maintain a permanent record of each dose of medicine that is administered (Figure 5–5). Include the:
   - date and time the medicine was given
   - name of the teacher administering the medication
   - dose of medication given
   - any unusual physical changes or behaviors observed after the medicine was administered
8. Inform the child's family of the dosage(s) and time medication was given, as well as any unusual reactions that may have occurred.
9. NOTE: Adults should never take any medication in front of children.

TeachSource Digital Download Download from CourseMate.

should be in writing, familiar to all staff members, filed in an accessible location, and distributed to every family (Figure 5–5).

When children are enrolled in part-day programs, families may be able to alter medication schedules and administer prescribed doses at times when children are home. However, this may not be an option for children who attend full-day school or early childhood programs. In these cases, families will need to make prior arrangements with the child's teachers or school nurse to have prescribed medications administered at the appropriate times.

Medications should never be given to children without their family's written consent and written instructions from a licensed physician. The label on a prescription drug is considered an acceptable physician's directive. In the case of nonprescription medicines, families should obtain written instructions from the physician stating the child's name, the medication to be given, the dose, frequency it is to be administered, potential reactions, and any special precautions that may be necessary. There are risks associated with giving children over-the-counter

FIGURE 5–5   **Sample medication recording form.**

ADMINISTRATION OF MEDICATION FORM

Child's name _____

Prescription number _____

Date of prescription _____

Doctor prescribing medicine _____

Medication being given for _____

Time medication is to be given by staff _____

Time medication last given by parent (guardian) _____

Amount to be given at each time (dosage): _____

I, _____ give my permission for the staff to administer the above prescription medication (according to the above guidelines) to _____ _____ . I understand that the staff cannot be held

           (child's name)

responsible for allergic reactions or other complications resulting from administration of the above medication when given according to the directions.

          Parent/guardian name (print) _____

          Signature _____

          Date _____

Staff Record

Staff member accepting medication and signing this form (print): _____

Is medication in its original container? _____

Is original label intact? _____

Is there written permission from the doctor attached (or the original prescription)? _____

        Signature of accepting staff _____

Administration Record

DATE	TIME	AMOUNT GIVEN	STAFF ADMINISTERING	INITIALS

medications that have not been authorized by a physician. It is the physician's professional and legal responsibility to determine which medication and exact dosage is appropriate for an individual child. Teachers can protect themselves from potential liability by refusing to give medications without a doctor's order.

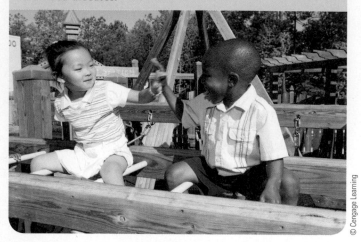

▼ **Immunizations protect children from many preventable childhood diseases.**

© Cengage Learning

5-4c Immunization

Immunization offers permanent protection against all preventable childhood diseases, including diphtheria, tetanus, whooping cough (pertussis), polio, measles, mumps, rubella, Haemophilus influenza, and chickenpox. However, outbreaks of some diseases continue to occur. Large-scale national, state, and local campaigns have successfully increased the number of children 19 to 35 months who have received all age-appropriate immunizations to approximately 90 percent (CDC, 2012). Yet, there are many adults and older children who are not current or fully immunized according to recommendations. Efforts to improve the immunization rates among all age groups remain a Healthy People 2020 priority (U.S. DHHS, 2012).

Why are some families so seemingly complacent about having their children immunized? Perhaps they do not realize that some communicable illnesses are still life-threatening and continue to pose a threat to children who are not protected. Recent outbreaks of mumps, measles, tuberculosis, and whooping cough, for example, have clearly demonstrated this potential (Luthy et al., 2013). Some families falsely believe that antibiotics are available to cure all infectious illness so they are willing to take a chance. Others have expressed concern about vaccine safety and the number of immunizations children must receive (Gidengil et al., 2012). Pharmaceutical companies continue to make strides in combining some vaccines to help reduce this number. Manufacturers have also eliminated questionable substances, such as thimerosal, from vaccines to improve their safety (Barile et al., 2012).

 CONNECTING TO EVERYDAY PRACTICE

Hand Washing Compliance

It is easy to assume that everyone knows how to wash their hands and understands the importance of doing so. However, multiple studies have shown that even health care workers fail to follow recommended hand washing guidelines approximately 40 to 50 percent of the time (White et al., 2012; Fuller et al., 2011). Serious concerns have been raised about the lack of hand washing compliance in light of an increase in antibiotic-resistant infections. The use of hand sanitizing gels has proven beneficial for preventing the spread of some communicable illnesses, but they are not considered effective against all infectious organisms.

Because schools and early childhood programs provide ideal settings for the spread of communicable illnesses, it is especially important that teachers practice careful hand washing. However, hand washing is not always followed rigorously in these settings. As a result, researchers continue to look for ways to improve hand washing compliance in health care facilities, schools, and early childhood programs including the use of surveillance cameras, training videos, sanitizing gels, sink placement, and checklists (Armellino et al., 2012; Wilson, Jacob, & Powell, 2011).

Think About This:

▶ Why do you think teachers often fail to wash their hands at the necessary times?

▶ What are the barriers?

▶ What would motivate teachers to improve their hand hygiene compliance?

▶ Should schools resort to high tech methods (i.e., video cameras) to ensure compliance?

▶ How would you respond if you observed a teacher who served the children lunch without first washing his or her hands?

Most states require children's immunizations to be current when they enter school or enroll in early childhood programs. In states where immunization laws are lax, teachers must insist that every child be fully immunized unless families are opposed on religious or medical grounds. (Luthy et al., 2013; Gaudino & Robison, 2012). Teachers should also be diligent in keeping their own immunizations up-to-date.

Vaccines work by triggering the body's immune system to produce protective substances called antibodies. This process is similar to what occurs when a person becomes ill with certain infectious diseases. Infants are born with a limited supply of antibodies, acquired from their mothers, which protect them against some communicable illnesses. However, this maternal protection is only temporary and, therefore, the immunization process must be initiated early in an infant's life. The immunization schedule jointly recommended by the Centers for Disease Control and Protection (CDC), the American Academy of Pediatrics (AAP), and the American Academy of Family Physicians (AAFP) appears in Figure 5–6. Similar recommendations are available for Canadians and children in other countries (Public Health Agency of Canada, 2012).

Infants and young children, especially those in group care, are encouraged to be immunized against Haemophilus influenza Type b (Hib), an upper respiratory infection and common cause of

FIGURE 5–6 Recommended childhood and adolescent immunization schedule, U.S. 2013.

Source: Centers for Disease Control and Prevention. (2013).

meningitis. (See Figure 5–6.) Vaccines for chickenpox (varicella) and hepatitis B, a viral infection spread through contact with body secretions and feces, are also required in some states and recommended in others (Abrevaya & Mulligan, 2011). Children who have special health conditions are often more susceptible to communicable illnesses and should be immunized against these diseases as a precautionary measure even though they may not be required. Immunizations can be obtained from most health care providers, neighborhood health clinics, or public health departments where the cost is often reduced or free.

Programs that employ more than one teacher (including aides and substitutes) are required to offer free hepatitis B immunizations to employees during the first 10 days of employment or within 24 hours following exposure to blood or body fluids containing blood (OSHA, 2011). Teachers are at high risk for exposure to hepatitis B and should protect themselves by completing the immunization series.

5-4d Environmental Control

Communicable illnesses can also be controlled through a variety of effective environmental practices and modifications (Cannon et al., 2012; Stebbins, Downs, & Vukotich, 2011). Teachers should be familiar with these methods and understand how to implement them in their classrooms. Written procedures should be posted where they are visible and reviewed periodically with all employees. Teachers must also take personal precautions, such as wearing gloves and practicing frequent hand washing, to protect themselves from unnecessary exposure to contaminated materials.

Because respiratory illnesses are common in group settings where there are children, special attention should be given to control measures that limit their spread. For example, children can be taught to cough and sneeze into their elbow or a tissue, dispose of tissues properly, and then wash their hands. Children must also be reminded frequently to keep hands out of their mouth, nose, and eyes to prevent self-infection and the spread of infection to others.

Universal Infection Control Precautions The U.S. Department of Labor's Occupational Safety and Health Administration (OSHA) is responsible for protecting employees' safety by ensuring that workplace environments and practices meet federal guidelines. Regulations passed by OSHA require child care programs (except those without paid employees) to develop and practice **universal infection control precautions** for handling contaminated body fluids. (See Teacher Checklist 5-2.) In addition, schools must have a written exposure control plan for

TEACHER CHECKLIST 5-2

Universal Precautions for Handling Body Fluids

Whenever handling body fluids or items contaminated with body fluids, be sure to:

- Wear disposable gloves when you are likely to have contact with blood or other body fluids (e.g., vomitus, urine, feces, or saliva).
- Remove glove by grasping the cuff and pulling it off inside out.
- Wash hands thoroughly. (Lather for at least 30 seconds.)
- Dispose of contaminated materials properly. Seal soiled clothing in plastic bags to be laundered at home. Dispose of diapers by tying them securely in garbage bags. Place broken glass in a designated container.
- Clean all surfaces with an approved disinfectant or chlorine bleach solution (check product label and mix fresh daily).
- Subsidize the cost of hepatitis B immunizations for all employees.

TeachSource Digital Download Download from CourseMate.

---

universal infection control precautions – *special measures taken when handling bodily fluids, including careful hand washing, wearing disposable gloves, disinfecting surfaces, and proper disposal of contaminated objects.*

handling potentially infectious material, provide annual training for employees, and maintain records of any contact (OSHA, 2003).

Universal precautions are designed to protect teachers from accidental exposure to blood-borne pathogens, including hepatitis B and C and HIV/AIDS. All body fluids are considered potentially infectious and, therefore, should be treated as such. Any material that has been contaminated with blood or other body fluids that might possibly contain blood, such as urine, feces, saliva, and vomitus, must be handled with caution, regardless of whether or not a child is known to be ill.

Disposable gloves should always be accessible to teachers; non-latex gloves must be provided if a teacher or child has a latex sensitivity. They must always be worn whenever handling soiled objects or caring for children's injuries. Gloves should be removed by pulling them off inside out and carefully discarding them after use with an individual child. Thorough hand washing must follow to prevent any further spread of infection; *wearing gloves does not eliminate the need for washing one's hands.* Children's hands and skin should also be washed with soap and running water to remove any blood. Washable objects, such as rugs, pillows, or stuffed toys that have been contaminated with body fluids should be laundered separately from other items. Children's clothing should be rinsed out, sealed in a plastic bag, and sent home to be washed. Bloodstains on surfaces must be wiped up and disinfected with a commercial germicide or chlorine bleach solution.

NOTE: Manufacturers have recently changed the strength of their chlorine bleach products. Also, be aware that not all bleach products are designed for disinfecting purposes—some are simply laundry products. Read manufacturers' labels carefully and follow their instructions for appropriate dilution and use. Updated safety information and mixing guidelines are posted on the National Resource Center for Health and Safety in Child Care and Early Education (NRC) website, *Caring for Our Children* (3rd ed.), Appendix J (http://cfoc.nrckids.org/Bleach /Bleach.cfm) and can also be obtained from your state or local health department.

Hand Washing Hand washing is perhaps the single most effective control measure against the spread of communicable and infectious illness in child care and school environments (Schulte et al., 2012). (See Teacher Checklist 5-3.)

Infants and toddlers who are crawling on the floor, eating with their hands, or sucking their thumbs or fingers should have their hands washed frequently, and especially after diaper changes. Individual washcloths moistened with soap and water can be used for this purpose; however, infants and toddlers should also have their hands washed under running water several times a day. Preschoolers and adults should always wash with soap and running water. Children must be taught the correct procedure and supervised so that each step is followed carefully. School-age children should be given several opportunities during the day to wash their hands. In addition, children should wash their hands before and after eating or whenever they have blown their nose, used the bathroom, played outdoors or in sand, or touched animals. Although sanitizing hand gels are beneficial for limiting the spread

Did You Know...

that hand washing can prevent more than 50 percent of all communicable illnesses?

© 2015 Cengage Learning

▶❙❙ **TeachSource** Video Connections

Promoting Children's Health: A Focus on Nutrition in Early Childhood Settings

Young children often experience multiple episodes of communicable illness throughout the year. Although it is not reasonable to think that all communicable illness can be prevented, there are steps teachers can take to improve children's resistance. As you watch the learning video, *Promoting Children's Health: A Focus on Nutrition in Early Childhood Settings,* consider the following questions:

1. What role does nutrition education play in reducing the incidence of communicable illness?

2. What additional control measures did the teacher take to limit the potential spread of disease-causing organisms?

3. Why is it important that teachers wash their hands at appropriate times?

4. When should children wash their hands?

Watch on CourseMate.

TEACHER CHECKLIST 5-3

How and When to Wash Hands

Following proper hand washing technique is critical for controlling the spread of infectious illnesses:

- Pull down paper towel.
- Turn on the water; wet hands and wrists under warm, running water.
- Apply soap and lather hands to loosen dirt and bacteria.
- Rub hands and wrists vigorously for a minimum of 20 seconds. Friction helps to remove microorganisms and dirt. (Have children sing the entire ABC or similar song while rubbing their hands with soap.)
- Pay special attention to rubbing soap on the backs of hands, between fingers, and around finger nails.
- Rinse hands thoroughly under running water to remove dirt and soap. Hold hands higher than wrists to prevent recontamination. Leave the water running.
- Dry hand and arms carefully with paper towel.
- Use the paper towel to turn off water faucets. (This prevents hands from becoming contaminated again.)
- Open bathroom door with paper towel and discard it in an appropriate receptacle.

Correct hand washing technique should always be used:

- upon arrival or return to the classroom
- before handling food or food utensils
- before and after feeding children
- before and after administering medication
- after changing diapers or handling items contaminated with mucus, urine, feces, vomitus, or blood
- after personally using the restroom
- after cleaning up from snack or play activities, emptying garbage, handling pets, or using art materials such as clay and paint
- after touching animals or playing in sand and dirt

TeachSource Digital Download) Download from CourseMate.

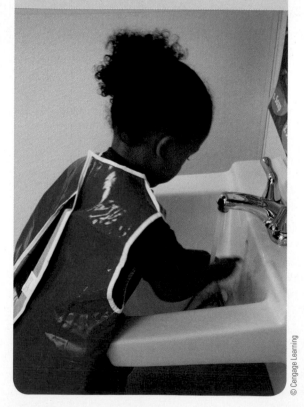

▼ **Frequent hand washing reduces the risk of communicable illness.**

© Cengage Learning

of communicable illness, they are not considered a substitute for thorough hand washing and should be used only when running water is not available (Gerald et al., 2012; Nandrup-Bus, 2011).

Cleaning Frequent cleaning of furniture, toys, and surfaces is also an effective method for limiting the spread of communicable illness (APHA & AAP, 2011). Changing tables, mats, and potty chairs should be constructed of nonporous materials and free of any tears or cracks for ease of cleaning. They should be disinfected thoroughly after each use with an approved solution that has been mixed according to the manufacturer's directions. (Refer to new bleach solution guidelines.) Surfaces contaminated with blood or large amounts of urine, stool, or vomitus require special cleaning and disinfecting measures.

Toys that children have placed in their mouths should be removed for cleaning before they are used by another child. Items should be washed with soap and warm water, rinsed in a disinfecting solution, and allowed to air-dry. Some toys can be sanitized in the dishwasher. Washable cloth and stuffed objects should be laundered between use by other children. Surfaces, such as tables, gate tops, car seats, and crib rails that children mouth or drool on should be scrubbed daily with soap and water and disinfected. Desktops and equipment in school-age classrooms should also be wiped off with a mild disinfectant at least once a week, or daily during the cold and flu season.

TEACHER CHECKLIST 5-4
Sanitary Diapering Procedure

The consistent implementation of sanitary diapering procedures is important for reducing the spread of disease. Teachers should follow these steps:

- Organize and label all supplies.
- Have all items for diaper changing within reach.
- Place a disposable covering (paper towel, paper roll) over a firm changing surface. Do not change children on fabric chairs or sofas that could become soiled.
- If using gloves, put them on.
- Pick up the child, holding him away from your clothing to avoid contamination.
- Place the child on the paper surface; fasten security belt. Remove the child's clothing and shoes if necessary to prevent them from becoming soiled.
- Remove the soiled diaper. Place disposable diapers in a covered, plastic-lined receptacle designated for this purpose; seal cloth diapers in a plastic bag and send home to be laundered.
- Clean the child's bottom with a disposable wipe and place the wipe in receptacle; pat skin dry with a paper towel.
- Remove the paper lining from beneath the child and discard.
- Wash your hands or wipe with a clean disposable wipe and discard. *Never leave the child alone.*
- Wash the child's hands under running water.
- Diaper and redress the child. Return the child to a play area.
- Disinfect the changing surface and any supplies or equipment that was touched with a chlorine bleach solution or other approved disinfectant.
- Remove gloves (if worn) and wash your hands again.

TeachSource Digital Download Download from CourseMate.

Diapering and Toileting Areas Children who are not toilet-trained can spread infectious illnesses through urine and feces. Maintaining separate diapering and toileting areas can significantly reduce contamination and the spread of infection from one child to another. Careful adherence to sanitary diapering procedures, disinfection of surfaces (free of cracks), and thorough hand washing will further reduce this risk. (See Teacher Checklist 5-4.) Teachers may choose to wear disposable gloves when changing infants or handling soiled diapers, but this is not essential. Even if gloves are worn, meticulous hand washing must follow because they do not prevent contamination. Soiled diapers (disposable) should be placed in a covered waste container (lined with a plastic bag) that is not accessible to children. Cloth diapers must be sealed in a plastic bag and sent home for parents to launder. Infants' hands should be washed under running water following each diaper change.

Family preferences and cultural differences will influence when and how toilet training is initiated (Gonzalez-Mena & Eyer, 2011; Rowe & Casillas, 2011). When toddlers are ready to begin potty training, small, child-sized toilets should be made available. (See Teacher Checklist 5-5.)

TEACHER CHECKLIST 5-5
Readiness Indicators for Toilet Training

Successful toilet training requires that children have basic motor and cognitive skills:

- an ability to understand the concepts of wet and dry
- a regularity to patterns of elimination (at least during daytime)
- language to express the need for elimination
- an ability to pull clothing up and down

TeachSource Digital Download Download from CourseMate.

Many states prohibit the use of shared potty-chairs in early childhood programs because they can spread infections if not properly disinfected. Families may wish to provide a chair for their child's sole use if the program's policy permits. However, teachers must still follow strict sanitizing procedures each time the chair is used. Any soiled material should first be removed with soap and water before spraying the surface with a disinfecting solution. Follow manufacturer's guidelines for mixing solutions and the length of time they must remain on surfaces to adequately disinfect. Teachers should wash their hands carefully after completing cleaning procedures and also be sure that children have washed their hands!

Room Arrangements Simple modifications in children's environments can also have a positive effect on the control of communicable illnesses. For example, room temperatures set at 68–70°F are less favorable for the spread of infectious illnesses and are often more comfortable for children. Their smaller body surfaces make children less sensitive than adults to cooler temperatures.

Rooms should be well ventilated to reduce the concentration of infectious organisms circulating within a given space. Doors and windows can be opened briefly, even on cool days, to introduce fresh air. Screens help to prevent disease-carrying flies and mosquitoes from coming indoors. Mechanical ventilating systems should undergo annual inspection and maintenance to improve air flow. Taking children outdoors, even in winter, also improves their resistance to illness.

The humidity level in rooms should also be checked periodically, especially in winter when rooms are heated. Extremely warm, dry air increases the risk of respiratory infection by causing the mucous linings in the mouth and nose to become dry and cracked. Moisture can be added to the air by installing a humidifier in the central heating system or placing a cool-mist vaporizer in individual rooms. Cool-mist units eliminate the risk of burns, but they must be emptied, washed out with soap and water, disinfected, and refilled with fresh distilled water each day to prevent bacterial growth. Plants or small dishes of water placed around a room also provide added humidity, but they can encourage the growth of mold spores, which may aggravate children's allergies and asthma (Nriagu et al., 2012).

The physical arrangement of a classroom also provides an effective method for controlling communicable and infectious illness. For example, separating older children from infants and toddlers who are not toilet-trained can significantly reduce the spread of intestinal illnesses. Surfaces such as floors, walls, counter tops, and furniture should be smooth and easy to clean. Laundry and food preparation areas should be separated from each other as well as from the classrooms. Pedal-operated sinks or faucets with infrared sensors encourage frequent hand washing and prevent recontamination.

Arranging children in small groups helps to limit close contact and enables teachers to more closely monitor behaviors that could potentially spread communicable illnesses. Children's rugs, cribs, and sleeping mats can be arranged in alternating directions, head to foot, to decrease talking, coughing, and breathing in each other's faces during naptimes. Individual lockers or storage spaces where children can store personal items, such as blankets, coats, hats, toys, and toothbrushes are also effective for reducing contact and transfer of infectious organisms.

Rearranging the environment can be an effective step in reducing the spread of communicable illness.

© Cengage Learning

Several additional areas of children's environments deserve special attention. Sandboxes should be covered to prevent contamination from animal feces. Water tables and wading pools need to be emptied and washed out daily to prevent bacterial growth and the spread of communicable disease; a water pH of 7.2–8.2 and chlorine level of 0.4–3.0 parts per million should be maintained in swimming pools at all times (as specified in commercial test kits). Items that children put on their heads, such as hats, wigs, and beauty parlor items can spread head lice and, therefore, may not be appropriate to use as play items in group settings unless they can be washed or disinfected. Play clothes should be laundered weekly or more often if communicable illnesses are present in the classroom.

5-4e Education

Teachers also make a valuable contribution to the control of communicable illness through the health promotion lessons they design for children. Educational activities that teach children about personal wellness, physical activity, and nutritious diet play an important role in improving resistance to illness and shortening convalescence if they do become ill (Gleddie, 2012; Johnson, Weed, & Touger-Decker, 2012). Examples of topics that are of interest and value to young children include:

- hand washing (appropriate technique and times)
- proper method for covering coughs, blowing noses, and disposing of tissues
- not sharing personal items, such as drinking cups, toothbrushes, shoes, hats, towels, eating utensils
- germs and how they spread
- dressing appropriately for the weather
- growing and cooking nutritious foods
- the importance of sleep
- fun ways to be physically active (and how this makes a body healthy)
- staying safe around animals

Communicable illness outbreaks provide excellent opportunities for teachers to review important preventive health concepts and practices with children. Learning is more meaningful for children when it is associated with real-life experiences, such as when a classmate has chickenpox, a cold, or pinkeye. Teachers can use these opportunities to review correct hand washing procedures, reinforce the importance of eating nutritious foods, conduct simple experiments to illustrate how germs spread, and model sound health practices for children to imitate. Children are far more likely to remember what they have seen than what they have been told.

Families must be included in any educational program that is aimed at reducing the incidence of communicable illness. They should be informed of health practices and information that is being taught to the children. Teachers can also reinforce the importance of (1) serving nutritious meals and snacks at home, (2) making sure that children get sufficient sleep and physical activity, (3) obtaining immunizations for infants, toddlers, and older children, (4) eliminating water sources where mosquitos can breed, and (5) scheduling routine medical and dental supervision. Successful control of communicable illness and the promotion of children's well-being depend on schools and families working together.

Did You Get It?

What is/are considered the earliest visible symptoms of an impending illness?
a. A drop in academic performance.
b. Concrete symptoms such as fever, cough, and sneezing.
c. Appearance and behavioral changes out of the ordinary for that child.
d. Increased appetite.

Take the full quiz on CourseMate.

PARTNERING with FAMILIES

Giving Children Medication

Dear Families,

Special precautions should be taken whenever administering medication to children. Their smaller bodies are more sensitive to many medications, and they may respond differently than an adult. It is also easy to give children too much of a medication because their dosages are typically quite small.

(continued)

PARTNERING with FAMILIES

Giving Children Medication   *(continued)*

Unattended medications may attract children's curiosity and must always be stored in a locked cabinet to prevent unintentional poisoning. Additional safety precautions that you can take include:

▶ Always check with your child's physician before giving over-the-counter medications, especially to children under 2 years.

▶ Read medication labels carefully. Be sure you are giving the correct medication to the right child at the appropriate time interval. Also, double-check the dose that has been prescribed, and administer only that amount. Make sure the medication is approved for children; many drugs are not advised for children younger than 12 years.

▶ Ask your pharmacist about potential drug interactions—with other medications or food— that should be avoided. Also, learn about possible reactions that should be noted before giving your child any new medication.

▶ Always follow the instructions for administering a medication and finish giving the full course that has been prescribed.

▶ Dispose of outdated medications. Old medications can lose their effectiveness and cause unexpected reactions. Always check with a pharmacist if in doubt.

▶ Store medications in their original container and according to instructions.

▶ Never tell children that medicines are "candy" and avoid taking medication in front of children.

CLASSROOM CORNER

Teacher Activities

Those Invisible Germs...

(**NHES** PreK–2, National Health Education Standard 1.2.3)

Concept: Germs are everywhere; germs are on the things we touch.

Learning Objectives

▶ Children will understand that germs are invisible and on most things we touch.

▶ Children will learn that correct hand washing removes germs.

Supplies

▶ Baby powder or glitter; small spray bottle with water; paper towel; hand lotion

Learning Activities

▶ Read and discuss one of the following books:

  ▶ *Germs Are Not for Sharing* by Elizabeth Verdick

  ▶ *Those Mean Nasty Dirty Downright Disgusting but . . . Invisible Germs* by Judith Rice

  ▶ *The Magic School Bus Inside Ralphie: A Book About Germs* (for older children) by Joanna Cole

  ▶ *The Berenstain Bears Come Clean for School* by Jan and Mike Berenstain

▶ Ask children if they know what a germ is and if they can describe what they look like. Ask them where germs are found and what we can do to protect ourselves from them.

▶ Lightly spray water on the hands of half of the children; sprinkle with baby powder or glitter. Ask children to shake hands with one another and then examine their hands.

▶ Coat children's hands with a thin layer of hand cream (make sure no one has any allergies). Sprinkle their hands lightly with glitter. Have them attempt to brush the "germs" off by

(continued)

CLASSROOM CORNER

Teacher Activities *(continued)*

Those Invisible Germs...

rubbing their hands together. Repeat this step using a paper towel. Finally, have children wash their hands with soap and warm water. After, ask the children which method was most effective for removing the "germs." Talk about why hand washing is important for keeping the germs away and staying healthy.

▶ Have children draw their own interpretations of what a germ looks like.

Evaluation

▶ Children can explain where germs are found and how they are spread.

▶ Children will demonstrate how to wash their hands correctly.

Additional lesson plans for grades 3–5 are available on CourseMate.

Summary

▶ Communicable illnesses are common in group settings where there are young children. Reasons for this include children playing in close proximity, immature development of children's respiratory system, children's play and personal hygiene habits, adult carelessness, and poor hand washing practices.

▶ To be communicable, an illness requires a pathogen, a susceptible host, and a method for successful transmission.

  • Transmission occurs via airborne, fecal-oral, direct, or indirect methods.

▶ Communicable illnesses develop in four stages: incubation, prodromal, acute, and convalescence.

▶ Effective practices for controlling and managing communicable illness in group settings include conducting daily observations, implementing health policies and sanitation procedures, enforcing immunization requirements, modifying the environment, working collaboratively with families, and educating children.

Terms to Know

antibodies *p. 113*	airborne transmission *p. 115*	prodromal *p. 116*
communicable *p. 114*	fecal-oral transmission *p. 115*	acute *p. 117*
pathogen *p. 114*	direct contact *p. 115*	convalescent *p. 117*
susceptible host *p. 114*	indirect contact *p. 116*	lymph glands *p. 117*
respiratory tract *p. 114*	incubation *p. 116*	universal infection control
immunized *p. 114*	contagious *p. 116*	precautions *p. 124*

Chapter Review

A. By Yourself:

1. Define each of the *Terms to Know* listed at the end of this chapter.

2. Describe two examples that illustrate how an illness can be spread via:

   a. airborne transmission

   b. indirect contact

3. What immunizations, and how many of each, are recommended for a 30-month-old child?

4. Where can families in your community obtain immunizations for their children?

5. During what stage(s) of communicable illnesses are children most contagious?

B. **As a Group:**

1. Identify and discuss three factors that are required for an infection to be communicable.

2. What early signs would you be likely to observe in a child who was coming down with a respiratory virus?

3. Discuss specific practices that teachers can use in their classrooms to limit the spread of illnesses transmitted via:

   a. the respiratory tract

   b. the fecal-oral route

   c. skin conditions

   d. contaminated objects such as toys, towels, or changing mats

4. Discuss when and how universal precautions should be implemented in the classroom.

5. What special accommodations would be necessary if a program wanted to allow mildly ill children to remain onsite?

Case Study

Laura arrived at the child care center with a runny nose and cough. Her mother informed the teachers that it was probably "just allergies" and left before Laura could be checked in. When the head teacher finally completed a health check, she discovered that Laura had a fever, red throat, and swollen glands. Laura's mother is a single parent, a student at the local community college, and also works part time at an early childhood program in another part of town.

1. How should the teachers handle Laura's immediate situation? Should she be allowed to stay or should they try to contact Laura's mother?

2. If Laura is allowed to stay at the center, what measures can be taken to limit the risk of spreading illness to other children?

3. If this is a repeated occurrence, what steps can be taken to make sure Laura's mother complies with the center's exclusion policies?

4. How can the center help Laura's mother avoid similar situations in the future?

Application Activities

1. Obtain several agar growth medium plates. With sterile cotton applicators, culture one toy and the top of one table. Observe the "growth" after 24 hours and again after 48 hours. Wash the same items with a mild chlorine bleach solution and repeat the experiment. Compare the results.

2. Contact the Office of Public Health in your state (province/territory). Obtain data on the percentage of children under 6 years of age who are currently immunized. How does this figure compare to national goals? What suggestions do you have for improving this rate in your community? What immunizations are children required to have before they can attend an early childhood or kindergarten program in your state.

3. Locate and read OSHA's regulations and guidelines for implementing a blood-borne pathogen workplace policy (document CFR 1910.1030) available on their website (http://www.osha .gov/SLTC/bloodbornepathogens/index.html). Develop a written compliance plan for an early childhood center or school building.

4. Discuss how you would handle the following situations:

   a. The father of a toddler in your center is upset because his child has frequent colds.

   b. You observe your teacher covering a cough with her hand and then continuing to prepare snacks for the children.

   c. Your toddler group has experienced frequent outbreaks of strep throat in the past six months.

   d. While reviewing immunization records, you discover that one child has received only one dose of DTaP, IPV, and Hib.

   e. Gabriel announces that he threw up all night. You notice that his eyes appear watery and his cheeks are flushed.

   f. You find that one of your aides has stored all of the children's toothbrushes together in a sealed, plastic container.

   g. You overhear one of your paraprofessionals offering to retrieve medication from her backpack for a child who is complaining of a headache.

5. Review and compare health care policies from an early childhood center, home-based program, Head Start program, and elementary school. How are they similar? How do they differ?

Helpful Web Resources

American Public Health Association	http://www.apha.org
Canadian Paediatric Society	http://www.cps.ca
Centers for Disease Control and Prevention (CDC)	http://www.cdc.gov
Maternal and Child Health Bureau	http://mchb.hrsa.gov
National Center for Emerging & Zoonotic Infectious Diseases (NCEZID)	http://www.cdc.gov/ncezid
National Foundation for Infectious Diseases	http://www.nfid.org
National Institutes of Health	http://www.nih.gov

 Visit the Education CourseMate for this textbook to access the eBook, Did You Get It? quizzes, Digital Downloads, TeachSource Video Cases, flashcards, and more. Go to CengageBrain.com to log in, register, or purchase access.

References

Abrevaya, J., & Mulligan, K. (2011). Effectiveness of state-level mandates: Evidence from the varicella vaccine, *Journal of Health Economics*, 30(5), 966–976.

American Public Health Association (APHA) & American Academy of Pediatrics (AAP). (2011). *Caring for our children. National health and safety performance standards: Guidelines for out-of-home care.* (3rd. ed.). Washington, DC.

Armellino, D., Hussain, E., Schilling, M., Senicola, W., Eichorn, A., Dlugacz, Y., & Farber, B. (2012). Using high-technology to enforce low-technology safety measures: The use of third-party remote video auditing and real-time feedback in healthcare, *Clinical Infectious Diseases*, 54(1), 1–7.

Barile, J., Kuperminc, G., Weintraub, E., Mink, J., & Thompson, W. (2012). Thimerosal exposure in early life and neuropsychological outcomes 7–10 years later, *Journal of Pediatric Psychology*, 37(1), 106–118.

Cannon, M., Westbrook, K., Levis, D., Schleiss, M., Thackeray, R., & Pass, R. (2012). Awareness of and behaviors related to child-to-mother transmission of cytomegalovirus, *Preventive Medicine*, 54(5), 351–357.

Centers for Disease Control and Prevention (CDC). (2012). U.S. vaccination coverage reported via NIS. Accessed on May 10, 2012 from http://www.cdc.gov/vaccines/stats-surv/nis/default.htm#nis.

Egger, J., Konty, K., Wilson, E., Karpati, A., Matte, T., Weiss, D., & Barbot, O. (2012). The effect of school dismissal on rates of influenza-like illness in New York City schools during the spring 2009 novel H1N1 outbreak, *Journal of School Health*, 82(3), 123–130.

Fuller, C., Savage, J., Besser, S., Hayward, A., Cookson, B., Cooper, B., & Stone, S. (2011). "The dirty hand in the latex glove": A study of hand hygiene compliance when gloves are worn, *Infection Control & Hospital Epidemiology*, 32(12), 1194–1199.

Gaudino, J., & Robison, S. (2012). Risk factors associated with parents claiming personal-belief exemptions to school immunization requirements: Community and other influences on more skeptical parents in Oregon, 2006, *Vaccine*, 30(6), 1132–1142.

Gerald, L., Gerald, J., Zhang, B., McClure, L., Bailey, W., & Harrington, K. (2012). Can a school-based hand hygiene program reduce asthma exacerbations among elementary school children?, *Journal of Allergy & Clinical Immunology*, 130(6), 1317–1324.

Gidengil, C., Lieu, T., Payne, K., Rusinak, D., Messonnier, M., & Prosser, L. (2012). Parental and societal values for the risks and benefits of childhood combination vaccines, *Vaccine*, 30(23), 3445–3452.

Gleddie, D. (2012). A journey into school health promotion: District implementation of the health promoting schools approach, *Health Promotion International*, 27(1), 82–89.

Gonzalez-Mena, J. & Eyer, D. (2011). *Infants, toddlers, and caregivers: A curriculum of respectful, responsive, relationship-based care and education*. (5th ed.). NY: McGraw-Hill.

Johnson, T., Weed, D., & Touger-Decker, R. (2012). School-based interventions for overweight and obesity in minority school children, *Journal of School Nursing*, 28(2), 116–123.

Luthy, K., Beckstrand, R., Callister, L., & Cahoon, S. (2013). Reasons parents exempt children from receiving immunizations, *The Journal of School Nursing*, 28(2), 153–160.

Nandrup-Bus, I. (2011). Comparative studies of hand disinfection and handwashing procedures as tested by pupils in intervention programs, *American Journal of Infection Control*, 39(6), 450–455.

Nriagu, J., Martin, J., Smith, P., & Socier, D. (2012). Residential hazards, high asthma prevalence and multimorbidity among children in Saginaw, Michigan, *Science of the Total Environment*, 416(1), 53–61.

Occupational Safety and Health Administration (OSHA). (2011). OSHA Fact Sheet: Hepatitis B vaccination protection. Accessed on May 10, 2012 from http://www.osha.gov/OshDoc/data_BloodborneFacts/bbfact05.pdf.

OSHA. (2003). Model plans and programs for the OSHA bloodborne pathogens and hazard communication standards. Accessed on May 12, 2012 from http://www.osha.gov/Publications/osha3186.html.

Public Health Agency of Canada (2012). Canadian immunization guide. Accessed on April 23, 2013 from http://www.phac-aspc.gc.ca/publicat/cig-gci/index-eng.php.

Rowe, M., & Casillas, A. (2011). Parental goals and talk with toddlers, *Infant & Child Development*, 20(5), 475–494.

Schulte, J., Williams, L., Asghar, J., Dang, T., Bedwell, S., Guerrero, K., Hamaker, D., Stonecipher, S., Zoretic, J., & Chow, C. (2012). How we didn't clean up until we washed our hands: Shigellosis in an elementary and middle school in North Texas, *Southern Medical Journal*, 105(1), 1–4.

Stebbins, S., Downs, J., & Vukotich, C. (2011). The effect of grade on compliance with nonpharmaceutical interventions to reduce influenza in an urban elementary school setting, *Journal of Public Health Management*, 17(1), 65–71.

Tak, S., Groenewold, M., Alterman, T., Park, R., & Calvert, G. (2011). Excess risk of head and chest colds among teachers and other school workers, *Journal of School Health*, 81(9), 560–565.

U.S. Department of Health & Human Services (DHHS). (2012). Healthy People 2020–Improving the life of Americans. Accessed on May 10, 2012 from http://www.healthypeople.gov.

Vermeer, H., van IJzendorn, M., Groeneveld, M., & Granger, D. (2012). Downregulation of the immune system in low-quality child care: The case of the secretory immunoglobulin A (Slg A) in toddlers, *Physiology & Behavior*, 105(2), 161–167.

White, C., Statile, A., Conway, P., Schoettker, P., Solan, L., Unaka, N., Vidwan, N., Warrick, S., Yau, C., & Connelly, B. (2012). Utilizing improvement science methods to improve physician compliance with proper hand hygiene, *Pediatrics*, 129(4), e1042–e1050.

Wilson, S., Jacob, C., & Powell, D. (2011). Behavior-change interventions to improve hand-hygiene practice: A review of alternatives to education, *Critical Public Health*, 21(1), 119–127.

chapter 6 Childhood Illnesses: Identification and Management

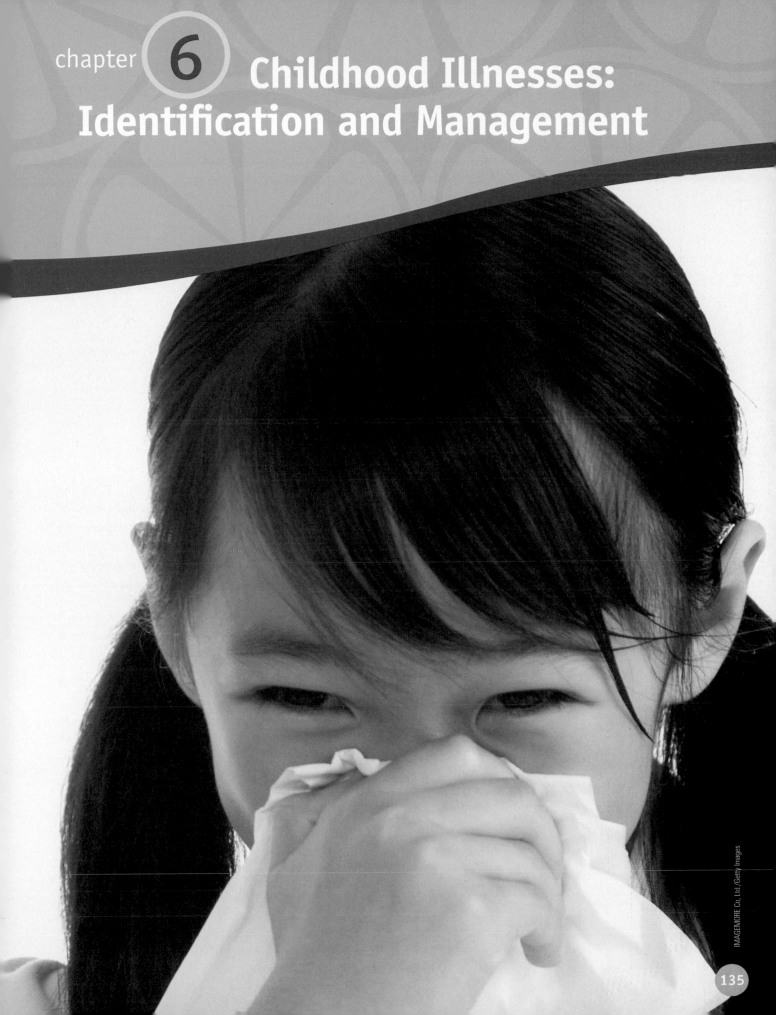

▶ **#1 a, b, and c:** Promoting child development and learning
▶ **#2 a, b, and c:** Building family and community relationships
▶ **#3 a, c, and d:** Observing, documenting, and assessing to support young children and families

Learning Objectives

After studying this chapter, you should be able to:

LO 6-1 Explain how communicable childhood illnesses such as chickenpox, colds, pinkeye, and head lice are spread and identify the appropriate control measures to be taken.

LO 6-2 Describe the teachers' role in addressing common acute childhood illnesses, such as ear infections, Lyme disease, and Sudden Infant Death Syndrome (SIDS).

Because young children are especially vulnerable to a variety of communicable and acute illnesses, classroom teachers must be prepared to identify and implement policies and practices designed to limit their spread. Teachers can best prepare themselves for this role by becoming familiar with the signs and **symptoms** of common childhood illnesses and the precautionary control measures appropriate for each. This knowledge can be useful for establishing program guidelines, creating meaningful lessons for children, and communicating important health information with families.

6-1 Common Communicable Childhood Illnesses

Protecting children's health in group settings requires teachers to have a sound understanding of common communicable illnesses—what causes them, how they are transmitted, and how they can be controlled (Table 6–1). Their knowledge of childhood illnesses and ability to implement infection control procedures, including hand washing and disinfection, are essential to children's well-being.

Teachers should be familiar with local public health regulations that specify which communicable illnesses must be reported. Notifying health officials of existing cases enables them to monitor communities for potential outbreaks and to provide additional information that can be shared with families.

---

symptoms – *changes in the body or its functions that are experienced by the affected individual.*

TABLE 6–1   Common Communicable Childhood Illnesses

Communicable Illness	Signs and Symptoms	Methods of Transmission	Incubation Period	Length of Communicability	Control Measures
Airborne Transmitted Illnesses					
Chickenpox	Slight fever, irritability, cold-like symptoms. Red rash that develops blister-like head, scabs later. Most abundant on covered parts of body, e.g., chest, back, neck, forearms.	Airborne through contact with secretions from the respiratory tract. Transmission from contact with blisters less common.	2–3 weeks after exposure.	2–3 days prior to the onset of symptoms until 5–6 days after first eruptions. Scabs are not contagious.	Specific control measures: (1) Exclusion of sick children. (2) Practice good personal hygiene, especially careful hand washing. Children can return to group care when all blisters have formed a dry scab (approximately 1 week). Immunization is now available.
Common cold	Highly contagious infection of the upper respiratory tract accompanied by slight fever, chills, runny nose, fatigue, muscle ache, and headaches. Onset may be sudden.	Airborne through contact with secretions from the respiratory tract, e.g., coughs, sneezes, eating utensils, etc.	12–72 hours.	About 1 day before onset of symptoms to 2–3 days after acute illness.	Prevention through education and good personal hygiene. Avoid exposure. Exclude first day or two. Antibiotics not effective against viruses. Avoid aspirin products (possible link to Reye's syndrome). Observe for complications, e.g., earaches, bronchitis, croup, pneumonia.
Fifth disease	Appearance of bright red rash on face, especially cheeks.	Airborne contact with secretions from the nose/mouth of infected person.	4–14 days.	Prior to appearance of rash; probably not contagious after rash develops.	Children don't need to be excluded once rash appears. Frequent hand washing; frequent washing/disinfecting of toys/surfaces. Use care when handling tissues/nasal secretions.
Haemophilus influenza Type b (Hib)	An acute respiratory infection; frequently causes meningitis. Other complications include pneumonia, epiglottitis, arthritis, infections of the bloodstream, and conjunctivitis.	Airborne via secretions of the respiratory tract (nose, throat). Some children are carriers and may/may not have symptoms.	2–4 days.	Throughout acute phase; as long as organism is present. Noncommunicable 36–48 hours after treatment with antibiotics.	Identify and exclude sick children. Treatment with antibiotics 3–4 days before returning to group care. Notify families of exposed children to contact their physician. Immunize children. Practice good hand washing techniques; sanitize contaminated objects.

(continued)

TABLE 6–1   Common Communicable Childhood Illnesses (*continued*)

Communicable Illness	Signs and Symptoms	Methods of Transmission	Incubation Period	Length of Communicability	Control Measures
Airborne Transmitted Illnesses (*continued*)					
Measles (Rubeola)	Fever, cough, runny nose, eyes sensitive to light. Dark red blotchy rash that often begins on the face and neck, then spreads over the entire body. Highly communicable.	Airborne through coughs, sneezes, and contact with contaminated articles.	8–13 days; rash develops approximately 14 days after exposure.	From beginning of symptoms until 4 days after rash appears.	Most effective control method is immunization. Good personal hygiene, especially hand washing and covering coughs. Exclude child for at least 4 days after rash appears.
Meningitis	Sudden onset of fever, stiff neck, headache, irritability, and vomiting; gradual loss of consciousness, seizures, and death.	Airborne through coughs, nasal secretions; direct contact with saliva/nasal discharges.	Varies with the infectious organism; 2–4 days average.	Throughout acute phase; noncommunicable after antibiotic treatment.	Encourage immunization. Exclude child from school until medical treatment is completed. Use universal precautions when handling saliva/nasal secretions, frequent hand washing, and disinfecting of toys/surfaces.
Mononucleosis	Characteristic symptoms include sore throat, intermittent fever, fatigue, and enlarged lymph glands in the neck. May also be accompanied by headache and enlarged liver or spleen.	Airborne; also direct contact with saliva of an infected person.	2–4 weeks for children; 4–6 weeks for adults.	Unknown. Organisms may be present in oral secretions for as long as 1 year following illness.	None known. Child should be kept home until over the acute phase (6–10 days). Use frequent hand washing and careful disposal of tissues after coughing or blowing nose.
Mumps	Sudden onset of fever with swelling of the salivary glands.	Airborne through coughs and sneezes; direct contact with oral secretions of infected persons.	12–26 days.	6–7 days prior to the onset of symptoms until swelling in the salivary glands is gone (7–9 days).	Immunization provides permanent protection. Peak incidence is in winter and spring. Exclude children from school or group settings until all symptoms have disappeared.
Roseola infantum (6–24 mos.)	Most common in the spring and fall. Fever rises abruptly (102–105°F) and lasts 3–4 days; loss of appetite, listlessness, runny nose, rash on trunk, arms, and neck lasting 1–2 days.	Person to person; method unknown.	10–15 days.	1–2 days before onset to several days following fading of the rash.	Exclude from school or group care until rash and fever are gone.

Disease	Symptoms	Mode of Transmission	Incubation	Communicability	Management
Rubella (German Measles)	Mild fever; rash begins on face and neck and rarely lasts more than 3 days. May have arthritis-like discomfort and swelling in joints.	Airborne through contact with respiratory secretions, e.g., coughs, sneezes.	4–21 days.	From one week prior to 5 days following onset of the rash.	Immunization offers permanent protection. Children must be excluded from school for at least 7 days after appearance of rash.
Streptococcal infections (strep throat, scarlatina, rheumatic fever)	Sudden onset. High fever accompanied by sore, red throat; may also have nausea, vomiting, headache, white patches on tonsils, and enlarged glands. Development of a rash depends on the infectious organism.	Airborne via droplets from coughs or sneezes. May also be transmitted by food and raw milk.	1–4 days.	Throughout the illness and for approximately 10 days afterward, unless treated with antibiotics. Medical treatment eliminates communicability within 36 hours. Can develop rheumatic fever or become a carrier if not treated.	Exclude child with symptoms. Antibiotic treatment is essential. Avoid crowding in classrooms. Practice frequent hand washing, educating children, and careful supervision of food handlers.
Tuberculosis	Many people have no symptoms. Active disease causes productive cough, weight loss, fatigue, loss of appetite, chills, night sweats.	Airborne via coughs or sneezes.	2–3 months.	As long as disease is untreated; usually noncontagious after 2–3 weeks on medication.	TB skin testing, especially babies and young children if there has been contact with an infected person. Seek prompt diagnosis and treatment if experiencing symptoms; complete drug therapy. Cover coughs/sneezes. Practice good hand washing.
Acquired Immuno-deficiency Syndrome (AIDS)	Flu-like symptoms, including fatigue, weight loss, enlarged lymph glands, persistent cough, fever, and diarrhea.	Children acquire virus when born to infected mothers, from contaminated blood transfusions, and possibly from breast milk of infected mothers. Adults acquire the virus via sexual transmission, contaminated drug needles, and blood transfusions.	6 weeks to 8 years.	Lifetime	Exclude children 0–5 years if they have open lesions, uncontrollable nosebleeds, bloody diarrhea, or are at high risk for exposing others to blood-contaminated body fluids. Use universal precautions when handling body fluids, including good hand washing techniques. Seal contaminated items, e.g., diapers, paper towels in plastic bags. Disinfect surfaces with bleach/water solution (1:10) or other disinfectant.

(continued)

TABLE 6–1 Common Communicable Childhood Illnesses *(continued)*

Communicable Illness	Signs and Symptoms	Methods of Transmission	Incubation Period	Length of Communicability	Control Measures
Blood-Borne Transmitted Illnesses					
Hepatitis B	Slow onset; loss of appetite, nausea, vomiting, abdominal pain, and jaundice. May also be asymptomatic.	Through contact with blood/body fluids containing blood.	45–180 days; average 60–80 days.	Varies; some persons are lifetime carriers.	Immunization is preferable. Use universal precautions when handling any blood/body fluids; use frequent hand washing.
Contact (Direct and Indirect) Transmitted Illnesses					
Conjunctivitis (Pinkeye)	Redness of the white portion (conjunctiva) of the eye and inner eyelid, swelling of the lids, yellow discharge from eyes, and itching.	Direct contact with discharge from eyes or upper respiratory tract of an infected person; through contaminated fingers; indirect contact with surfaces and objects (tissues, towels).	1–3 days.	Throughout active infection; several days up to 2–3 weeks.	Antibiotic treatment. Exclude child for 24 hours after medication is started. Frequent hand washing and disinfection of toys/surfaces is necessary.
Cytomegalovirus (CMV)	Often no symptoms in children under 2 years; sore throat, fever, fatigue in older children. High risk of fetal damage if mother is infected during pregnancy.	Person-to-person contact with body fluids, e.g., saliva, blood, urine, breast milk, in utero.	Unknown; may be 4–8 weeks.	Virus present (in saliva, urine) for months following infection.	No need to exclude children. Always wash hands after changing diapers or contact with saliva. Avoid kissing children's mouths or sharing eating utensils. Practice careful hand washing with children; wash/disinfect toys and surfaces frequently.
Hand-foot-and-mouth disease	Affects children under 10 years. Onset of fever, followed by blistered sores in the mouth/cheeks; 1–2 days later raised rash appears on palms of hands and soles of feet.	Person-to-person through direct contact with saliva, nasal discharge, or feces.	3–6 days.	7–10 days.	Exclude sick children for several days. Practice frequent hand washing, especially after changing diapers. Clean/disinfect surfaces.

asymptomatic — *having no symptoms.*

Illness	Symptoms	Method of spread	Incubation period	Period of communicability	Control measures
Herpes simplex (cold sores)	Clear blisters develop on face, lips, and other body parts that crust and heal within a few days.	Direct contact with saliva, on hands, or sexual contact.	Up to 2 weeks.	Virus remains in saliva for as long as 7 weeks following recovery.	No specific control. Frequent hand washing. Child does not have to be excluded from school.
Impetigo	Infection of the skin forming crusty, moist lesions usually on the face, ears, and around the nose. Highly contagious. Common among children.	Direct contact with discharge from sores; indirect contact with contaminated articles of clothing, tissues, etc.	2–5 days; may be as long as 10 days.	Until treated with antibiotics and all lesions are healed.	Exclude from group settings until lesions have been treated with antibiotics for 24–48 hours. Cover areas with bandage until treated.
Lice (head)	Lice are seldom visible to the naked eye. White nits (eggs) are visible on hair shafts. The most obvious symptom is itching of the scalp, especially behind the ears and at the base of the neck.	Direct contact with infected persons or with their personal articles, e.g., hats, hair brushes, combs, or clothing. Lice can survive for 2–3 weeks on bedding, carpet, furniture, car seats, clothing, etc.	Nits hatch in 1 week and reach maturity within 8–10 days.	While lice remain alive on infested persons or clothing; until nits have been destroyed.	Exclude infected children until treated. Wash hair with a special medicated shampoo; follow with a vinegar/water rinse (any concentration will work) to make nit removal easier (use a fine-toothed comb). Heat from a hair dryer helps to destroy eggs. All friends and family should be carefully checked. Thoroughly clean child's environment: vacuum carpets, furniture, car seats; wash/dry clean bedding, clothing, hairbrushes. Seal nonwashable items (hair ribbons, clips) in plastic bag and freeze for 1 week.
Ringworm	A fungal infection of the scalp, skin, or nails. Causes flat, spreading, oval-shaped lesions that may become dry and scaly or moist and crusted. When it is present on the feet it is commonly called athlete's foot. Infected nails may become discolored, brittle, or chalky or they may disintegrate.	Direct or indirect contact with infected persons, their personal items, swimming pools, theater seats, etc. Dogs and cats may also be infected and transmit it to children or adults.	4–10 days (unknown for athlete's foot).	As long as lesions are present.	Exclude children from gyms, pools, or activities where they are likely to expose others. May return to group care following treatment with a fungicidal ointment. All shared areas, such as pools and showers, should be thoroughly cleansed with a fungicide.

(continued)

TABLE 6-1   Common Communicable Childhood Illnesses *(continued)*

Communicable Illness	Signs and Symptoms	Methods of Transmission	Incubation Period	Length of Communicability	Control Measures
Contact (Direct and Indirect) Transmitted Illnesses *(continued)*					
Rocky Mountain spotted fever	Onset usually abrupt; fever (101–104°F); joint and muscle pain, severe nausea and vomiting, and white coating on tongue. Rash appears on 2nd to 5th day over forehead, wrist, and ankles; later covers entire body. Can be fatal if untreated.	Indirect transmission: tick bite.	2–14 days; average 7 days.	Not contagious from person to person.	Prompt removal of ticks; not all ticks cause illness. Administration of antibiotics. Use insect repellent on clothes when outdoors.
Scabies	Characteristic burrows or linear tunnels under the skin, especially between the fingers and around the wrists, elbows, waist, thighs, and buttocks. Causes intense itching.	Direct contact with an infected person. Indirect contact with towels, bedding, and personal items of infected person.	Several days to 2–4 weeks.	Until all mites and eggs are destroyed.	Children should be excluded from school or group care until treated. Affected persons should bathe with prescribed soap and carefully launder all bedding and clothing. All contacts of the infected person should be notified.
Tetanus	Muscle spasms and stiffness, especially in the muscles around the neck and mouth. Can lead to convulsions, inability to breathe, and death.	Indirect: organisms live in soil and dust; enter body through wounds, especially puncture-type injuries, burns, and unnoticed cuts.	4 days to 2 weeks.	Not contagious.	Immunization every 8–10 years affords complete protection.
Fecal/Oral Transmitted Illnesses					
Dysentery (shigellosis)	Sudden onset of vomiting; diarrhea, may be accompanied by high fever, headache, abdominal pain. Stools may contain blood, pus, or mucus. Can be fatal in young children.	Fecal-oral transmission via contaminated objects; indirectly through ingestion of contaminated food or water, and via flies.	1–7 days.	Variable; may last up to 4 weeks or longer in the carrier state.	Exclude child during acute illness. Careful hand washing after bowel movements. Proper disposal of human feces; control of flies. Strict adherence to sanitary procedures for food preparation.

E. coli	Diarrhea, often bloody.	Spread through contaminated food, dirty hands.	3–4 days; can be as long as 10 days.	For duration of diarrhea; usually several days.	Exclude infected children until no diarrhea; practice frequent hand washing, especially after toileting and before preparing food.
Encephalitis	Sudden onset of headache, high fever, convulsions, vomiting, confusion, neck and back stiffness, tremors, and coma.	Indirect spread by bites from disease-carrying mosquitoes; in some areas transmitted by tick bites.	5–15 days.	Not contagious.	Spraying of mosquito breeding areas and use of insect repellents; public education.
Giardiasis	Many persons are asymptomatic. Typical symptoms include chronic diarrhea, abdominal cramping, bloating, pale and foul-smelling stools, weight loss, and fatigue.	Fecal-oral transmission; through contact with infected stool (e.g., diaper changes, helping child with soiled underwear), poor hand washing; passed from hands to mouth (toys, food). Also transmitted through contaminated water sources.	7–10 days average; can be as long as 5–25 days.	As long as parasite is present in the stool.	Exclude children until diarrhea ends. Scrupulous hand washing before eating, preparing food, and after using the bathroom. Maintain sanitary conditions in bathroom areas.
Hepatitis (infectious; type A)	Fever, fatigue, loss of appetite, nausea, abdominal pain (in region of liver). Illness may be accompanied by yellowing of the skin and eyeballs (jaundice) in adults, but not always in children. Acute onset.	Fecal-oral route. Also spread via contaminated food, water, milk, and objects.	10–50 days (average range 25–30 days).	7–10 days prior to onset of symptoms to not more than 7 days after onset of jaundice.	Exclude from group settings a minimum of 1 week following onset. Special attention to careful hand washing after going to the bathroom and before eating is critical following an outbreak. Report disease incidents to public health authorities. Immunoglobulin (IG) recommended for protection of close contacts.

(continued)

TABLE 6-1 Common Communicable Childhood Illnesses *(continued)*

Communicable Illness	Signs and Symptoms	Methods of Transmission	Incubation Period	Length of Communicability	Control Measures
Fecal/Oral Transmitted Illnesses *(continued)*					
Pinworms	Irritability, and itching of the rectal area. Common among young children. Some children have no symptoms.	Infectious eggs are transferred from person to person by contaminated hands (oral-fecal route). Indirect spread through contaminated bedding, food, clothing, swimming pool.	Life cycle of the worm is 3–6 weeks; persons can also re-infect themselves.	2–8 weeks or as long as a source of infection remains present.	Infected children must be excluded from school until treated with medication; may return after initial dose. All infected and non-infected family members must be treated at one time. Frequent hand washing is essential; discourage nail biting or sucking of fingers. Daily baths and change of linen are necessary. Disinfect school toilet seats and sink handles at least once a day. Vacuum carpeted areas daily. Eggs are also destroyed when exposed to temperatures over 132°F. Education and good personal hygiene are vital to control.
Salmonellosis	Abdominal pain and cramping, sudden fever, severe diarrhea (may contain blood), nausea and vomiting that lasts 5–7 days.	Fecal-oral transmission via dirty hands. Also spread via contaminated food (especially improperly cooked poultry, milk, eggs), water, and infected animals.	12–36 hours.	Throughout acute illness; may remain a carrier for months.	Attempt to identify source. Exclude children/adults with diarrhea; may return when symptoms end. Carriers should not handle or prepare food until stool cultures are negative. Practice good hand washing and sanitizing procedures.

▼ Identifying the early signs of childhood illnesses is an important control measure.

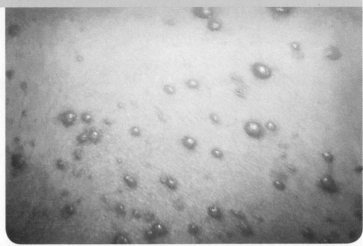

© http://phil.cdc.gov/phil

Did You Get It?

Chicken pox is a highly infectious disease caused by the varicella zoster virus. A child who has had chickenpox can return to the classroom when all blisters have:

  a. disappeared completely
  b. formed dry scabs
  c. started oozing
  d. started to decrease in number

Take the full quiz on CourseMate.

6-2 Common Acute Childhood Illnesses

Children experience many forms of acute illness; however, not all of these are contagious (Fiore et al., 2012; Sun & Sundell, 2011). Teachers must be able to distinguish conditions that are communicable from those that are limited to an individual child. *However, teachers must never attempt to diagnose children's health conditions.* Their primary responsibilities are to identify children who are ill, make them comfortable until parents arrive, and advise the family to contact their health care provider. The remainder of this chapter is devoted to descriptions of several common childhood illnesses and acute health conditions.

6-2a Colds

Children may experience as many as seven to eight colds during a typical year. This number tends to decrease as children mature and their respiratory passageways increase in size, their immune systems become more effective at warding off illness, and they begin to develop healthy personal habits. Cold symptoms can range from frequent sneezing and runny nose to fever, sore throat, cough, headache, and muscle aches.

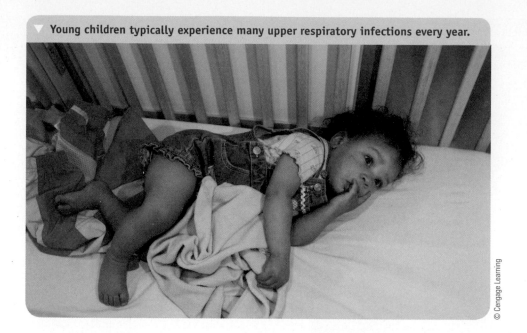

▼ **Young children typically experience many upper respiratory infections every year.**

© Cengage Learning

Cause Most colds are caused by a viral **infection**, primarily rhinoviruses and coronoviruses. They spread rapidly and have a short incubation stage of 1 to 2 days.

Management Because colds are highly contagious during the first day or two, it is best to exclude children from group settings. Rest and increased fluid intake (water, fruit juices, soups) are recommended. Non-aspirin fever-reducing medication is usually adequate treatment for a cold and may help children rest more comfortably. (Note: Schools must obtain a physician's approval before administering any medication.)

Antibiotics are not effective against most viruses and are therefore of limited value for treating simple colds. However, a physician may prescribe antibiotics to treat complications or secondary infections, such as fever, red throat, white patches on tonsils (one indication of strep throat), or yellow nasal drainage. Toddlers and young children are more susceptible to these conditions and should be observed closely. Families should be advised to seek immediate medical attention for children who do not improve after 4 to 5 days or if they develop any secondary complications.

Some children who have developmental disabilities such as Down syndrome or special medical conditions such as leukemia, or allergies, may experience chronic cold-like symptoms including runny nose and a productive cough. It isn't necessary for these children to be excluded from school unless they also show signs of a secondary infection (e.g., fever, yellow nasal discharge, productive cough).

6-2b Diaper Rash (Diaper Dermatitis)

Diaper rash is an irritation of the skin in and around the buttocks and genital area. Infants who have sensitive skin or who are formula-fed versus breast-fed are more likely to experience periodic outbreaks of diaper rash (Hockenberry & Wilson, 2012).

Cause Prolonged contact with ammonia in urine and organic acids in stools can burn an infant's skin and cause patches of red, raised areas, or tiny pimples. In severe cases, areas that are open and weeping may become infected with yeast or bacteria. Reactions to fabric softeners, soaps, lotions, powders, antibiotics, foods, and certain brands of disposable diapers may also cause some infants and toddlers to develop diaper rash.

infection – *a condition that results when a pathogen invades and establishes itself within a susceptible host.*

Management   Prompt changing of wet or soiled diapers followed by a thorough cleansing of the skin is often sufficient to prevent and treat diaper rash. Baby products, such as powders and lotions, should be avoided because they can encourage bacterial growth when combined with urine and feces. In addition, infants are apt to inhale fine powder particles and some products contain phthalates, which may have harmful effects on children's development and reproductive systems (Lampel & Jacob, 2011). A thin layer of petroleum jelly or zinc oxide ointment applied to irritated areas will help to protect the skin. Allowing the infant to go without diapers (when at home) and exposing affected areas to the air can also speed the healing process. If the diaper rash does not improve in 2 or 3 days, parents should be encouraged to contact their health care provider.

6-2c Diarrhea

The term "diarrhea" refers to frequent watery or very soft bowel movements. At times they may be foul-smelling or contain blood or mucus, especially if a child is taking antibiotics or has an intestinal infection. It is not uncommon for young children to experience occasional episodes of diarrhea in response to dietary changes or food sensitivities. However, diarrhea that is frequent (more than seven or eight stools in 8 hours) or prolonged (lasting 6 or 7 days) and accompanied by fever, vomiting, and dehydration requires medical attention.

Cause   Diarrhea can either be infectious or noninfectious. Infectious forms of diarrhea include:

▶ viral or bacterial infections, such as rotavirus, hepatitis A, or salmonellosis
▶ parasitic, such as giardia

Causes of noninfectious diarrhea can include:

▶ fruit juices containing fructose and sorbitol (Jones et al., 2013)
▶ antibiotic therapy
▶ recent dietary changes
▶ food allergies, such as lactose or gluten intolerance
▶ food poisoning
▶ illnesses, such as earaches, colds, strep throat, or cystic fibrosis

Until new vaccines became available in 2006, approximately 55,000–70,000 children were hospitalized each year for severe diarrhea caused by rotavirus (Dennehy, 2012). Because children under age 3 are the most frequent victims of this illness, infants are now being immunized against the disease at 2, 4, and 6 months of age. Consequently, the numbers of children who experience rotavirus infections and hospitalizations have declined significantly.

Frequent or prolonged diarrhea can result in **dehydration**, especially in infants and toddlers. Dehydration involves a loss of body water and can occur quickly in young children due to their poor fluid regulation and small body size. Because excessive dehydration can be fatal in infants and young children, they should be observed closely for:

- dryness of the mouth
- **listlessness**
- sunken eyes
- absence of tears
- decreased or no urinary output
- rapid, weak pulse
- skin that loses elasticity and becomes dough-like

Management It is important to monitor and record the frequency (number) and amount (small, large) of bowel movements. The color, consistency, and presence of any blood, mucus, or pus should also be noted. Be sure to check the child's temperature and observe for any signs of discomfort. Prompt medical advice should be sought if diarrhea is severe or prolonged, or the child becomes lethargic or drowsy. Adults and children should practice meticulous hand washing to avoid infecting themselves and others.

Most cases of diarrhea can be treated by temporarily replacing solid foods in the child's diet with a commercially prepared electrolyte solution. This solution supplies important fluids and salts lost through diarrhea and helps to restore normal function. Liquids and soft foods can gradually be added back into the child's diet once the diarrhea has ended. Any complaint of pain that is continuous or located in the lower right side of the **abdomen** should be reported promptly to the child's family and checked by a physician.

Children who have experienced diarrhea during the past 24 hours should be excluded from group settings. Exceptions to this policy would include children whose diarrhea resulted from noncontagious conditions such as food allergies, dietary changes, or recent antibiotic treatment. However, even these children may not feel well enough to attend school and to participate in the day's activities. The problem and inconvenience of frequent accidental soiling may also be too time-consuming for teachers to manage.

Diarrhea lasting longer than a week should be cause for concern, especially if it is accompanied by bloating, change of appetite, or weight loss. The child should remain at home until a cause is determined and conditions such as giardia, dysentery, or hepatitis A have been ruled out.

6-2d Dizziness

It is not unusual for children to complain of momentary dizziness or a spinning sensation after vigorous play. However, repeated complaints of dizziness should be noted and reported to the child's family. They should be advised to contact the child's physician to determine a possible underlying cause.

Cause Dizziness can be a symptom of other health conditions, including:

- ear infections
- fever

---

dehydration – *a state in which there is an excessive loss of body fluids or extremely limited fluid intake. Symptoms may include loss of skin tone, sunken eyes, and mental confusion.*
listlessness – *a state characterized by a lack of energy or interest in one's affairs.*
abdomen – *the portion of the body located between the diaphragm (located at the base of the lungs) and the pelvic or hip bones.*

- headaches
- head injuries
- anemia
- nasal congestion and sinus infections
- brain tumor (rare)

Management Temporary episodes of dizziness usually respond to simple first aid measures. Have the child lie down quietly or sit with head resting on or between the knees until the sensation has passed. Quiet play can be resumed when the child no longer feels dizzy. Inform the child's family of this experience so they can continue to monitor the condition at home.

If dizziness is accompanied by any loss of balance or coordination, parents should be encouraged to check with the child's physician at once. Dizziness that results from an underlying health problem will usually not respond to most first aid measures.

6-2e Earaches

Ear infections, also known as otitis media, are relatively common during the first three or so years of a child's life and affect boys more often than girls. More than half of all infants, especially those who are not breast-fed, experience an ear infection before their first birthday (Salone, Vann, & Dee, 2013). However, by age 5, children usually begin to have fewer ear infections as their resistance (antibody production) improves and structures in the ear, nose, and throat increase in size.

Certain groups of children appear to be more susceptible to ear infections. Children of Native American and Eskimo ethnicity are known to experience a higher rate of ear infections, possibly related to structural differences in the ear canal (Said et al., 2011). Children who are exposed to second-hand smoke are also at greater risk (Jones et al., 2012). Ear infections are also more common among children who have medical conditions such as cleft palate or developmental disabilities such as Williams syndrome, Turner's syndrome, Down syndrome, fragile X, or autism (Schieve et al., 2012). Infants who are fed in a reclining position experience more ear infections because milk can enter the Eustachian tube (passageway connecting the ear, nose, and throat) when the baby swallows. For this reason, it is important to always hold an infant in a semi-upright position (with head slightly elevated) during feedings. Additionally, studies have shown that children in group care are exposed to more upper respiratory infections and, thus, also experience more ear infections than those who remain at home (AAO-HNS, 2012).

Cause Ear infections are generally caused by a bacterial or viral infection that affects the middle ear (behind the ear drum). The resulting inflammation and fluid buildup (effusion) can result in considerable ear pain, fever, irritability, and temporary hearing loss. Ear pain in children can also be caused by several additional conditions, including:

- allergies
- nasal congestion
- dental cavities and eruption of new teeth
- excessive ear wax
- foreign objects, such as plastic beads, food, small toy pieces, or stones
- feeding infants in a reclining position

Young children, especially infants and toddlers who have limited language, should be closely monitored for signs of a potential ear infection, including:

- nausea, vomiting, and diarrhea
- tugging or rubbing of the affected ear
- refusal to eat or swallow
- redness of the outer ear
- fever
- dizziness or unsteady balance
- irritability

▶ discharge from the ear canal
▶ difficulty hearing
▶ crying when placed in a reclining position

Management Ear infections are not contagious, but the bacteria or virus that caused the initial upper respiratory infection (such as a cold) is easily spread. For this reason, children who develop otitis media may not need to be excluded from group settings unless they are too ill to participate in daily activities or have other symptoms that are contagious. Teachers may be able to provide temporary relief from earache pain by having the child lie down with the affected ear on a soft blanket; the warmth helps to soothe discomfort. A small, dry cotton ball placed in the outer ear may also help reduce pain by keeping air out of the ear canal. If excess wax or a foreign object is causing the child's ear pain, it must be removed only by a health care provider.

Persistent complaints of ear pain or earache should not be ignored and need to be checked by the child's health care provider if symptoms last longer than 3 or 4 days. In most cases, the infection and fluid will resolve without treatment. However, some children may develop chronic otitis media and continue to have middle ear fluid even though the initial infection has cleared up. If left untreated, this condition can interfere with a child's speech and language development (Cunningham et al., 2012; Boudewyns et al., 2011; Danhauer, Johnson, & Caudle, 2011).

Physicians now use several approaches to treat acute bacterial ear infections. Current guidelines recommend taking a wait-and-see approach and limiting the use of antibiotics to reduce the potential of drug resistance. If children are placed on oral antibiotics, it is important that all medication be taken; failure to finish medication can result in a recurrence of the infection. Children's ears should be rechecked by a health care provider after the prescribed course of medication has been completed to be certain the infection and fluid are gone. In some cases, a second round of medication may be needed. Children who have recurrent infections and chronic fluid buildup may have small plastic tubes surgically inserted in the eardrum to drain the fluid and decrease the risk of permanent hearing loss (Robb & Williamson, 2012). Teachers should be alert to any children who have tubes in their ears. Special precautions must be taken to avoid getting water in the outer ear canal during activities that involve water play, such as swimming, bathing, or playing in pools or sprinklers. Ear plugs or a special plastic putty are commonly used for this purpose.

▼ The frequency of ear infections decreases as children grow older.

© Cengage Learning

6-2f Fainting

Fainting, a momentary loss of consciousness, occurs when blood supply to the brain is temporarily reduced.

Cause Possible causes for this condition in young children include:

▶ anemia
▶ breath-holding
▶ **hyperventilation**
▶ extreme stress, excitement, or hysteria
▶ drug reactions
▶ illness, infection, or extreme pain
▶ poisoning

hyperventilation – *rapid breathing often with forced inhalation; can lead to sensations of dizziness, lightheadedness, and weakness.*

Management   Children may initially complain of feeling dizzy or weak. Their skin may appear pale, cool, and moist shortly before they collapse. If this occurs, lay the child down, elevate the legs 8 to 10 inches on a pillow or similar object, and observe breathing and pulse frequently. A light blanket can be placed over the child for extra warmth. Clothing should be loosened from around the neck and waist to make breathing easier. No attempt should be made to give the child anything to eat or drink until consciousness is regained. The child's family should be notified and encouraged to consult with their health care provider.

6-2g Fever

Fever is not an illness, but it is the body's way of indicating that a system is not functioning properly or is trying to fight infection. Activity, age, eating, sleeping, and the time of day can cause normal fluctuations in children's temperature. However, a persistent elevated **temperature** should be evaluated, especially if the child also complains of headache, coughing, nausea, or sore throat.

Cause   Common causes of fever in children include:

- viral and bacterial illnesses, such as ear, skin, and upper respiratory infections
- urinary tract infections
- heat stroke and overheating

Changes in children's appearance and behavior may be an early indication of **fever**. Other signs may include:

- flushed or reddened face
- listlessness or desire to sleep
- "glassy" eyes
- loss of appetite
- complaints of not feeling well
- chills
- warm, dry skin; older children may have increased perspiration

Management   Children's temperature should be checked if there is reason to believe that they may have a fever. Only digital and infrared **tympanic** thermometers are recommended for use in schools and group-care settings because of safety and liability concerns (Table 6–2). These thermometers are quick and efficient to use, especially with children who may be fussy or uncooperative, and they provide readings that are reasonably accurate (Table 6–3) (Padilla-Raygoza et al., 2011). Infrared forehead thermometers are currently being marketed, but studies have shown them to be unreliable. Glass mercury thermometers are considered unsafe to use with young children and also pose hazardous environmental concerns.

TABLE 6–2   Preferred Methods for Checking Children's Temperature in Group Settings (in Rank Order)

Age	Method
Infants and toddlers	axillary
2-5 year-olds	tympanic
	axillary
	oral
5 years and older	oral
	tympanic
	axillary

temperature – *a measurement of body heat; varies with the time of day, activity, and method of measurement.*
fever – *an elevation of body temperature above normal; a temperature over 99.4°F or 37.4°C orally is usually considered a fever.*
tympanic – *referring to the ear canal.*

TABLE 6-3   A Comparison of Thermometer Options

Type	Advantages	Disadvantages	Normal Range	How to Use	How to Clean
Digital thermometer	Can be used to check oral and axillary temperatures.	Takes 1–2 minutes to obtain a reading.	(Axillary) 94.5–99.0°F (34.7–37.2°C)	Turn switch on; wait for beep to signal ready.	Remove disposable cover.
	Safe, unbreakable.	Requires child to sit still.	(Oral) 94.5–99.5°F (34.7–37.5°C)	Apply disposable sanitary cover (optional).	Wipe with alcohol or clean with soap and cool water.
	Numbers are easy to read.	Axillary readings are less accurate than oral.		Place under tongue (oral) or in crease of armpit; hold in place; wait for beep to signal reading.	
	Beeps when ready.	Must purchase batteries and disposable covers.			
	Easy to clean.				
Tympanic thermometer	Yields a quick reading.	Thermometer is expensive to buy (approximately $40–60).	96.4–100.4°F (35.8–38°C)	Apply disposable earpiece.	Wipe instrument (probe) with alcohol.
	Easy to use.	Accuracy of reading depends on correct positioning in child's ear canal (differs from child to child).		Turn on start button.	
	Can check child's temperature while asleep.	Must purchase batteries and disposable ear piece coverings.		Insert probe carefully into ear canal opening; reading appears in seconds.	
	Requires limited child cooperation.				

Children with an axillary temperature over 99.1°F (37.2°C) or a tympanic reading over 100.4°F (38°C) should be observed carefully for other symptoms of illness. Unless a program's exclusion policies require children with fevers to be sent home, they can be moved to a separate room or quiet area in the classroom and monitored closely. If there are no immediate indications of acute illness, children should be encouraged to rest. Lowering the room temperature, removing warm clothing, and offering extra fluids can also help to make a child feel more comfortable. Fever-reducing medications should be administered only with a physician's approval. Families should also be notified so they can decide whether to take the child home or wait to see if any further symptoms develop.

6-2h Headaches

Headaches are not a common complaint of young children, but when they do occur they are usually a symptom of some other condition. Repeated complaints of headache should be brought to the family's attention.

Cause Children may experience headaches as the result of several conditions, including:

- bacterial or viral infections
- allergies
- head injuries
- emotional tension or stress
- reaction to medication
- lead poisoning
- hunger
- eye strain
- nasal congestion
- brain tumor (rare)
- constipation
- carbon monoxide poisoning

Management In the absence of any fever, rash, vomiting, or **disorientation**, children who experience headaches can remain in care but should continue to be observed for other indications of illness or injury. Frequently, their headaches will disappear with rest. However, patterns of repeated or intense headaches should be noted and families encouraged to discuss the problem with the child's physician.

6-2i Heat Rash

Heat rash is most commonly seen in infants and toddlers.

Cause Heat rash is caused by a blockage in the sweat glands. It occurs more commonly during the summer months, but can also develop when an infant or child is dressed too warmly. Some children have sensitive skin and may develop a heat rash from clothing made of synthetic fabrics.

Management Heat rash is not contagious. However, several measures can be taken to make a child more comfortable. Affected areas can be washed with cool water, dried thoroughly, and dusted sparingly with cornstarch.

6-2j Lyme Disease

Lyme disease is a tick-borne infection most prevalent along the East Coast, although it has been identified in nearly every U.S. state and many provinces of Canada (Eisen et al., 2012). The number of cases continues to increase. There were approximately 22,000 confirmed cases and 7,000 probable cases reported in 2010, with children ages birth to 15 years (especially boys 5 to 9 years) experiencing the highest incidence (CDC, 2012b).

....

disorientation – *lack of awareness or ability to recognize familiar persons or objects.*
Lyme disease – *bacterial illness caused by the bite of infected deer ticks found in grassy or wooded areas.*

TEACHER CHECKLIST 6-1

Measures to Prevent Tick Bites

- Encourage children to wear long pants, a long-sleeved shirt, socks, shoes, and a hat; light-colored clothing makes it easier to spot small deer ticks.
- Apply insect/tick repellent containing DEET to clothing and exposed skin areas. Be sure to follow manufacturer's directions and avoid aerosol sprays that children might inhale.
- Discourage children from rolling in the grass or sitting on fallen logs.
- Remove clothing as soon as children come indoors and check all body areas (under arms, around waist, behind knees, in the groin, on neck) and hair.
- Bathe or shower to remove any ticks.
- Wash clothing in soapy water and dry in dryer. (Heat will destroy ticks.)
- Continue to check children for any sign of ticks that may have been overlooked on a previous inspection.
- Promptly remove any tick discovered on the skin and wash the area carefully. (See Chapter 9).

TeachSource Digital Download   Download from CourseMate.

Cause   This bacterial illness is caused by the bite of a tiny, infected deer tick; however, not all deer ticks are infected, nor will everyone who is bitten develop Lyme disease. Many species of the deer tick are commonly found in grassy and wooded areas during the summer and fall months.

Management   The most effective way to prevent Lyme disease is to take preventive measures whenever children will be spending time outdoors, especially in grassy or wooded areas (Teacher Checklist 6-1). It is important that these practices also be followed while children are attending school (Hamlen, 2012).

Because deer ticks are exceptionally small, they are easily overlooked. Development of any unusual symptoms following a tick bite should be reported immediately to a physician. However, Lyme disease can be difficult to diagnose in some cases because the early symptoms are easily mistaken for other less serious illnesses. In the early weeks following a bite, a small, red, and flat or raised area may develop at the site, followed by a localized rash that gradually disappears. Flu-like symptoms, including fever, chills, fatigue, headache, and joint pain, may also be experienced during this stage. If the bacterial infection is not diagnosed early and treated with antibiotics, complications, including arthritis, heart, or neurological problems can develop within 2 years of the initial bite. A simple blood test is available for early detection.

6-2k Sore Throat

Sore throats are a relatively common complaint among young children, especially during the fall and winter seasons. Teachers must rely on their observations to determine when infants and toddlers may be experiencing a sore throat because children of this age are unlikely to verbalize their discomfort. Fussiness, lack of interest in food or refusal to eat, difficulty swallowing, enlarged lymph glands, fever, and fatigue may be early indications that the child is not feeling well.

Cause   Most sore throats are caused by a viral or bacterial infection. However, some children may experience a scratchy throat as the result of sinus drainage, mouth breathing, or allergies.

Management   It is extremely important not to ignore a child's complaint of sore throat. A small percentage of sore throats are caused by a highly contagious streptococcal infection (Table 6–1). Although most children are quite ill with these infections, some may experience only mild symptoms, such as headache or stomachache and fever, or none at all. Unknowingly, they may also become carriers of the infection and capable of spreading it to others. A routine throat culture is necessary to determine if a strep infection is present and which antibiotic will provide the most effective treatment. If left untreated, strep throat can lead to serious health complications, including rheumatic fever, arthritis, heart valve damage, and kidney disease (Hockenberry & Wilson, 2012).

Sore throats resulting from viral infections are not usually harmful, but they may cause the child considerable discomfort. Cool beverages (and popsicles) can soothe an irritated throat. Antibiotics are not effective against viral infections and, therefore, seldom prescribed.

6-2l Stomachaches

Most children experience an occasional stomachache from time to time. However, children may use this term to describe a range of discomforts, from hunger or a full bladder to actual nausea, cramping, or emotional upset. Teachers can use their observation and questioning skills to determine a probable cause.

Cause   Children's stomachaches are often a symptom of some other condition. There are many possible causes, including:

- food allergies or intolerance
- appendicitis
- **intestinal** infections (e.g., giardiasis, salmonella, E. coli)
- urinary tract infections
- gas or constipation
- side effect to medication, especially antibiotics
- change in diet
- emotional stress or desire for attention
- hunger
- diarrhea and vomiting
- strep throat

Management   There are several ways to determine whether or not a child's stomach pain is serious. Is the discomfort continuous or a cramping-type pain that comes and goes? Does the child have a fever? Is the child able to continue playing? If no fever is present, the stomachache is probably not serious. Encourage the child to use the bathroom and note if **urination** or having a bowel movement relieves the pain. Have the child rest quietly to see if the discomfort goes away. Check with the child's family to determine if there has been a dietary change or new medication prescribed. Stomach pain or stomachaches should be considered serious if they:

- disrupt a child's activity, such as running, playing, eating, sleeping
- cause tenderness of the abdomen
- are accompanied by diarrhea, vomiting, or severe cramping
- last longer than 3 to 4 hours
- result in stools that are bloody or contain mucus

If any of these conditions occur while the child is attending school or group care, the family should be notified and advised to seek prompt medical attention.

6-2m Sudden Infant Death Syndrome (SIDS)

Sudden infant death syndrome (SIDS) refers to the unexplainable death of an infant under 12 months of age. It is a leading cause of infant mortality and typically peaks between the second and fourth months. Deaths are more likely to occur during sleep (nighttime and naps), and especially during the fall and winter months. Despite aggressive awareness campaigns, approximately 2,200 infants die each year (CDC, 2012d).

---

intestinal – *pertaining to the intestines and intestinal tract.*
urination – *the act of emptying the bladder of urine.*

Cause It was previously thought that infants who died of SIDS were otherwise healthy. However, new evidence suggests that defects may exist in areas of the infant's brain (brainstem) that control breathing, temperature regulation, heart rate, and sleep patterns (Rand et al., 2013). These abnormalities appear to increase the infant's vulnerability to certain environmental conditions, such as second-hand smoke and respiratory infections, that would not pose the same risk for typically developing babies. Additional factors that increase an infant's risk of dying from SIDS include:

- prematurity
- weighing less than 3.5 pounds at birth
- being a male child
- being of African American or American Indian/Alaska Native ethnicity (CDC, 2012c)
- having a sibling who also died of SIDS
- family poverty
- prenatal exposure to alcohol or illicit drugs, such as cocaine, heroin, or methadone
- maternal smoking (during and after pregnancy) (Trachtenberg, et al, 2012)
- being born to a teenage mother

Children born into families with limited education and financial resources seem to experience the highest rate of SIDS deaths (Rowley & Hogan, 2012). Many of these mothers failed to obtain routine prenatal care or they engaged in unhealthy practices during and after their pregnancy. Infants who die of SIDS often experience repeated interruptions of breathing called **apnea**. Researchers continue to investigate possible connections between this breathing disturbance and other factors, including:

- toxic mattress fumes
- immunizations
- use of pacifiers
- air pollution
- bed sharing or co-sleeping with parents
- respiratory infections (such as colds and flu)
- swaddling

To date there has been no scientific evidence linking toxic mattress fumes or immunizations to SIDS. In fact, infants who are immunized are less likely to die from SIDS (AAP, 2011). Positive relationships between SIDS and air pollution have led to recommendations that families avoid exposing infants to second-hand smoke and other indoor pollutants. The practice of bed-sharing has also been linked to an increased risk of SIDS and is strongly discouraged (Schnitzer, Covington, & Dykstra, 2012).

Management An infant's sleeping position has proven to be the most effective practice for preventing SIDS. This discovery led to a nationwide "Back to Sleep" campaign, which has been ongoing and credited with significantly reducing SIDS deaths (NICHD, 2012). Multiple child and maternal government and private agencies continue to educate parents about proper sleep positioning for infants—*that babies must always be placed on their backs for sleeping*—and have extended their efforts to include early childhood teachers and caregivers. Although fewer than 20 percent of SIDS fatalities occur while infants are being cared for outside of their home, it is essential that teachers take the same precautionary steps to avoid any preventable death (AAP, 2012a). Despite ongoing educational efforts, researchers have found that many non-parental caregivers continue to place infants in unsafe conditions and sleeping positions. As a result, many states now address infant sleep position in their child care licensing regulations so that programs will no longer be able to ignore this critical safety practice.

Initial fears that infants would be more likely to choke when placed on their back for sleeping have not proven true. It isn't clear whether back-sleeping improves infants' oxygen intake or reduces their breathing in of carbon dioxide. However, the SIDS death rate

apnea – *momentary absence of breathing.*

TEACHER CHECKLIST 6-2

Practices to Reduce the Risk of Sudden Infant Death Syndrome (SIDS)

- Always put infants to sleep on their back for naptimes and bedtimes unless a health condition prevents this.
- Use a firm mattress that fits snugly in a safety-approved crib; cover mattress with a tight-fitting sheet. Never place infants on a waterbed, sheepskin, comforter, sofa cushions, or other soft bedding material.
- Remove pillows, thick or fluffy blankets, bumper pads, positioning wedges, and soft toys from an infant's bed.
- Cover infants with a thin blanket, tucking the bottom half under the mattress (never cover their head) (Figure 6–1).
- Dress infants in light sleepwear and maintain room temperature between 68–72° F to avoid overheating.
- Remove all objects in the surrounding area that could cause entrapment, such as window blind cords, baby monitors, light or appliance cords, and mobiles.
- Offer a pacifier to infants who use them; breast-fed infants should be offered a pacifier only after feeding.
- Avoid exposing infants to second-hand smoke, car exhaust, wood smoke, and other air pollutants.
- Limit infants' exposure to persons who have colds or other respiratory infections.
- Provide brief periods of tummy time so infants build stronger neck muscles and don't develop flat spots on their heads.
- Encourage mothers to obtain professional prenatal care for themselves *and* recommended well-child checkups and immunizations for their infant.
- Encourage and support breastfeeding for as long as mothers are able; breast milk aids in protecting infants against SIDS.
- Know how to respond to medical emergencies.

TeachSource Digital Download Download from CourseMate.

has decreased by nearly 50 percent since this practice was initially recommended (CDC, 2012d).

Infants should not share a crib with another infant nor sleep in a bed with adults; both of these practices have been found to increase the risk of SIDS. However, researchers have also discovered that the risk of SIDS is reduced when an infant's crib is placed in the same room with parents (Vennemann et al., 2012). The use of pacifiers has also been shown to reduce SIDS deaths although it is unclear why this practice is beneficial (Trachenberg et al., 2012). Additional guidelines for safe infant sleep are outlined in Teacher Checklist 6-2.

Because infants spend many hours sleeping, it is important to change their position often during times when they are awake. Weak neck muscles make it difficult for infants to turn their head from side to side. As a result, flat spots may develop if an infant is left in the same position for extended periods. These can be prevented by placing the infant on her tummy for brief periods or propping her on either side when she is awake. Alternating an infant's position in the crib is also beneficial—one day the head should be placed at the head of the crib, the following day the head should be placed at the foot of the bed. This prevents the infant from consistently laying on the same side of his or her head every day.

Because there is often no identifiable cause for SIDS, families tend to blame themselves for having been negligent or using poor judgment. They may believe that somehow this tragedy could have been prevented. Consequently, families who have experienced the unexpected death of an infant from SIDS require special emotional support and counseling. Siblings may also be affected by an infant's death and should be included in counseling therapy. Information and

Figure 6–1 Putting infants to sleep on their backs significantly reduces the risk of SIDS.

support groups are available to help families cope with their grief, including local chapters of several national SIDS organizations:

- First Candle/SIDS Alliance (http://www.sidsalliance.org)
- American SIDS Institute (http://www.sids.org)
- National SUID/SIDS Resource Center (http://www.sidscenter.org)
- Association of SIDS and Infant Mortality Programs (http://www.asip1.org)
- Canadian Foundation for the Study of Infant Deaths (http://www.sidscanada.org)

6-2n Teething

Teething is a natural process. Infants usually begin getting their first teeth around 4 to 7 months of age. Older children will begin the process of losing and replacing their baby teeth with a permanent set about the time they reach their fifth or sixth birthday.

Cause New teeth erupting through gum tissue can cause some children mild discomfort. However, most children move through this stage with relatively few problems.

Management Increased drooling and chewing activity may occur for several days or weeks before a tooth erupts and may be the only indication that an infant is teething. Some infants become a bit more fussy, run a low-grade fever (under 100°F), and may lose interest in eating. High fevers, diarrhea, and vomiting are usually not caused by teething, but may be an indication of illness. Chilled teething rings and firm objects for children to chew often provide comfort and relief to swollen gums.

6-2o Toothache

Young children do not typically experience toothaches. They may have temporary periods of discomfort during times when a tooth is being lost or new teeth are erupting. However, untreated oral health problems can cause significant pain and suffering, interfere with speech and language development, make eating difficult, affect school performance, and lead to early tooth loss. For this reason, it is important that children practice preventive measures such as brushing, eating a healthy diet, and seeing a dentist regularly. Limited finances should not prevent families from seeking necessary dental treatment for children. Low-cost insurance (CHIP), Medicaid, and community resources such as clinics and dental schools, are often available to help families obtain essential dental care (Kenney et al., 2011).

Cause Although tooth decay is the most common cause of toothache, gum disease and injury can also be quite painful. Children may complain of a throbbing discomfort that sometimes radiates into the ear. Redness and swelling may also be observed around the gumline of the affected tooth. Foods that are hot or very sweet may intensify pain.

▶❚❚ **TeachSource** Video Connections

Video supplied by the BBC Motion Gallery

SIDS: Is There a Biological Cause?

The possibility that an infant may stop breathing is a frequent and genuine concern of parents and caregivers. Although many preventive measures can be taken to reduce the risk of SIDS, only recently have we learned that a biological defect may be involved. As you watch the learning video, *SIDS: Is There a Biological Cause?*, consider the following questions:

1. What is Sudden Infant Death Syndrome?
2. What is serotonin, and what biological functions does it regulate?
3. Note the crib bumper pads that appear in an early scene. Why should they never be used in an infant's crib?
4. How do you think that knowing SIDS is caused by a genetic abnormality will help parents who have lost an infant to the condition?

Watch on CourseMate.

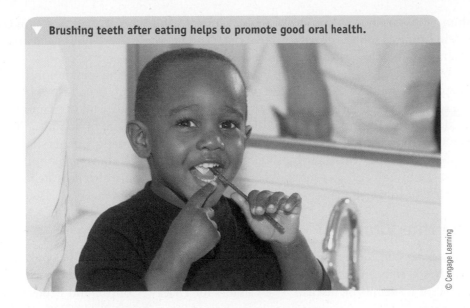

▼ **Brushing teeth after eating helps to promote good oral health.**

© Cengage Learning

Management Complaints of toothache require prompt dental attention. In the meantime, an icepack applied to the cheek on the affected side may make the child feel more comfortable. Aspirin-free products can also be given for temporary pain relief. However, prevention, including proper brushing after eating and reduction of dietary sugars, is always the preferred approach for limiting tooth decay.

6-2p Vomiting

Vomiting can be a frightening and unpleasant experience for children. True vomiting is different from an infant who simply spits up after eating. Vomiting is a symptom often associated with an acute illness or other health problem (Hockenberry & Wilson 2012).

Cause A number of conditions can cause children to vomit, including:

- emotional upset
- viral or bacterial infection, such as stomach flu or strep throat
- drug reactions
- ear infections
- meningitis
- **salmonellosis**
- indigestion
- severe coughing
- head injury
- poisoning

Management The frequency, amount, and composition of vomited material is important to observe and record. Dehydration and disturbances of the body's chemical balance can occur with prolonged or excessive vomiting, especially in infants and toddlers. Children should be observed carefully for:

- high fever
- abdominal pain
- signs of dehydration
- headache
- excessive drowsiness
- difficulty breathing
- sore throat
- exhaustion

salmonellosis – *a bacterial infection that is spread through contaminated drinking water, food, or milk or contact with other infected persons. Symptoms include diarrhea, fever, nausea, and vomiting.*

Children who continue to vomit and show signs of a sore throat, fever, or stomach pains should be sent home as soon as possible until a cause can be determined. The teacher should also advise the child's family to contact their physician for further advice.

In the absence of any other symptoms, a single episode of vomiting may simply be due to an emotional upset, food dislike, excess mucus, or reaction to medication. Usually the child feels better immediately after vomiting and should be encouraged to rest quietly while remaining at school.

In addition to not feeling well, some children are upset by the act of vomiting itself. Extra reassurance and comforting can help make the experience less traumatic. Infants should be positioned on their stomachs, with their hips and legs slightly raised to allow any vomited material to flow out of the mouth and prevent choking. Older children should also be watched closely so they don't choke or inhale vomitus.

6-2q West Nile Virus

Humans have long considered mosquitoes to simply be annoying insects that buzz in the ear, feast on exposed skin, and leave an itchy raised welt as their calling card. However, they are also capable of transmitting disease. The Centers for Disease Control and Protection (CDC) reported 712 West Nile virus cases in the United States during 2011 (CDC, 2012a); a total of 110 cases were reported in Canada for 2011 (Public Health Agency of Canada, 2012).

A majority of persons infected with the West Nile virus will have no symptoms of the illness. Some people will experience mild flu-like symptoms; a small percent will develop more serious symptoms, such as high fever, muscle weakness, rash, stiff neck, tremors, disorientation, coma, and even death. Young children and the elderly are at the greatest risk for developing the West Nile virus.

Did You Know...

there is no treatment to kill the West Nile virus? That is why prevention is so critical.

Cause West Nile virus is caused by the bite of an infected mosquito. The incidence is highest during the summer and fall seasons. However, there have also been limited reports of transmission via blood transfusion, organ donation, and the breast milk of an infected mother.

Management Prevention is the most important and effective strategy for avoiding this infectious illness (AAP, 2012b). Eliminating standing water in flower pots, water fountains, bird baths, buckets, tire swings, small pools, and similar sources removes mosquito breeding sites. A number of products containing natural chemicals and bacteria are available to spray or to use in ponds that cannot be drained. Additional precautionary measures include applying mosquito repellents containing DEET (maximum of 30 percent) whenever going outdoors, wearing protective clothing (long sleeves, long pants), staying indoors during early morning and evening hours when mosquitoes are at their peak activity, making sure that screen doors and windows are in good repair, and placing mosquito netting over infant strollers. In most cases, persons with mild symptoms will recover without medical treatment. However, prompt medical attention should be sought for prolonged illness or if any serious complications develop.

Finally, rely on your intuition. Don't hesitate to call the doctor if you are unsure about the symptoms your child may be experiencing. Most physicians would rather be notified of a child's condition than to be called only when there is a crisis.

Did You Get It?

A typically healthy and energetic kindergarten student is complaining of dizziness and seems unsteady. These symptoms might indicate:

a. dehydration

b. anemia

c. an ear infection

d. food poisoning

Take the full quiz on CourseMate.

PARTNERING with FAMILIES

When to Call the Doctor

Dear Families,

It is not uncommon for young children to experience frequent illness. With time, their bodies will mature, resistance (immunity) to many illnesses will develop, and their immunizations will have been completed. In the meantime, families may face the difficult task of deciding at what point a child is sick enough to warrant calling the doctor. Although each child's symptoms and needs are different, there are guidelines that may be helpful in making this decision. Call the physician if your child:

▶ Experiences serious injury, bleeding that cannot be stopped, or excessive or prolonged pain.

▶ Is less than one month old and develops a fever, or is between 1 and 3 months of age and has a rectal temperature over 100.4°F. Call if the child's fever lasts more than 3 days.

▶ Has difficult, rapid, or noisy breathing.

▶ Experiences any loss of consciousness, including a seizure.

▶ Complains of unusual pain in an arm or leg. X-rays may be necessary to rule out a fracture.

▶ Has repeated episodes of vomiting or diarrhea and is unable to keep down liquids. Symptoms of dehydration include urination fewer than three times per day, dry lips or tongue, headache, lack of tears, and excessive drowsiness. A sunken fontanel (soft spot) is an additional symptom in infants. Young children can become dehydrated quickly.

▶ Develops an unusual skin rash, especially one that spreads.

▶ Has blood in her vomit, urine, or stool.

▶ Suffers an eye injury or develops an eye discharge. Children who have sustained an eye injury should always be seen by a physician.

▶ Develops stomach pain that is prolonged or interferes with appetite or activity.

▶ Becomes excessively sleepy or difficult to arouse.

CLASSROOM CORNER

Teacher Activities

Gear Up for Health...

Concept: Physical activity is important for staying healthy. (Grades 3–5; National Health Education Standards 1.5.1 and 6.5.1)

Learning Objectives

▶ Children will learn the importance of moving to stay healthy.

▶ Children will improve their aerobic condition.

Supplies

▶ worksheet for recording activities

▶ kick balls

(continued)

CLASSROOM CORNER

Teacher Activities   *(continued)*

Gear Up for Health...

▶ pedometers

▶ charts or graph paper

▶ Mylar balloons

▶ masking tape

Learning Activities

▶ Read and discuss any of the following books:

  ● *Anna Banana: 101 Jump-Rope Rhymes* by Joanna Cole

  ● *Norma Jean, Jumping Bean* by Joanna Cole

  ● *Song and Dance Man* by Karen Ackerman

  ● *Snow Dance* by Lezlie Evans

▶ As a group, discuss the benefits of physical activity in terms of improving the body's immune system to fight off germs and protect against illness. Encourage the children to brainstorm activities that will increase their respiratory and heart rates (jumping rope, running, riding bikes, going for a walk, playing soccer, etc.).

▶ Introduce the terms *aerobic* (activities that increase heart and breathing rates) and *anaerobic* (activities that improve muscle strength) and explain the differences. Prepare a worksheet with two columns: one headed "aerobic activities," the other "anaerobic activities." Have the children list as many activities as they can in each appropriate column. As a group, ask the children to share one activity listed on their sheet and compile a master class list. Challenge the children to engage in at least one of these activities each day.

▶ Set up a game of kickball and give each child a pedometer to wear during the activity. At the end of 15 minutes, have each child record the number of steps he has taken. As an alternative, set up two cones and have children run laps; each week, increase the distance or number of laps children must run. Older children can graph their data (number of steps) while younger children might simply keep a daily tally. Varying the distance between cones, the number of laps run, or the length of playing time is an effective way to help children grasp the relationship between activity and health benefits. Children can also set weekly goals for themselves and gradually increase the number of steps they want to accumulate on their pedometer.

▶ Play balloon volleyball (great indoor activity). Group children into small teams, place a tape line on the floor, and instruct children to keep the balloon in motion by batting it back and forth. Have the children compare and describe how they felt before (heart beating slowly, easy to breathe) and after (breathing hard, heart beating fast, sweaty) the activity.

Evaluation

▶ Children will describe how physical activity improves health.

▶ Children will improve aerobic capacity by setting goals and recording their progress.

Additional lesson plans for grades PreK–2 are available on this text's Education CourseMate website.

Summary

▶ Communicable illnesses are common among young children in group settings.

- Teachers can utilize multiple strategies to control the spread of communicable illnesses:
  - continuous observation and early identification of sick children
  - implementation of exclusion policies
  - thorough hand washing
  - environmental sanitation
  - ongoing health education

▶ Teachers should also be familiar with the signs and symptoms, method of transmission, and control measures of common acute childhood illnesses.

Terms to Know

symptoms *p. 136*   hyperventilation *p. 150*   intestinal *p. 155*
asymptomatic *p. 140*   temperature *p. 151*   urination *p. 155*
infection *p. 146*   fever *p. 151*   apnea *p. 156*
dehydration *p. 148*   tympanic *p. 151*   salmonellosis *p. 159*
listlessness *p. 148*   disorientation *p. 153*
abdomen *p. 148*   Lyme disease *p. 153*

Chapter Review

A. By Yourself:

1. Define each of the *Terms to Know*.

2. Match each of the following signs and symptoms in Column I with the correct communicable illness in Column II.

Column I	**Column II**
1. swelling and redness of white portion of the eye	a. chickenpox
2. frequent itching of the scalp	b. strep throat
3. flat, oval-shaped lesions on the scalp, skin; infected nails that become discolored, brittle, chalky, and may disintegrate	c. head lice
	d. shigellosis
4. high fever; red, sore throat	e. conjunctivitis
5. mild fever and rash that lasts approximately 3 days	f. ringworm
6. irritability and itching of the rectal area	g. German measles
7. red rash with blister-like heads; cold-like symptoms	h. scabies
8. sudden onset of fever; swelling of salivary glands	i. pinworms
9. burrows or linear tunnels under the skin; intense itching	j. mumps
10. vomiting, abdominal pain, diarrhea that may be bloody	k. Lyme disease

B. As a Group:

1. Discuss what a teacher should do in each of the following situations:

   a. You have just finished serving lunch to the children, when Kara begins to vomit.

   b. The class is involved in a game of keep-away. Theo suddenly complains of feeling dizzy.

   c. During check-in, a parent mentions that his son has been experiencing stomachaches every morning before coming to school.

    d. Lucy wakes up from her afternoon nap crying and is holding her ear.

    e. You have just changed a toddler's diaper for the third time in the last hour because of diarrhea.

    f. Chris enters the classroom sneezing and blowing his nose.

    g. While you are helping Jasmine put on her coat to go outdoors, you notice that her skin feels very warm.

    h. Randy refuses to eat his lunch because it makes his teeth hurt.

    i. While you are cleaning up the blocks, Sean tells you that his throat is sore and it hurts to swallow.

    j. You have just taken Monique's temperature (orally) and it is 102°F.

    k. Your assistant teacher mentions that his son has chickenpox and that he has never had it.

2. The concepts of illness and pain are often viewed differently by various cultural groups. Select two or three predominant cultures and research their beliefs about illness, pain, and traditional medicine. How might these differences in cultural values and beliefs influence your response in each of the situations described in Question #1?

◖ Case Study

The teacher noticed that Carrie seemed quite restless today and was having difficulty concentrating on any task that she started. She continuously squirmed, whether in her chair or sitting on the floor. On a number of occasions the teacher also observed Carrie tugging at her underwear and scratching her bottom. She recalled that Carrie's mother had mentioned something about getting her younger brother tested for pinworms and wondered if this might be what she was observing.

1. If you were the teacher, what actions would you take in this situation?

2. What control measures should be implemented? At school? At home?

3. When can Carrie return to school?

4. Is this a reportable illness in your state?

5. If Carrie does have pinworms, for what length of time should the other children be observed for similar problems?

6. What special personal health measures should be emphasized with the other children?

◖ Application Activities

1. With a partner, practice taking each other's axillary, oral, and tympanic temperatures. Follow steps for the correct cleaning of the thermometer between each use. Were there differences in the readings you obtained?

2. Divide the class into groups of five to six students. Discuss how each member feels about caring for children who are ill. Could they hold or cuddle a child with a high fever or diarrhea? What are their feelings about being exposed to children's contagious illnesses? How might they react if an infant just vomited on their new sweater? If they feel uncomfortable around sick children, what steps could they take to better cope with the situation?

3. Select another student as a partner and observe that person carefully for 20 seconds. Now look away. Write down everything you can remember about this person, such as eye color, hair color, scars or moles, approximate weight, height, color of skin, shape of teeth, clothing, and so on. What can you do to improve your observational skills?

4. Do you know if your immunizations are up-to-date with current recommendations? Take the quiz on the CDC's immunizations website: http://www.cdc.gov/vaccines/schedules/index.html. What boosters or newer immunizations do you need? Why is it especially important that teachers keep their immunizations current?

Helpful Web Resources

Center for Disease Control	http://www.cdc.gov
Health Canada	http://www.hc-sc.gc.ca
Keep Kids Healthy	http://www.keepkidshealthy.com
Morbidity & Mortality Weekly	http://www.cdc.gov/mmwr
National Initiative for Children's Healthcare Quality (special needs)	http://www.nichq.org/
National Institutes of Health	http://www.nih.gov
Office of Minority Health	http://minorityhealth.hhs.gov

Visit the Education CourseMate for this textbook to access the eBook, Did You Get It? quizzes, Digital Downloads, TeachSource Video Cases, flashcards, and more. Go to CengageBrain.com to log in, register, or purchase access.

References

American Academy of Otolaryngology—Head and Neck Surgery (AAO-HNS). (2012). *Fact sheet: Day care and ear, nose, and throat problems.* Accessed on May 29, 2012 from http://www.entnet.org/HealthInformation/dayCareENT.cfm.

American Academy of Pediatrics (AAP). (2012a). A child care provider's guide to safe sleep. Accessed on May 30, 2012 from, http://www.healthychildcare.org/pdf/SIDSchildcaresafesleep.pdf.

AAP. (2012b). Preventing West Nile virus. Accessed on May 30, 2012 from, http://www.healthychildren.org/English/health-issues/conditions/skin/Pages/Preventing-West-Nile-Virus.aspx.

AAP. (2011). Technical Report –SIDS and other sleep-related infant deaths: Expansion of recommendations for a safe infant sleeping environment, *Pediatrics*, 128(5), e1341–e1367.

Aschenbrenner, D. (2012). Safety warnings for new concentration of liquid acetaminophen, *American Journal of Nursing*, 1112(4), 28–29.

Boudewyns, A., Declau, F., Van den Ende, J., Kerschaver, E., Dirckx, S., Hofkens-Van den Brandt, A., & Van de Heyning, P. (2011). Otitis media with effusion: An underestimated cause of hearing loss in infants, *Otology & Neurotology*, 32(5), 799–804.

Centers for Disease Control & Prevention (CDC). (2012a). Final 2011 West Nile virus human infections in the United States. Accessed on May 30, 2012 from, http://www.cdc.gov/ncidod/dvbid/westnile/surv&controlCaseCount11_detailed.htm.

CDC. (2012b). Lyme disease data—2001 to 2010. Accessed on May 29, 2012, from http://www.cdc.gov/lyme/stats/index.html.

CDC. (2012c). Postneonatal mortality among Alaska native infants—Alaska, 1989–2009, *Morbidity & Mortality Weekly Report (MMWR)*, 61(1):1–5.

CDC. (2012d). Sudden Unexpected Infant Death (SUID). Accessed on May 30, 2012 from, http://www.cdc.gov/SIDS/index.htm.

Cunningham, M., Guardiani, E., Kim, H., & Brook, I. (2012). Otitis media, *Future Microbiology*, 7(6), 733–753.

Danhauer, J., Johnson, C., & Caudle, A. (2011). Survey of K–3rd grade teachers' knowledge of ear infections and willingness to participate in prevention programs, *Language, Speech, & Hearing Services in Schools*, 42(2), 207–222.

Dennehy, P. (2012). Effects of vaccine on rotavirus disease in the pediatric population, *Current Opinion in Pediatrics*, 24(1), 76–84.

Eisen R., Piesman, J., Zielinski-Gutierrez, E., & Eisen, L. (2012). What do we need to know about disease ecology to prevent Lyme disease in the Northeastern United States?, *Journal of Medical Entomology*, 49(1), 11–22.

Fiore, A., Epperson, S., Perrotta, D., Bernstein, H., & Neuzil, K. (2012). Expanding the recommendations for annual influenza vaccination to school-age children in the United States, *Pediatrics*, 129(2), S54–S62.

Hamlen, R. (2012). Tick-borne infections—A growing public health threat to school-age children: Prevention steps that school personnel can take, *NASN School Nurse*, 27(2), 94–100.

Hockenberry, M., & Wilson, D. (2012). *Wong's essentials of pediatric nursing*. (9th ed.). New York: Mosby.

Isbister, G., Prior, F., & Kilham, H. (2012). Restricting cough and cold medicines in children, *Journal of Paediatrics*, 48(2), 91–98.

Jones, H., Butler, R., Moore, D., & Brooks, D. (2013). Developmental changes and fructose absorption in children: Effect on malabsorption testing and dietary management, *Nutrition Reviews*, 71(5), 300–309.

Jones, L., Hassanien, A., Cook, D., Britton, J., & Leonardi-Bee, J. (2012). Parental smoking and the risk of middle ear disease in children, *Archives of Pediatrics & Adolescent Medicine*, 166(1), 18–27.

Kenney, G., Marton, J., Klein, A., Pelletier, J., & Talbert, J. (2011). The effects of Medicaid and CHIP policy changes on receipt of preventive care among children, *Health Services Research*, 46(1), 298–318.

Lampel, H., & Jacob, S. (2011). Phthalates in baby skin care products, *Dermatitis*, 22(5), 272–276.

National Institute of Child Health & Human Development (NICHD). (2012). Back to sleep public education campaign. Accessed on May 30, 2012 from http://www.nichd.nih.gov/sids/.

Padilla-Raygoza, N., Diaz-Guerrero, R., Garcia-Valenzuela, G., & Pantoja-Hernandez, P. (2011). Comparison of measurements of body temperature with four thermometers in a children health care setting, *The Internet Journal of Pediatrics & Neonatology*, 13(2). Accessed online from http://www.ispub.com/journal/the-internet-journal-of-pediatrics-and-neonatology/volume-13-number-2/comparison-of-measurements-of-body-temperature-with-four-thermometers-in-a-children-health-care-setting-comparison-of-thermometers.html.

Public Health Agency of Canada. (2012). West Nile virus monitor. Accessed on April 30, 2013 from http://www.phac-aspc.gc.ca/wnv-vwn/mon-hmnsurv-eng.php.

Rand, C., Patwari, P., Carroll, M., & Weese-Mayer, D. (2013). Congenital central hypoventilation syndrome and sudden infant death syndrome: Disorders of autonomic regulation, *Seminars in Pediatric Neurology*, 20(1), 44–55.

Robb, P., & Williamson, I. (2012). Otitis media with effusion in children: Current management, *Paediatrics & Child Health*, 22(1), 9–12.

Rowley, D., & Hogan, V. (2012). Disparities in infant mortality and effective, equitable care: Are infants suffering from benign neglect?, *Annual Review of Public Health*, 33, 75–87.

Said, M., O'Brien, K., Nuorti, J., Singleton, R., Whitney, C., & Hennessy, T. (2011). The epidemiologic evidence underlying recommendations for use of pneumococcal polysaccharide vaccine among American Indian and Alaska Native populations, *Vaccine*, 29(33), 5355–5362.

Salone, L., Vann, W., & Dee, D. (2013). Breastfeeding: An overview of oral and general health benefits, *The Journal of the American Dental Association,* 144(2), 143–151.

Schieve, L., Gonzalez, V., Boulet, S., Visser, S., Rice, C., Van Naarden Braun, K., & Boyle, C. (2012). Concurrent medical conditions and health care use and needs among children with learning and behavioral disabilities, National Health Interview Survey, 2006–2010, *Research in Developmental Disabilities,* 33(2), 467–476.

Schnitzer, P., Covington, T., & Dykstra, H. (2012). Sudden unexpected infant deaths: Sleep environment and circumstances, *American Journal of Public Health*, 102(6), 1204–1212.

Sun, Y., & Sundell, J. (2011). Early daycare attendance increase the risk for respiratory infections and asthma of children, *Journal of Asthma*, 48(8), 790–796.

Trachtenberg, F., Haas, E., Kinney, H., Stanley, C., & Krous, H. (2012). Risk factor changes for sudden infant death syndrome after initiation of back-to-sleep campaign, *Pediatrics*, 129(4), 630–638.

Vennemann, M., Hense, H., Bajanowski, T., Blair, P., Complojer, C., Moon, R., & Kiechl-Kohlendorfer, U. (2012). Bed sharing and the risk of Sudden Infant Death Syndrome: Can we resolve the debate?, *The Journal of Pediatrics*, 160(1), 44–48.

Keeping Children Safe

chapter 7 Creating High-Quality Environments

◗ **#1 a, b, and c:** Promoting child development and learning
◗ **#4 a, b, and d:** Using developmentally effective approaches to connect with children and families
◗ **#6 b, c, d, and e:** Becoming a professional
◗ Field experiences

Learning Objectives

After studying this chapter, you should be able to:

LO 7-1 Discuss how to identify high-quality programs.

LO 7-2 Explain how licensure and registration of early childhood programs differ.

LO 7-3 Identify the features of high-quality programs and discuss how teachers' educational preparation affects children's development.

LO 7-4 Describe at least ten ways to make children's indoor and outdoor environments safe.

Children's growth and development are continually being shaped and influenced by their **environment**. Growth is enhanced through nurturing and responsive care, a healthy diet, homes and schools that are clean and safe, access to dental and health care, and communities free of drugs, violence, excessive traffic, and air pollution. Children's intellectual and psychological development are fostered through environments that provide new challenges, opportunities for learning, and positive social interactions. For these reasons, careful attention must be given to creating physical, **cognitive**, and psychological settings that will have positive effects on children's growth and development.

7-1 Identifying High-Quality Programs

Families frequently rely on out-of-home arrangements for child care. Some families simply want their children to benefit from enrichment experiences and opportunities to socialize with their peers. Others may enroll children with special developmental needs in early intervention programs where they can receive individualized learning experiences and intervention services such as speech or physical therapy (Allen & Cowdery, 2012). Older children may require a safe, educational place to stay before and after regular school hours. Regardless of their reasons, families often find it challenging to identify and secure high-quality, affordable

▼ **Environments should support and promote children's growth and development.**

© Cengage Learning

environment – *the sum total of physical, emotional, cultural, and behavioral features that surround and affect an individual.*
cognitive – *the aspect of learning that refers to the development of skills and abilities based on knowledge and thought processes.*

programs for children. New programs are continuously being opened to meet increased demand, but quality is not always a priority.

Research continues to demonstrate that high-quality programs make a difference in children's development and family relationships (Tucker-Drob, 2012). Children enrolled in high-quality care show long-term gains in language and cognitive skills, improved readiness for school, and fewer problem behaviors (Sripada, 2012; Wen et al., 2012). Although most families would prefer to have their child in an excellent program, the urgency and, at times, desperation of simply finding an available opening may force them to overlook this important issue. Cost and location considerations may understandably overshadow a family's concern about quality.

It is also true that many families simply do not know how to determine the quality of a program or even what features to look for. Some parents feel uncomfortable questioning teachers. Others may not be able to find a convenient high-quality program in their area even when they are dissatisfied with poor conditions in a current arrangement.

7-1a Educating Families

Advocacy groups and professional organizations have launched initiatives to help educate families about the characteristics associated with excellence in early childhood programs. Families can also retrieve similar information from a number of professional websites.

Researchers have identified three characteristics common to high-quality early childhood programs (Ma et al., 2013; Hebbeler, Spiker, & Kanhn, 2012):

- small group size
- low teacher-child ratio (fewer children per teacher)
- teachers who have advanced educational training in early childhood education and child development

Families should always take time to observe any new program they are considering for their child and determine how the program measures up to these criteria. Additional areas that should also be noted include:

- physical facilities (clean, safe, spacious, licensed)
- program philosophy; developmentally appropriate goals and objectives
- nutritious meals and snacks
- opportunities for family involvement
- attention to diversity
- toys and educational activities (developmentally appropriate, variety, adequate in number, organized learning experiences)
- health services (trained personnel, established policies, and procedures)

Educating families about how to identify high-quality programs has obvious benefits for children. Programs that fail to improve their services may be forced out of business as demand for higher quality increases.

7-1b Resource and Referral Services

Many communities have resource and referral agencies devoted to helping families locate center- and home-based early childhood programs, as well as before- and after-school care. Families can request a list of available openings based on their specific child care needs, such as location, cost, preferred hours, philosophy, and child's age. Many independent agencies have been networked into state and national computerized databases; Child Care Aware (formerly the National Association of Child Care Resource and Referral Agencies) is one of the largest.

Child care resource and referral agencies do not necessarily restrict their listings to high-quality programs. Some agencies will include any program with available openings, while others screen programs carefully to ensure high standards. Consequently, families must spend time investigating individual programs to find one that best suits their needs and personal preferences.

Resource and referral agencies in many areas also play an active role in educating families about how to select an early childhood program. They are also vocal advocates for improved program quality and are committed to providing inservice training for early childhood teachers.

7-1c Professional Accreditation

A national system of voluntary **accreditation** for early childhood programs was established in 1985 by the National Association for the Education of Young Children (NAEYC). Its primary objective is aimed at promoting excellence and improving the quality of early education through a process of self-study (NAEYC, 2012). The accreditation process identifies and recognizes outstanding early-education programs and provides an added credential that acknowledges a commitment to quality. Programs are accredited for 3 years, at which time they must reapply. NAEYC continuously updates its accreditation standards to reflect the latest research findings and promote better quality in early childhood classrooms (http://www.naeyc.org/academy).

A number of organizations, including Head Start, the National Association for Family Child Care (NAFCC), and the National AfterSchool Association, have developed similar endorsement plans to recognize outstanding programs. Individual states have also begun to establish their own quality standards and voluntary accreditation systems.

> **Did You Get It?**
>
> Which environmental factor is not likely to foster healthy intellectual and psychological development for young children?
> **a.** positive social interactions
> **b.** new and continuously available challenges
> **c.** opportunities for learning and "teachable moments"
> **d.** rigid expectations and constant feedback
>
> Take the full quiz on CourseMate.

7-2 Early Childhood Program Licensure

Licensing standards are established by individual states. They represent an attempt to ensure that environments are safe, appropriate, and healthful for young children. However, these regulations typically reflect only minimal health and safety requirements and also vary considerably from one state to another (Hillemeier et al., 2012). They in no way guarantee high-quality conditions, programs, or child care. This is an issue of great concern, as programs are increasing their numbers of infants and young children who have special behavior, developmental, and medical needs.

Licensing **regulations** serve a twofold purpose. First, they are aimed at protecting children's physical and psychological well-being by monitoring environmental and program safety. Second, they afford minimal protection to the program and its personnel. Programs that comply with licensing regulations are less likely to overlook situations that could result in negligence charges.

Early attempts to regulate child care programs dealt primarily with the sanitation and safety of physical settings. However, most current licensing regulations go beyond this narrow scope to also address teacher qualifications and the educational content of programs planned for children.

Each state has a designated agency that is authorized and responsible for conducting inspections and issuing or revoking licenses to operate. This agency also oversees the review and development of licensing standards and methods for enforcing **compliance**. Again, there are significant differences in licensing standards and levels of enforcement from one state to another. This fragmented approach also lacks a system for ensuring that individual states are actually performing their licensing responsibilities.

accreditation – *the process of certifying an individual or program as having met certain specified requirements.*
licensing – *the act of granting formal permission to conduct a business or profession.*
regulations – *standards or requirements that are set to ensure uniform and safe practices.*
compliance – *the act of obeying or cooperating with specific requests or requirements.*

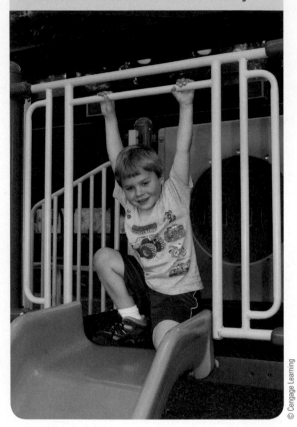

▼ Licensing standards help to ensure that children's environments are safe and healthy.

In many states, home-based child care programs are governed by a separate set of regulations that often include an option for becoming either licensed or registered. Those choosing to be licensed are inspected by a licensing agent and required to meet specific standards. In contrast, the requirements for **registration** are often minimal. Teachers may simply be asked to place their name on a list, complete a self-administered checklist attesting to safe conditions, and attend a brief preservice informational program. An on-site home inspection is seldom conducted unless a complaint is registered. Child care programs based in churches and public schools and relative care are exempt from licensing regulation in many states.

Controversy continues to surround the issue of early childhood program licensure. Establishing licensing requirements that adequately protect young children's health and safety—yet are realistic for teachers and programs to achieve—can be challenging. In addition, some people believe that too much control or standards that are set too high will reduce the number of available openings and programs. The licensing process is also costly to administer and often difficult to enforce, so that lowering the standards may be a tempting option. On the other hand, many families and teachers favor stricter regulations to ensure higher-quality programs and improved respect for the early childhood profession.

Despite the ongoing controversy, licensing of early childhood programs is necessary. Ideally, licensing standards should adequately safeguard children, yet not be so overly restrictive that qualified individuals and programs are eliminated.

7-2a Obtaining a License

A license permits an early childhood program to operate on a routine basis. As previously mentioned, the process for obtaining a license differs from state to state. However, the steps described here are generally representative of the procedure involved. In some cases, the process may require considerable time and effort, especially if major renovations must be made to the proposed facility. For others, approval may be obtained in a reasonably short time. Persons interested in operating an early childhood or after-school program should first contact their state or local licensing agency. Questions regarding the applicant's qualifications and specific program requirements can usually be answered at this time.

Child care facilities must comply with local laws and ordinances in addition to state licensing regulations. Zoning codes must be checked carefully to determine whether or not a program can be operated in a given location or neighborhood. Often this requires meeting with local planning authorities and reviewing proposed floor plans. Programs located in public school buildings may also be required to meet state building codes and regulations.

Buildings that house early childhood programs must also pass a variety of inspections to ensure they meet fire, safety, and sanitation codes. These inspections are usually conducted by personnel from the local fire and public health departments. Any renovations necessary to comply with licensing regulations will be determined during the inspections. In most cases, the changes are relatively simple; in other cases, the required changes may not be feasible or economical to make.

registration – *the act of placing the name of a child care program on a list of active providers; usually does not require on-site inspection.*

Application for a permanent license can be made once all these steps have been completed. Licensing authorities may also request copies of the program's plans for review. Final approval usually includes an on-site inspection of the facilities to ensure that all requirements and recommendations have been satisfied.

7-2b Federal Regulations

In addition to meeting state licensing requirements, early childhood programs that receive federal funds, such as Head Start, Early Head Start, and Even Start programs, must comply with an additional set of regulations. All schools and child care facilities, with the exception of religion-affiliated programs, built or remodeled after 1990 must also meet standards established by the Americans with Disabilities Act (ADA) (Child Care Law Center, 2009).

> **Did You Get It?**
>
> **Child care licensing regulations:**
> a. are uniform from state to state
> b. ensure that programs are safe and of high quality
> c. protect children from physical and emotional harm
> d. reflect minimal standards
>
> **Take the full quiz on CourseMate.**

7-3 Features of High-Quality Programs

Researchers are continually studying children in schools, home-, and center-based programs to determine what conditions and experiences are best for promoting learning and healthy development. Through the years, they have identified several key components that distinguish high-quality programs from those considered to be of mediocre or poor value (Belsky & Pluess, 2012). NAEYC, the largest organization representing early care and education in the United States, and similar professional organizations have embraced these findings and incorporated them into their accreditation standards and recommended guidelines (APHA & AAP, 2011).

7-3a Teacher Qualifications

Perhaps one of the weakest areas in many state licensing regulations pertains to staff qualifications. Primary attention is often focused on the safety of the physical setting, while staff requirements, such as years of experience, educational preparation, and personal qualifications are often lacking or poorly defined. Even when these issues are addressed in the licensing regulations, there is little consistency from one state to another.

Research has documented a positive correlation between a teacher's educational preparation and the ability to provide high-quality early childhood education (Dennis & O'Connor, 2013; Whitebook & Ryan, 2011). Teachers who have a strong background in child development, value family involvement and communication, understand and respect diversity, and know how to create developmentally appropriate experiences are more effective in facilitating positive learning outcomes for children (Essa, 2014). As increasing numbers of children with behavior problems, developmental disabilities, and medical conditions are enrolled in early childhood programs, teachers must also be prepared to meet their special needs (Fults & Harryl, 2012). In addition, teachers must be able to work and communicate effectively with all children and families of diverse abilities, languages, and backgrounds.

Unfortunately, the licensing requirements in many states do not reflect what we currently know about the importance of employing teachers with formal training in early childhood education. Often, a person who is 18 years of age, has a high school diploma, and passes a background check is qualified to be hired as an early childhood teacher. As a result, many of these individuals are not prepared to effectively handle the daily challenges involved in working with young children (Nicholson & Reifel, 2011). The combination of low salaries, long working hours, and lack of preparation contribute to a high turnover rate which, in turn, has a negative effect on children's development (Tran & Winsler, 2011). Initiatives to improve teacher preparation and salaries are being studied, funded, and incorporated into licensing regulations in an effort to improve the quality of care and education that young children receive. However, teachers must also take steps to continue their education and prepare themselves to work with increasingly challenging child populations. Scholarship programs and professional opportunities are available to assist teachers in pursuing advanced education, including:

- on-the-job training/inservice training
- CDA (Child Development Associates credential)
- 1-year vocational training; child care or child development certificate
- 2-year associate degree (A.A.) (community college)
- 4-year bachelor degree (B.A.)
- advanced graduate training (M.A. and Ph.D.)

Although many of these degree programs are offered on traditional campuses, an increasing number are now available online.

At a minimum, all directors and head teachers should have a 2-year associate degree with specialized training in early childhood (Rhodes & Huston, 2012; Whitebook & Ryan, 2011). However, in many areas of the country, teachers and directors with advanced preparation are in short supply. Individual states are beginning to establish director credentialing programs in an effort to improve the quality of care and leadership provided in early childhood centers.

Early childhood programs often include paraprofessionals as part of their teaching team. These individuals may be aides who work for wages or are unpaid volunteers. Regardless of their position or previous experience, it is essential that paraprofessionals receive a thorough orientation to their job responsibilities and program procedures before they work in the classroom. This preparation enables paraprofessionals to provide safe and effective care when they assume their role and also improves employee retention.

Teachers who work in high-quality programs often bring many special personal qualities and skills to their position. They value communication and know how to develop meaningful relationships with children, families, and colleagues. They understand and respect diversity and make it a priority. They also possess qualities of warmth, patience, sensitivity to children's needs, respect for individual differences, and a positive attitude. They have the ability to plan, organize, make decisions, and resolve conflict. They also enjoy good personal health, which allows them to cope with the physical and emotional demands of long, action-packed days. Individuals with these qualities are not only better teachers, but also are more likely to have a positive effect on young children's lives.

7-3b Staffing Ratios

Staff/child ratios are determined by individual states and typically reflect only the minimal number of adults considered necessary to protect children's well-being. However, the ability to provide positive learning experiences, individualized care, and conditions that safeguard children's health and safety requires more teachers than are generally mandated.

Ideally, high-quality early childhood programs provide one full-time teacher for every seven to eight children 3 to 6 years of age. Programs serving children who have behavioral or developmental disabilities should be staffed with one teacher for every four to five children, depending on the age group and severity of their needs. If children younger than 2 years are included, there should be at least one full-time teacher for every three to four children. A list of substitutes should also be available in the event of teacher illness or other absence.

Research suggests that small group size and low teacher/child ratios improve the quality of educational experiences that children receive (Rhodes & Huston, 2012). However, low ratios do not always guarantee that children will be safer. Much depends on the knowledge and supervisory skills of individual teachers.

Teachers who are part of high-quality programs understand the importance of continuing their professional education by attending professional conferences, inservice programs, workshops, and college classes. Participation in these experiences exposes teachers to new concepts, ideas, and approaches and promotes continued professional growth and competence. They also provide forums where teachers can discuss common problems, share ideas, and discover unique solutions.

These opportunities are especially important for teachers who work in home-based programs and have limited interaction with other educators.

7-3c Group Size and Composition

When a license is issued to an early childhood program, specific conditions and restrictions under which it is allowed to operate are clearly defined. These conditions usually spell out:

- ages of children that can be enrolled
- group size per classroom
- maximum enrollment per program
- special populations of children to be served (e.g., children with behavior problems, children who have developmental disabilities, infants, school-age, etc.)
- teacher-child ratios

For example, a program might be licensed to provide three half-day sessions for children 3 to 5 years of age, with a maximum enrollment of eighteen children and two teachers per classroom. An in-home program might be licensed for a total of six children, ages birth to 4 years.

Group size is also recognized as an important indicator of high-quality programs (NAEYC, 2012). For this reason, restrictions are typically placed on the number of children a program is permitted to enroll. This figure is determined by the square footage of available space, children's ages, and any special needs children may have, as well as the number of teachers on site. However, it should be remembered that state regulations allow group sizes that are often much larger than is ideal for quality care.

A program's educational philosophy and range of services provided should be described in the admission policies. The age range, special needs, and total number of children that a program is licensed to serve must also be clearly stated to avoid parent misunderstandings.

Video supplied by the BBC Motion Gallery

▶❚❚ **TeachSource Video Connections**

Signs Of Good Child Care

▶ A Caring Relationship
▶ Discipline That Teaches
▶ Good Adult-Child Ratio

The Quality of Child Care

Numerous studies have demonstrated positive outcomes for children who are enrolled in high-quality early childhood and after-school programs. As you watch the learning video, *The Quality of Child Care*, consider the following questions:

1. What features are associated with high-quality programs?
2. What have the studies shown us about the effects that attending an early childhood program can have on children from disadvantaged families?
3. What is temporary distress syndrome? What should parents do if their child exhibits these behaviors?

Watch on CourseMate.

7-3d Program Curriculum

The benefits children derive from participating in high-quality early childhood programs have been consistently documented (Ma et al., 2013; Rhodes & Huston, 2012). Because many children spend the majority of their waking hours in out-of-home early childhood programs, it is essential that **developmentally appropriate practices (DAP)**—learning environments and enriching opportunities—be provided. High-quality early education programs plan learning experiences that address children's needs across all developmental areas, including:

- physical
- cognitive
- motor
- social-emotional
- language
- self-care

developmentally appropriate practices (DAP) – *learning experiences and environments that take into account children's individual abilities, interests, and diverse needs. DAP also reflects differences among families and values them as essential partners in children's education.*

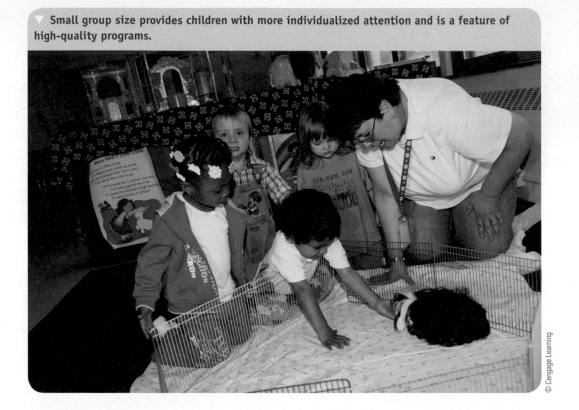

▼ Small group size provides children with more individualized attention and is a feature of high-quality programs.

© Cengage Learning

Curriculum delivery and content should be designed to address children's interests and to help them acquire new developmental skills. Learning experiences should be planned to take advantage of times when children are most likely to learn. Activities that alternate active and quiet play reduce the risk of children becoming overly fatigued and/or of losing interest. For example, a vigorous walk outdoors might be followed by a teacher-directed flannel board story or puppet show. It is also important that daily activity schedules and lesson plans be posted where families can learn what children will be doing throughout the day.

7-3e Health Services

Safeguarding children's health and well-being is a fundamental responsibility of teachers and school administrators (Green et al., 2012; APHA & AAP, 2011). Only when children are healthy can they fully benefit from everyday experiences and learning opportunities. High-quality programs take this role seriously and address children's health needs by:

▶ having written policies and procedures
▶ maintaining comprehensive health and safety records
▶ training personnel to administer first aid and emergency care
▶ providing clean, safe indoor and outdoor environments
▶ developing emergency response plans
▶ planning for health, safety, and nutrition education

State child care licensing regulations generally determine the types of policies and records that programs are required to maintain. Similar guidelines are issued by state departments of education for public schools. Although states' requirements differ, high-quality programs may find it prudent to take a more comprehensive approach to recordkeeping for improved understanding and legal protection. Basic records that are important for programs to maintain include:

▶ children's health assessments
▶ attendance
▶ emergency contact information

- developmental profiles
- staff health assessments
- fire and storm drills
- injuries
- daily health checks

Licensing authorities will review information in these records carefully during their renewal visits. Teachers in high-quality early childhood programs are trained to handle emergencies and to provide first aid and emergency care to ill or injured children. They also have completed training in cardiopulmonary resuscitation (CPR). Programs choosing to only meet minimal standards should have at least one staff member who is trained in these techniques and always available to respond to an emergency.

Notarized emergency contact forms, similar to the one shown in Figure 7–1, listing the name, address, and telephone number of the child's family and health care provider, should be completed at the time a child is enrolled. This step ensures that teachers can respond promptly, administer emergency care, and have a child transported to an emergency medical facility if necessary. Emergency numbers for fire, police, ambulance, and poison control should be posted next to the telephone for quick reference.

Programs that provide care for mildly ill children must establish policies that address their special health needs. A quiet area should be provided in either a separate corner of the classroom or a room designated specifically for this purpose so sick children can rest and not expose others to their illnesses. Medical supplies, equipment, and hand washing facilities should be located nearby so they are easy to access.

Early childhood programs must also have emergency plans and procedures in place so teachers are prepared to respond to unexpected events in a prompt and organized manner (Teacher Checklist 7-1). These plans should outline steps for protecting children's safety in emergencies, including fire, severe storms such as tornadoes, major disasters such as earthquakes, floods, or hurricanes, and unauthorized intruders. Representatives from local fire and law enforcement departments, the Red Cross, and emergency preparedness groups are available to assist programs in developing their emergency plans. Families should receive a copy of this information so they know what to expect in the event of an emergency and can also use it to develop similar procedures at home.

Did You Get It?

Staffing an institution properly is an ultimate and attainable goal. One of the weakest areas in many state licensing regulations is that of staff:

a. motivation
b. qualification
c. education
d. multiculturalism

Take the full quiz on CourseMate.

TEACHER CHECKLIST 7-1
Principles of Emergency Preparedness

- Remain calm—do not panic.
- Be informed. Tune in to a local station on your battery-powered radio.
- Move to a safe place. Develop and practice an appropriate disaster plan.
- Keep a first aid kit, bottled water, and flashlight (along with extra batteries) handy.
- Take along children's health forms, emergency contact information, attendance records, and a cell phone.
- Learn basic emergency and first aid procedures.

TeachSource Digital Download Download from CourseMate.

notarized – *official acknowledgment of the authenticity of a signature or document by a notary public.*

FIGURE 7–1   Sample emergency contact information form.

EMERGENCY CONTACT INFORMATION

Child's Name _____ Date of Birth _____

Address _____ Home Phone _____

Mother's Name _____ Business Phone _____

Father's Name _____ Business Phone _____

Name of other person to be contacted in case of an emergency:

1. _____ Address _____

    Relationship (sitter, relative, friend, etc.) _____ Phone _____

2. _____ Address _____

    Relationship (sitter, relative, friend, etc.) _____ Phone _____

Authorization is hereby given for the Child Development Center Staff to release the above named child to the following persons, provided proper identification is first established (list all names of authorized persons, including immediate family):

1. _____ Relation: _____

2. _____ Relation: _____

3. _____ Relation: _____

Physician to be called in an emergency:

1. _____ Phone _____ or _____

2. _____ Phone _____ or _____

Dentist to be called in an emergency:

1. _____ Phone _____ or _____

I, the undersigned, authorize the staff of the Child Development Center to take what emergency medical measures are deemed necessary for the care and protection of my child enrolled in the Child Development Center program.

_____
(Signature of Parent or Guardian/date)

Signature witnessed by:
(Notary)

_____
(Signature of Parent or Guardian/date)

The above statement sworn before me on:

_____

_____

7-4 Guidelines for Safe Environments

Nowhere is health and safety more important than in group programs serving young children. When families enroll children in a program, they expect teachers to safeguard their child's well-being. They assume the facilities, toys, and equipment will be safe for children's use, that teachers will carefully supervise their children's activities, that the environment is clean, and the food is safe and nutritious.

Although no uniform child care licensing standards currently exist in this country, several organizations have developed recommendations for out-of-home programs based on years of research data. NAEYC has consistently defined and supported high standards for early-childhood programs. The American Public Health Association (APHA) and American Academy of Pediatrics (AAP) have released their newly revised document, *Caring for Our Children: National Health and Safety Performance Standards Guidelines for Out-of-Home Child Care Programs* (3rd ed.), in which they identify approximately 180 regulation standards and recommended safety practices. The remainder of this chapter addresses features in children's indoor and outdoor environments that require special attention. An indoor and outdoor safety checklist is provided in Teacher Checklist 7-4.

7-4a Indoor Safety

A great deal of thought and preparation is needed to create rooms that are safe for children. Everything from the traffic flow, furniture arrangement, and choice of floor coverings to the design of changing tables, sink placement, and proper storage requires careful study. Knowledge of children's abilities at each stage of development plays a key role in anticipating and eliminating potential safety hazards. (Refer to Table 8–2.) A safe environment encourages children to explore and learn through play, and is also less stressful for adults to work in (Vidoni & Ignico, 2011).

Building and Site Location In a time of shrinking budgets and increasing demand for child care, the selection of an appropriate building site often requires a creative approach. Although it would be ideal to plan and design a facility specifically for this purpose, few programs have sufficient funds for new construction. More often, existing buildings such as unused classrooms in public schools, older houses, unoccupied stores, church basements, or places of business such as factories or hospitals are modified or remodeled to make them suitable for children. Although renovations can be expensive, it may be possible to reduce the cost by recruiting families and volunteers to assist with a portion of the work. In some cases, remodeling may simply not be a practical solution.

With the exception of church-affiliated programs, home- and center-based programs are considered public facilities under the 1990 Americans with Disabilities Act (ADA) even if they are privately owned (Child Care Law Center, 2009). Consequently, they too must comply with guidelines set forth in this historical piece of legislation, which requires the removal of physical barriers that would otherwise deny access to individuals who have disabilities. Early childhood programs cannot refuse to admit children on the basis of their disabilities. Program directors are expected to make reasonable adjustments in policies, practices, and facilities in order to accommodate all children. Admission can be denied only in special circumstances, such as if the required modifications are unreasonably difficult or costly to complete, or if there is no alternative solution for meeting a child's special needs (U.S. Department of Justice, 1997). Consequently, this law has important implications throughout the site selection, building, or remodeling stages as more children with disabilities are enrolling in early childhood programs.

© 2015 Cengage Learning

▶II TeachSource Video Connections

Creating a Safe Physical Environment for Toddlers

Toddlers are notorious for their boundless energy, curiosity, and questioning ways. However, these endearing qualities also place children at greater risk for unintentional injury. Teachers who work with toddlers must take extra care to safeguard children's well-being by creating safe environments and providing continuous supervision. As you watch the learning video, *Creating a Safe Physical Environment for Toddlers*, consider the following questions:

1. What safety features did you observe in this classroom?
2. What steps has the program taken to accommodate children who have special needs?
3. What qualities make toys safe for toddlers?
4. What security measures has the program implemented to protect the children's safety?

Watch on CourseMate.

Security in Early Childhood Programs

Media reports of school shootings, child mistreatment, unauthorized visitors, and workplace violence have heightened concerns about security. Although many public schools have installed additional security devices in buildings and enhanced their security procedures, early childhood programs have been somewhat slower to respond (Hong & Eamon, 2012). Employee background checks, photo identification cards for teachers and staff, and signed release forms authorizing child pickups are a few of the more common safety measures that programs utilize. Some centers have begun to install technology devices, such as touch keypads, Internet cameras that allow families to view children from work, and electronic surveillance cameras to improve security in their buildings (Bracy, 2011). However, the cost of these systems is simply more than many programs can afford.

Think About This:

▶ What resources are available to schools and community-based early childhood programs for addressing basic security issues and improvement measures?

▶ What workplace policies and procedures can programs implement to protect the safety of children and teachers?

▶ Are there any disadvantages to increasing security? What might they be?

▶ What message does the need for increased security in schools and early childhood programs say about contemporary society?.

Location is always important to consider when selecting an appropriate site. However, local zoning codes may make it difficult to locate programs in residential neighborhoods where they are often most needed. Ideally, buildings housing early childhood programs should be situated away from heavy traffic, excessive noise, air pollution, animals, ground contaminants (chemicals), bodies of water, large equipment, and other similar hazards to protect children's health and safety. Programs located in inner city and rural areas may find it difficult to avoid these conditions. It then becomes important to devote additional time and effort to safety awareness, policy development, and providing educational programs for children, teachers, and families. Buildings and building sites should be tested for radon, a colorless and odorless radioactive gas known to cause lung cancer (EPA, 2012). Inexpensive testing kits can be purchased locally or online or a certified radon professional can be hired to test the facilities. (The EPA also encourages individuals to test their personal homes for radon gas.)

Local fire codes will also affect building selection. Older buildings and those not originally designed for infants and young children may require extensive changes before they pass inspection. Rooms that children occupy must have a minimum of two exits, one leading directly outdoors. All doors should be hinged so they swing out of the room; this prevents doors from slowing the evacuation process in an emergency. Programs located on upper levels should have an enclosed stairwell for safe escape in the event of a fire.

How much space is needed depends to some extent on the type of program and services that will be offered. A minimum of 40 square feet of usable floor space per child is considered adequate for child care. However, teachers often find this amount of space crowded and difficult to work in. High-quality programs often provide 45 to 50 square feet of space per child for improved functionality and classroom safety. Additional space may be needed to accommodate large indoor play structures, special equipment for children with physical disabilities, or cribs for infants. However, it should also be kept in mind that large spaces are more difficult to supervise. Ground floor levels are always preferable for infants and preschool-aged children, although basement areas can be used for several hours at a time provided there are at least two exits.

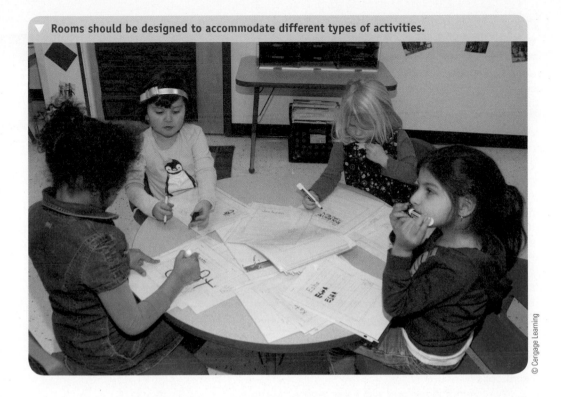

▼ Rooms should be designed to accommodate different types of activities.

© Cengage Learning

Space The arrangement of space, or basic floor plan, should be examined carefully to determine the ease of conducting specific activities. For example, the traffic flow should allow ample room for children to arrive and depart without disturbing others who are playing. It should also accommodate separate areas for active or noisy play and quiet activities. Small rooms that lack storage space, adequate lighting, accessible bathrooms, or suitable outdoor play areas are inconvenient and frustrating for the staff and children.

Play spaces for infants and toddlers should be separated from those of older children to avoid injuries, confrontations, and the spread of illness. Large, open space that is free of obstacles encourages young children to move about and to explore without hesitation.

Building Security Added precautions should be taken to protect children from unauthorized individuals while ensuring that families and legitimate visitors have safe access (Teacher Checklist 7-2). Buildings and outdoor play spaces should be evaluated carefully to determine if they are secure. Safety measures, such as locking outside doors and gates, issuing card keys (used in hotels), or installing keypads (with security codes) or buzzers on doors can be implemented to control unauthorized visitors. Teachers and staff members should always be alert to persons entering the building and acknowledge their presence by making a point to greet them. Surveillance cameras can also be installed to monitor entrances and exits. Programs should develop and review plans for handling unauthorized visitors and summoning assistance in the event of an emergency. They may also want to establish a safe area of the building where children can be moved for added protection.

Fire Safety Local fire officials can assist schools and in-home programs in the development and review of emergency procedures. They can be invited to tour the building layout and offer expert advice about planning efficient evacuation routes and notification procedures. Copies of the floor plans should be given to local fire authorities so they can familiarize themselves with the building layout and design. This will enable them to respond more efficiently if there is an actual emergency.

TEACHER CHECKLIST 7-2

Inventory Checklist: Planning for Program Security

Program administrators should work closely with local law enforcement, fire, and safety officials to assess a program's risk and to develop security plans that will protect children and staff members. Critical documents should be prepared and stored in a designated folder or box. All program staff should be familiar with its location and contents for quick retrieval in an emergency, such as fire, earthquake, hurricane, or unauthorized intruders. Items that should be addressed when planning for program security include:

• Obtaining a copy of the building floor plan or blueprint
• Preparing a list of employees by name and room, and attaching their photograph
• Preparing a roster of the children by room and attaching their photograph; note any children who have special needs
• Knowing where all shut-off valves are located and how to turn them off
• Preparing an evacuation plan with alternate exit routes
• Posting evacuation plans in each classroom and reviewing them periodically with teachers
• Conducting monthly evacuation drills with children
• Maintaining hallways and exits that are clear of obstructions
• Making copies of parent authorization forms and emergency contact information
• Compiling a list of emergency personnel and telephone numbers
• Assigning specific emergency responsibilities to individual personnel and outlining each role on a master plan
• Informing families about the program's security plans and including the information in parent handbooks
• Keeping an emergency food and water supply on hand

TeachSource Digital Download   Download from CourseMate.

Smoke and carbon monoxide detectors should be present in rooms occupied by children, especially those where infants and young children will be sleeping. Detectors should be tested monthly to be sure they are functioning properly and have the batteries replaced annually (unless the system is wired). All floor coverings and draperies should be flame-retardant and at least one multipurpose fire extinguisher should be available. Staff should be familiar with the location of building exits and emergency evacuation procedures. Monthly fire drills should be conducted with the children so they become familiar with the routine and are less likely to be frightened in an actual emergency (Teacher Checklist 7-3). Alternate evacuation routes should be planned and practiced so teachers will know where to exit the building if an area is blocked by fire. Plans for evacuating children with special needs should also be given careful attention.

Extension cords should not be used in classrooms. All electrical outlets should be covered with safety caps, which can be purchased in most grocery or hardware stores. However, remember that caps are only a temporary solution. They are frequently removed by teachers and cleaning personnel, not always replaced, and pose a choking hazard for young children if they are left lying around. An electrician can replace conventional outlets with childproof receptacles that do not require safety covers.

Bathroom Facilities Adequate bathroom facilities are essential for convenience and health concerns. They should be accessible to both indoor and outdoor play areas. Installation of child-sized fixtures, including sinks, toilets, soap dispensers, and towel racks, allow children to care for their own needs. If only adult-sized fixtures are available, foot stools, large wooden

▼ **Child-sized fixtures encourage independence.**

© Cengage Learning

TEACHER CHECKLIST 7-3
How to Conduct a Fire Drill

Develop an Evacuation Plan

- Plan at least one alternate escape route from every room.
- Post a written copy of the plan by the door of each room.
- Review plans with new personnel.

Assign Specific Responsibilities

- Designate one person to call the fire department, preferably from a telephone outside of the building. Be sure to give the fire department complete information: name, address, approximate location of the fire in the building, and whether or not anyone remains inside. Do not hang up until the fire department does so first.
- Designate several adults to assemble children and lead them out of the building; assign extra adults, such as cooking or clerical staff, to assist with the evacuation of younger children or those needing extra help.
- Designate one adult to bring a flashlight and the notarized emergency cards or class list.
- Appoint one person to turn off the lights and close all classroom doors.

Establish a Meeting Place

- Once outside, meet at a designated location so everyone can be accounted for.
- DO NOT GO BACK INTO THE BUILDING!

Practice Fire Evacuation Drills

- Conduct drills at least once a month; plan some of these to be unannounced.
- Practice alternate routes of escape.
- Practice fire evacuation safety; for example, feel closed doors before opening them, select an alternate route if hallway or stairwells are filled with smoke, stay close to the floor (crawl) to avoid heat and poisonous gases, learn the stop-drop-roll technique.
- Use a stopwatch to time each drill and record the results; strive for improvement.

TeachSource Digital Download   Download from CourseMate.

---

blocks, or platforms securely anchored to the floor will facilitate children's independence. One toilet and sink should be available for every ten to twelve children. Programs serving children with disabilities should be designed to meet their special needs and comply with ADA standards (Child Care Law Center, 2009). A separate bathroom area should also be available for adults.

Hand-washing facilities located near toilets and sleeping areas encourage children and teachers to wash their hands when needed. Hot water temperatures should be maintained between 105°F (40.5°C) and 120°F (48.9°C) to protect children from accidental burns. Liquid or foam soap dispensers placed near sinks encourage hand washing, are easier for children to use, and less likely (than bar soap) to end up on the floor. The use of individual paper towels and cups improves sanitation and limits the spread of infectious illnesses. Smooth surfaces on walls and floors facilitate cleaning. Light-colored paint on walls makes dirty areas easy to notice and more likely to be cleaned.

> **Did You Know...**
> that room colors are thought to affect human mood and behavior? Red, yellow, and orange are energizing; blue, pink, and brown are calming; green is restful; and purple fosters creativity.

Fixtures such as mirrors, light switches, and towel dispensers placed within children's reach, adequate lighting, and bright paint create a functional and pleasant atmosphere in which young children can manage self-care skills.

Surface and Furnishings Furniture and equipment should be selected to be comfortable, nontoxic, and safe. Children are less likely to be injured if chairs and tables are appropriately proportioned and safely constructed. Furniture should meet federal safety standards and be sturdy enough to withstand frequent use. (See Chapter 8.) Items with sharp corners or edges should be avoided; many manufacturers now construct children's furniture with rounded corners.

Bookcases, lockers, pianos, televisions, and other heavy objects must be anchored securely to the wall or floor to prevent children from tipping them over. Tall bookshelves should be replaced or cut in half to scale them down to child-size. Children should also not have access to adult exercise equipment.

Materials such as tile, vinyl, and plastics (free of BPA, PVC, or phthalates) are ideal for wall and floor coverings because they are easy to clean. However, floors covered with any of these materials can become quite slippery when wet. Injuries can be avoided by taking extra precautions such as positioning non-skid rugs or newspapers where liquids are likely to be spilled and wiping up any spills immediately. Rooms that include a combination of carpeted and tiled areas address children's needs for soft, comfortable play spaces and areas for potentially messy activities.

Each child should have an individual storage space, cubby, or locker where personal belongings can be kept. A child's private space is particularly important in group settings where most other things must be shared. Individual cubbies also help to minimize the loss of prized possessions and aid in controlling infectious illnesses that can be transmitted through direct and indirect contact (such as head lice and pinkeye).

Additional features that make children's classrooms safer include having locked cabinets for storing medicines and other potentially poisonous substances, such as cleaning products and paint. A telephone should also be located conveniently in the building along with a list of emergency phone numbers (e.g., fire, police, hospital, ambulance, poison control center) posted directly nearby. A sample checklist for evaluating the safety of indoor and outdoor areas is provided in Teacher Checklist 7-4.

▼ **Space should be provided where children can store their personal items.**

© Cengage Learning

Lighting and Ventilation Low windows and glass doors should be constructed of safety glass to prevent serious injuries if they are broken. Colorful pictures or decals placed at children's eye level will help prevent children from accidently walking into the glass. Doors and windows should be covered with screens to keep out unwanted insects; screens that can be locked also prevent children from falling out. Drapery and blind cords should hang freely (not be knotted or looped together) to prevent strangulation and also be fastened up high and out of children's reach.

Adequate lighting is essential in classrooms and hallways. Natural light from windows and glass doors creates rooms that are bright, attractive, and inviting to teachers and children. Sunlight is also a cost-free, sustainable resource known to have a positive psychological effect on children's and adults' moods (Veitch & Galasiu, 2012).

Proper arrangement of artificial lighting is equally as important as the amount of brightness it produces. Additional lighting may be needed in areas such as reading and art centers. Compact fluorescent lights are ideal for this purpose because they give off more light, create less glare, cost less to operate, and are environmentally friendly.

Heating and cooling systems should be energy efficient and maintained annually. Room temperatures set between 68°F (20°C) and 85°F (29.4°C) year-round are ideal for children. Hot radiators, exposed pipes, furnaces, fireplaces, portable heaters, or fans should not be accessible

Teachers' Safety Checklist: Indoor and Outdoor Spaces

Indoor Areas	Date Checked	Pass/Fail	Comments

1. A minimum of 35–40 square feet of usable space is available per child.
2. Room temperature is between 68°–85°F (20°–29.4°C).
3. Rooms have good ventilation:
   a. Windows and doors have screens.
   b. Mechanical ventilation systems are in working order.
4. There are two exits in all rooms occupied by children.
5. Carpets and draperies are fire-retardant.
6. Rooms are well lighted.
7. Glass doors and low windows are constructed of safety glass.
8. Walls and floors of classrooms, bathrooms, and kitchen appear clean; floors are swept daily, bathroom fixtures are scrubbed at least every other day.
9. Tables and chairs are child-sized and sturdy.
10. Electrical outlets are covered with safety caps.
11. Smoke detectors are located in appropriate places and in working order.
12. Furniture, activities, and equipment are set up so that doorways and pathways are kept clear.
13. Play equipment and materials are stored in designated areas; they are inspected frequently and safe for children's use.
14. Large pieces of equipment (e.g., lockers, piano, TV, bookshelves) are firmly anchored to the floor or wall.
15. Cleaners, chemicals, and other poisonous substances are locked up.
16. If stairways are used:
    a. Handrail is placed at children's height.
    b. Stairs are free of toys and clutter.
    c. Stairs are well-lighted.
    d. Stairs are covered with a nonslip surface.
17. Bathroom areas:
    a. Toilets and washbasins are in working order.
    b. One toilet and washbasin is available for every 10–12 children; potty chairs are provided for children in toilet training.
    c. Water temperature is no higher than 120°F (48.9°C).
    d. Powdered or liquid soap is used for hand-washing.
    e. Individual or paper towels are used for each child.
    f. Diapering tables or mats are cleaned after each use.
18. At least one fire extinguisher is available and located in a convenient place; extinguisher is checked annually by fire-testing specialists.
19. Premises are free from rodents and undesirable insects.
20. Food preparation areas are maintained according to strict sanitary standards.
21. At least one individual on the premises is trained in emergency first aid and CPR; first aid supplies are readily available.
22. All medications are stored in a locked cabinet or box.
23. Fire and storm/disaster drills are conducted monthly.

(continued)

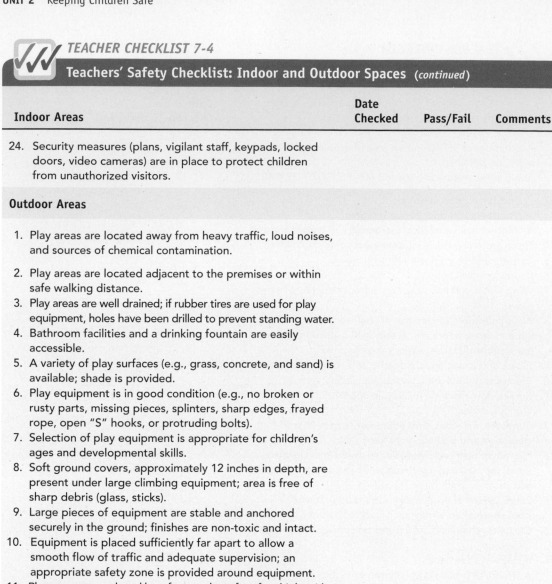

TEACHER CHECKLIST 7-4

Teachers' Safety Checklist: Indoor and Outdoor Spaces (continued)

Indoor Areas	Date Checked	Pass/Fail	Comments
24. Security measures (plans, vigilant staff, keypads, locked doors, video cameras) are in place to protect children from unauthorized visitors.			

Outdoor Areas

1. Play areas are located away from heavy traffic, loud noises, and sources of chemical contamination.
2. Play areas are located adjacent to the premises or within safe walking distance.
3. Play areas are well drained; if rubber tires are used for play equipment, holes have been drilled to prevent standing water.
4. Bathroom facilities and a drinking fountain are easily accessible.
5. A variety of play surfaces (e.g., grass, concrete, and sand) is available; shade is provided.
6. Play equipment is in good condition (e.g., no broken or rusty parts, missing pieces, splinters, sharp edges, frayed rope, open "S" hooks, or protruding bolts).
7. Selection of play equipment is appropriate for children's ages and developmental skills.
8. Soft ground covers, approximately 12 inches in depth, are present under large climbing equipment; area is free of sharp debris (glass, sticks).
9. Large pieces of equipment are stable and anchored securely in the ground; finishes are non-toxic and intact.
10. Equipment is placed sufficiently far apart to allow a smooth flow of traffic and adequate supervision; an appropriate safety zone is provided around equipment.
11. Play areas are enclosed by a fence at least four feet high, with a gate and workable lock for children's security and safety.
12. There are no poisonous plants, shrubs, or trees in the area.
13. Chemicals, insecticides, paints, and gasoline products are stored in a locked cabinet.
14. Grounds are maintained on a regular basis and are free of debris; grass is mowed; broken equipment is removed.
15. Wading or swimming pools are always supervised; water is drained when not in use.

TeachSource Digital Download Download from CourseMate.

to children; if they cannot be removed, protective insulation or wire screening must be placed around them to prevent injuries.

Indoor Air Quality Every day, children are exposed to a variety of indoor air pollutants, including formaldehyde (in carpet and building materials), carbon monoxide, radon, asbestos, cigarette smoke, paint fumes, lead, numerous household chemicals, and pesticides (EPA, 2013). Studies continue to demonstrate a close relationship between these pollutants and an increased rate of childhood respiratory illnesses, allergies, asthma, and cancer (Lin et al., 2012). Because children's bodies

TABLE 7–1   Common Air Pollutants and Their Health Effects

Sources

- organic particles (e.g., dust mites)
- molds
- pollen
- carbon monoxide
- formaldehyde and other VOCs
- insulation (e.g., asbestos, fiberglass)
- ozone

Common Health Effects

- chronic cough
- headache
- dizziness
- fatigue
- eye irritation
- sinus congestion
- skin irritation
- shortness of breath
- nausea

are still growing and maturing, they are especially vulnerable to the toxic chemicals found in these substances (Table 7-1).

Although it is not possible to avoid exposure to all toxic chemicals in an environment, steps can be taken to increase awareness and eliminate some sources. For example, labels on toys and art materials should always be checked to make certain they are nontoxic. Indoor air quality can be significantly improved by simply increasing ventilation (opening doors and windows daily, turning on the air conditioning), maintaining heating and cooling systems, and avoiding the use

▼ Children's toys should always be made of nontoxic materials.

© Cengage Learning

of aerosol sprays around children. Many new alternative building materials (low volatile organic compounds [VOC]) and cleaning products, often labeled as "green products" or "building green," are being manufactured without toxic chemicals. Information about green school initiatives, alternative cleaning products, and safer cleaning practices can be accessed on the Environmental Protection Agency's website (www.epa.gov/sc3), the Children's Environmental Health Network website (http://www.cehn.org), and from several other organizations dedicated to maintaining healthy environments.

7-4b Outdoor Safety

The outdoors provides an exciting environment for children's learning and imaginative play. It also offers important health benefits by encouraging children to be physically active. Studies continue to link time spent in outdoor play with reductions in childhood obesity, diabetes, mental health disorders, and behavior problems (Copeland et al., 2012; Milteer & Ginsburg, 2012). However, children's outdoor play areas are also a major source of unintentional injury and, therefore, require a heightened awareness of design, maintenance, and supervisory strategies. Schools that use public parks for outdoor recreation should be particularly alert to safety hazards, such as animal waste, needles, glass, and poorly maintained play equipment (CPSC, 2012b).

Space Safety must be a primary consideration in the design of outdoor play spaces. Separate play areas should be designated for infants and toddlers, preschoolers, and school-age children to accommodate their different developmental needs and abilities. A minimum of 75–100 square feet per child (using the area at the same time) is necessary to encourage active play and to reduce the potential for unintentional injury. The National Health and Safety Performance Standards recommend that play areas for infants include a minimum of 33 square feet per child; 50 square feet per child is suggested for toddlers (APHA & AAP, 2011). Ideally, play areas should be located adjacent to the building so that bathrooms are readily accessible and children are not required to walk long distances. Traveling even a short distance to playgrounds with young children requires considerable time and effort, and often discourages spontaneous outdoor play.

A fence at least 4 to 5 feet in height should surround the play area and include two exits with latched gates to prevent children from wandering away. Railings or slats should be spaced less than 3½ inches or more than 9 inches apart to prevent children's heads or bodies from becoming entrapped. Sharp wire and picket-type fences are inappropriate and should not be used around young children.

An important design element in children's play areas involves how the space will be used (Dotterweich, Greene, & Blosser, 2012; Woolley & Lowe, 2012). Play areas should be arranged so children are clearly visible from all directions. Large open areas encourage activities such as running and tossing balls. Hard, flat surfaces allow children to use riding toys and to play outdoors during inclement weather, especially if these areas are covered. Flower beds provide children with space for gardening, whereas sand and water promote imaginative play. Grassy areas and trees create a natural touch and offer protection from the sun. If trees are not available, large colorful canvas sails can be purchased from play equipment companies or home improvement stores to provide shade. Separate areas designed for quiet and active play also help to reduce potential injuries. Always check with a local nursery or county extension office to be sure that flowers, trees, and other plantings are not poisonous to children. (See Figure 7-2 and Table 7-2 for a partial list.) Photographs and a comprehensive listing of poisonous plants are also available from the Cornell University Department of Animal Science website (http://www.ansci.cornell.edu/plants; click on "Find - by common name.")

FIGURE 7–2 **Examples of common poisonous vegetation.**

Oak

Lily of the Valley

Daffodil & Crocus Bulbs

English Ivy

Designing outdoor playgrounds so they can be enjoyed by children of all abilities presents another unique challenge. Solid, flat surfaces at least 3½ feet wide allow children to maneuver safely in wheelchairs. Bright colors, textures, ramps, and handrails can easily be incorporated into play environments to improve their visibility and accessibility. Most manufacturers now offer a selection of modified outdoor play equipment designed for children who have a range of abilities and special needs. ADA guidelines for planning accessible facilities and playgrounds are available on their website (http://www.ada.gov; click on "ADA design standards".)

Equipment Each year approximately 220,000 children under the age of 14 are treated in emergency rooms for playground-related injuries (Safe Kids USA, 2011). Because most injuries involve play equipment, careful attention must be given to its selection, placement, and maintenance (Teacher Checklist 7-5; also see Chapter 8). Equipment choices should be based on:

- amount of available play space
- age and developmental appropriateness
- variety of learning experiences provided
- quality and safety of construction
- accessibility to all children

Large pieces of equipment and portable climbing structures should be securely anchored in the ground; posts should be sunk 12 to 18 inches below the ground surface if anchored with

TABLE 7–2   Examples of Common Poisonous Vegetation

Vegetation	Poisonous Part	Complications
Bittersweet	Berries	Causes a burning sensation in the mouth. Nausea, vomiting, dizziness, and convulsions.
Buttercup	All parts	Irritating to the digestive tract. Causes nausea and vomiting.
Castor bean	Beanlike pod	Extremely toxic. May be fatal to children and adults.
Daffodil, hyacinth, narcissus, jonquil, iris	Bulbs Underground roots	Nausea, vomiting, and diarrhea. Can be fatal.
Dieffenbachia	Leaves	Causes immediate burning and swelling around mouth.
English ivy	Leaves and berries	Ingestion results in extreme burning sensation.
Holly	Berries	Results in cramping, nausea, vomiting, and diarrhea.
Lily of the valley	Leaves and flowers	Nausea, vomiting, dizziness, and mental confusion.
Mistletoe	Berries	Extremely toxic. Diarrhea and irregular pulse.
Oleander	Flowers and sap	Highly toxic; can be fatal. Causes nausea, vomiting, diarrhea, and heart irregularities.
Philodendron	Leaves	Ingestion causes intense irritation and swelling of the lips and mouth.
Rhubarb	Raw leaves	Can cause convulsions, coma, and rapid death.
Sweet pea	All parts, especially the seeds	Shallow respirations, possible convulsions, paralysis, and slow pulse.
Black locust tree	Bark, leaves, pods, and seeds	Causes nausea and weakness, especially in children.
Cherry tree	Leaves and twigs	Can be fatal. Causes shortness of breath, general weakness, and restlessness.
Golden chain tree	Beanlike seed pods	Can cause convulsions and coma.
Oak tree	Acorns and leaves	Eating large quantities may cause poisoning. Gradually causes kidney failure.
Rhododendron	All parts	Causes vomiting, convulsions, and paralysis.
Wisteria	Seed pods	Causes severe diarrhea and collapse.
Yews	Berries and foliage	Foliage is very poisonous and can be fatal. Causes nausea, diarrhea, and difficult breathing.

metal pins or at least 6 inches if set in concrete. The safe height of play equipment should be determined by the age of children who will be using it (Table 7–3). Stationary equipment should be located at least 6 to 8 feet from other equipment or hard surfaces such as concrete and asphalt to avoid injury in the event of a fall; this distance should be increased to 15 feet if the equipment has moving parts such as swings.

TABLE 7–3   Recommended Equipment Heights

Age Group	Maximum Equipment Height
Infants & toddlers	32 inches
Preschoolers	48 inches
School-age	6–6 1/2 feet

Many states no longer recommend or permit programs to include swings and teeter-totters on newly constructed playgrounds because they are a frequent source of injury. The Consumer Product Safety Commission (CPSC) also discourages swings in public parks unless they meet strict safety standards (CPSC, 2012b). Existing swing seats should be constructed of plastic or rubber to decrease the risk of impact injuries. Holes must be drilled in tire swings to prevent mosquitoes from breeding in water that may collect. The size of any opening on equipment should also be carefully checked (openings must be less than 3½ inches or greater than 9 inches) to prevent children's heads from becoming entrapped.

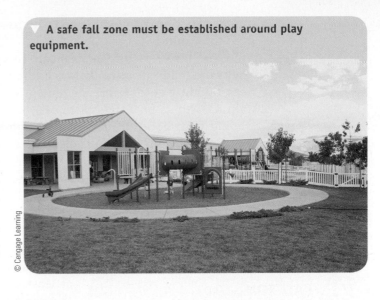

▼ A safe fall zone must be established around play equipment.

© Cengage Learning

Large trampolines have increased in popularity but are not appropriate in early childhood programs or school settings. The American Academy of Pediatrics discourages families from having trampolines in their backyards or schools from using them for physical education classes or athletic activities. Trampolines are also not recommended for use by children younger than 6 years due to the risk of serious injury (Lovejoy et al., 2012).

For many years, decks and children's climbing structures were constructed with chromated copper arsenic (CCA)-treated lumber, which gave it a green tint. CCA-treated lumber is no longer sold because there are health risks associated with these chemicals, which can rub off on children's hands. However, many play structures constructed with this material still exist on playgrounds and in children's backyards. Researchers have determined that an annual application of oil-based sealant significantly reduces children's exposure to the arsenic-based chemicals (CPSC, 2012a; Hayward, Lebow, & Brooks, 2011). Soil around the base of treated timbers should be

Did You Know...

that plastic, rubber, and other non-metal surfaces on outdoor play equipment can become hot enough on a sunny day to cause serious burns?

TEACHER CHECKLIST 7-5

General Guidelines for Purchasing Outdoor Play Equipment

Consider:

- Height of platforms and decks; no higher than 32 inches for infants and toddlers, 4 feet for preschoolers, and 6–6 1/2 feet for school-age children.
- Railings (height and design) present on all decks and platforms, especially those more than 30 inches above ground.
- The size of all openings (including those between rungs and guardrails) should be less than 3½ inches or greater than 9 inches apart to prevent entrapment.
- Hardware such as "S" hooks, protruding nuts and bolts, or moving pieces of rope that could injure fingers or catch on clothing; rope swings that could cause strangulation.
- Materials used in construction. (Wood/wood products require maintenance to avoid splintering and deterioration. Metal is strong, but becomes hot in sunlight and slippery when wet. Paints and chemicals used for wood treatment must be nontoxic.)
- The type of surface material that will be needed under equipment.
- The amount of area required for safe installation. (A clearance area of 9 feet is necessary for stationary equipment; 15 feet is needed for equipment with moving parts such as swings.)
- Ladders that are set straight up and down (vs. on an angle) encourage children to hold onto rungs more securely when climbing.

removed periodically or covered with fresh surface material because these chemicals also leach into the ground.

Sand boxes require special care to keep them safe for children (Teacher Checklist 7-6). Play sand made specifically for children's sandboxes can be purchased from local garden centers, building contractors, or cement suppliers. (**Note:** Sands used in construction may contain hazardous materials, such as asbestos, and should not be used for children.) Sandboxes should have good drainage and a tightly fitting cover to keep out animals and insects. If they cannot be covered, sand should be raked and inspected daily for animal feces, spiders, insects, sticks, stones, or other sharp debris before children begin to play. Locating sandboxes in wind-protected areas decreases the chances of having sand blown into children's eyes. Adjoining surfaces, especially sidewalks, should be swept frequently to reduce the potential for slipping and falling.

Wading or swimming pools can add interest to outdoor play areas. However, they require extra supervision, safety, and sanitation precautions. Every teacher should be familiar with water safety procedures and rescue breathing procedures, and at least one adult on site should be CPR certified. Limiting the number of children participating in water activities at any given time improves teachers' ability to monitor and improve safety. Safety rules should be carefully explained to the children before a water activity begins and then strictly enforced.

It is essential that pool water be tested and disinfected (7.2–7.7 ph) prior to use by each group of children to prevent the spread of diseases such as giardia and **cryptosporidiosis**. (See Table 6–1.) Inexpensive water-quality test kits are available from pool supply stores. Disinfecting chemicals must be guarded closely and removed from the area once they have been used to protect children from accidental poisoning. Permanent pools and natural bodies of water must be fenced (at least 5 feet in height; be sure to check local codes) and have self-closing gates. Gate alarms, pool safety covers, motion alarms, and the availability of proper flotation and rescue devices provide additional protection against accidental drownings.

Tricycles and other small riding toys are always children's favorites. However, they also are involved in many serious childhood injuries and are a common cause of head trauma. Children should always wear bike helmets when they are riding, but it is also important that the helmets fit properly, are worn correctly, and meet safety standards established by the Consumer Product Safety Commission (Figure 7–3). *Warning*: Children must not wear helmets while on play equipment to prevent entrapment and strangulation. A designated area located away from where other children are playing can make riding activities less hazardous. Safe

> ⚠️ **CAUTION**
>
> *Children must never be left unattended around any source of water, including sprinklers, wading pools, water tables, puddles, ditches, fountains, buckets, or toilets.*

✔✔ **TEACHER CHECKLIST 7-6**

Teacher Checklist: Sandbox Care and Maintenance

Purchase only special play sand for children's sandboxes.

- Make sure there is adequate drainage to prevent water from pooling.
- Rake and check sand daily for spiders, stones, and sharp objects.
- Cover sand if at all possible; if not, be sure to check for animal feces before children play.
- Sweep adjoining surfaces to prevent slipping and falling.

 TeachSource Digital Download   Download from CourseMate.

---

cryptosporidiosis – *an infectious illness caused by an intestinal parasite. May be present in water (e.g., swimming pools, hot tubs, streams) contaminated with feces or from unwashed hands. Often causes severe diarrhea in children.*

riding rules should be determined and explained to the children. For example, only one child should be allowed on a bike or wheeled-toy and all bikes should be ridden in the same direction to avoid collisions and subsequent injury.

Impact Surface Materials Protective materials that are soft and resilient should be placed under all play equipment and extend approximately 4 to 6 feet out in all directions to create an adequate fall zone (Table 7–4) (CPSC, 2012b). These materials must be loosened frequently to prevent them from compacting and replaced periodically to maintain the recommended depths. Impact surface materials must also be checked daily for any sharp debris or animal waste. Special rubber matting has been developed as an alternative to natural fall zone materials and can be purchased through most outdoor equipment catalogues. Although the initial costs may be considerably greater, rubber matting tends to last longer under children's constant wear. Synthetic grasses, sprinkled with finely ground rubber tire particles for added cushioning, are being installed more often in city parks and school playgrounds. Questions have been raised about the safety of chemicals used in manufacturing these products and the potential for children inhaling or ingesting the fine, rubber particles (Kim et al., 2012).

FIGURE 7–3 **Helmets must fit and be worn properly to protect children from serious head injury.**

Maintenance Hazardous conditions can often be spotted if outdoor play areas are inspected carefully each day before children begin to play. Equipment with broken pieces, jagged or sharp edges, loose screws or bolts, or missing parts should be removed or made off-limits to children. Frequent inspections of play areas and removal of any poisonous vegetation, snakes, rodents or other small animals, sharp sticks, fallen branches, broken glass, or other harmful debris is essential for preventing unintentional injury. Play equipment with wooden surfaces should be sanded and repainted regularly.

Supervision Although adults may go to great lengths to design attractive playgrounds and safe equipment, there is no substitution for first-rate supervision. Children must never be left unattended, and the younger they are the more closely adults need to supervise their play. Teacher supervision and safety management will be addressed in greater detail in Chapter 8.

7-4c Transportation

Some early childhood programs transport children to and from other school settings or on occasional field trips. Large passenger vans are often used for this purpose, but they are not considered safe and, in the event of an accident, may actually place occupants at increased risk for serious injury. Vans have a tendency to roll over and offer passengers limited structural protection. As a result, federal transportation officials currently recommend that early childhood programs replace existing passenger vans with small-scale school buses. These buses are designed with improved structural safety features (roof and fuel tanks) and, thus, offer greater protection.

Any vehicle used to transport children should be fitted with an appropriate safety restraint system (based on height, weight, and age) for each child: an infant-only carrier for infants

TABLE 7-4   Comparison of Impact Surface Materials

Material	Advantages	Disadvantages	Protects to Fall Height (feet)
Gravel, pea (3/8-inch diameter) (9-inch depth)	• Relatively inexpensive • Readily available • Long-lasting; won't decompose • Drains quickly • Doesn't attract animals • Easy to install	• Requires a barrier for containment • Becomes compact if wet and freezes • Must be replenished periodically; may mix with soil below • Not recommended with children under 5 years; small pebbles may be thrown or stuffed into noses, ears, or mouths • Not wheelchair accessible; hazardous if gravel is scattered on hard surfaces nearby; can cause slipping and falls	5
Wood mulch (9-inch depth)	• Inexpensive • Easy to install • Drains quickly • Readily available	• Decomposes rapidly • Must be contained with barriers; can wash away with heavy rains • Absorbs moisture and freezes • Compacts easily • Difficult to find sharp objects (e.g., broken glass, sticks, nails, stones) in loose mulch • Prone to microbial infestations	7
Wood chips (9-inch depth)	• Air trapped between chips promotes cushioning effect • Low in cost • Accessible to wheelchairs	• Washes away with heavy rains • Decomposes and must be replenished to maintain cushioning effect • May be thrown about by children but not likely to cause injury	10
Sand (coarse or masonry sand) (9-inch depth)	• Easy to obtain • Inexpensive • Does not deteriorate over time • Easy to install • Not as prone to microbial or insect infestation • Accessible by wheelchairs	• Must be replenished periodically to maintain cushioning effect • May be thrown about or eaten by children • Gets into shoes and clothing • Hazardous when spilled onto nearby hard surfaces such as cement and tile floors; can cause slipping and falls • Attractive to animals (especially cats) if area is not covered • Must be raked and sifted frequently to check for undesirable objects (e.g., sticks, broken glass, stones) • Requires good drainage beneath	4
Shredded rubber (6-inch depth)	• Relatively low initial cost • Doesn't deteriorate over time • Not as likely to compact • Less conducive to microbial and insect infestation • Wheelchair accessible	• Is flammable • May stain clothing if not treated • May contain metal particles from steel belted tires • Easily thrown about by children but unlikely to cause injury • Requires good drainage system	10

(continued)

TABLE 7–4   Comparison of Impact Surface Materials *(continued)*

Material	Advantages	Disadvantages	Protects to Fall Height (feet)
Rubber tiles or mat systems (check manufacturer's recommendations)	• Uniform cushioning effect • Easy to clean and maintain • Material remains in place • Foreign objects are easily noticed • Wheelchair accessible	• Expensive to install • Requires a flat surface; difficult to use on hills or uneven area • Mat or tile edges may curl up and present a tripping hazard • Some materials affected by frost	Varies by manufacturer

Note: Suggested material depths (noncompacted).
Source: *Public Playground Safety Handbook*, U.S. Consumer Product Safety Commission (CPSC) (2012). (http://www.cpsc.gov/PageFiles/116134/325.pdf).

(birth–1 year) weighing up to 22 pounds (9.9 kg) (installed in the back seat, facing the rear of the car) with a three- or five-point harness. A convertible safety seat for heavier infants should be purchased for children under 1 year who weigh 20–35 pounds (9.1–15.9 kg).

▶ a child safety seat for children (1–4 years) weighing 20–40 pounds (9.1–18.1 kg) and who are able to sit up by themselves (installed in the back seat, facing forward)
▶ a booster seat, secured in the back seat, used in combination with a lap belt and shoulder harness for children (4–8 years) who have outgrown child safety seats and are under 4 feet 9 inches (57 inches; 144.8 cm) in height
▶ a vehicle lap belt and shoulder harness for children (age 8 years and older) who are at least 55–58 inches (139.7–147.3 cm) in height; children should always ride in the back seat.

It is also critical that safety seats and restraints be installed according to manufacturer's specifications and used correctly whenever children are in transit:

▶ They must be installed correctly (facing the front or back as is appropriate) and securely anchored in the vehicle.
▶ They must meet federal manufacturing standards. (See, http://www.nhtsa.gov/nhtsa_eou/info.jsp?type=all for car seat ratings.) Additional child car seat guidelines and comparison lists are posted at www.healthychildren.org. (Click on "Safety and Prevention," "On the Go.")
▶ Children must always be buckled into the seat.

Children and adults must be buckled in securely on every trip even though it may be a time-consuming process. Young children should always ride in the back seat of a vehicle to avoid injury from airbags.

Designated drivers must be responsible individuals who are in good health and possess a current license appropriate for the vehicle-type and number of passengers they will be transporting. They should present evidence of a safe driving history and have no criminal convictions. In addition, they must abstain from alcohol, drug, and tobacco use for several hours prior to and while driving. Families of children who are transported on a regular basis should get to know the driver so they feel comfortable with the arrangement. Written parental permission and special instructions should always be obtained from families before children are transported in any vehicle.

Transport vehicles must be inspected and maintained regularly to ensure their safe performance. Air conditioning and heating should be operational to protect children from temperature extremes. An ABC-type fire extinguisher should be secured in the front of the vehicle where it is accessible for emergencies. Liability insurance should be purchased to cover the vehicle, driver, and maximum number of intended passengers. Copies of children's health forms and emergency contact information should always be stored safely in the vehicle.

Special off-street areas should be designated for the sole purpose of loading and unloading children. If programs do not have space sufficient to accommodate this activity, they will need to dedicate additional effort to providing safety education for children and families. Children should always enter

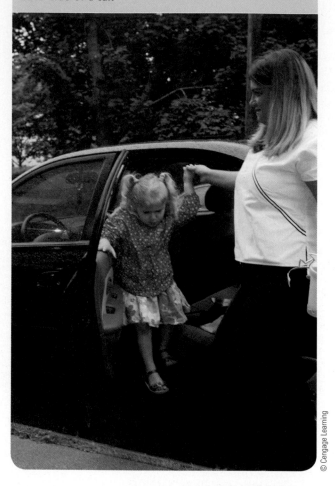

▼ **Children should always enter and exit from the curb-side of a car.**

© Cengage Learning

and exit vehicles from the curb-side rather than the street-side. Adequate parking should be available around school buildings to reduce traffic congestion and protect children's safety. Families must also be reminded *never* to leave children alone in a vehicle, even for a few minutes, to prevent abduction or overheating. (**Note:** Temperatures inside of a vehicle can become dangerously high in a short time even on mild or cloudy days.)

Families are sometimes asked to provide transportation for off-site field trips. However, this practice is risky and has the potential for creating serious legal problems in the event of an accident. Programs have no guarantee that privately owned vehicles or individual drivers meet the standards and qualifications previously discussed. As a result, programs may be even more vulnerable to lawsuits and charges of negligence. To avoid this risk, programs may opt to use public transportation, such as a city bus, or contract with a private transportation company.

When private vehicles are used for transportation, several steps can be taken to protect children's safety. Travel routes should be planned in advance, reviewed with the director, and followed precisely by all drivers. Names of drivers, supervising adults, and children riding in each vehicle, as well as anticipated departure and arrival times, should be left with a program administrator. Rules for safe traveling should be reviewed with all drivers and children before each excursion. Plans for handling an unplanned emergency, such as an ill child, flat tire, carjacking, or unusual weather, should also be discussed and gone over carefully with drivers. At least one adult traveling with the group should have first aid and CPR training.

Did You Get It?

_____ is an important design feature to consider when planning a new indoor or outdoor space for children.
- **a.** Cost
- **b.** Ease of supervision
- **c.** Visual appeal
- **d.** Staffing

Take the full quiz on CourseMate.

PARTNERING with FAMILIES

How to Identify High-Quality Programs

Dear Families,

Choosing an early childhood or after-school program that is right for your child can be a challenging task. It is important to take time and to carefully research each program until you are satisfied with the arrangement. Note how well the program measures up to the three key indicators of a quality program: small group size; a low ratio of adults to children; and, teachers who have educational preparation in child development and early childhood education. Spend

(continued)

PARTNERING with FAMILIES

How to Identify High-Quality Programs   *(continued)*

time visiting and observing each program and seek answers to the following questions before enrolling your child:

▶ Does the environment appear to be clean, safe, and appealing to children? For example, are electrical outlets covered, are poisonous and sharp items stored out of children's reach, is the carpet intact and free of snags or stains, and do children wash their hands before eating and at other appropriate times?

▶ Is the program accredited or licensed?

▶ Do the children seem happy and under control? Are children encouraged in their efforts and allowed to express their feelings? Are teachers playing and talking with the children? Do they involve children in solving their own problems?

▶ Are children treated with respect and as individuals? Is the teacher's tone of voice warm and friendly versus harsh, demanding, or demeaning?

▶ Is there adequate adult supervision? Are there sufficient numbers of adults present who can respond to an injured child or classroom emergency while ensuring the safety of other children?

▶ Are there a sufficient number and variety of toys and materials for all children to use, or must children wait for others to finish? Are items easily accessible to children? Do some of the toys reflect the diversity of children enrolled?

▶ Is the food served to children nutritious, age appropriate, and adequate in amount? Is food stored, prepared, and served in a safe manner? If your child has food allergies, would her special needs be accommodated? Are weekly menus posted?

▶ Have the teachers been trained to work with young children? Do they appear to enjoy interacting with the children and take pride in their efforts? Are they knowledgeable about how to facilitate children's development, identify problems, and support diversity? Be sure to ask about their educational preparation and years of experience.

▶ Do you feel welcomed and encouraged to ask questions? Are there opportunities for you to become involved in your child's classroom?

▶ Are learning experiences planned for children, or are they left to wander or to watch television?

▶ Is a schedule of the children's daily activities posted for you to read?

▶ Do you agree with the program's philosophy, and is it appropriate for your child's needs?

▶ Have the program's policies been explained clearly, and are they acceptable to you?

CLASSROOM CORNER

Teacher Activities

Recycle Everyday

(**NHES** PreK–2; National Health Education Standard 2.2.2)

Concept: You can recycle items instead of throwing them away in the trash.

Learning Objectives

▶ Children will learn that items can be recycled and then made into other products.

▶ Children will learn how to sort different items.

(continued)

CLASSROOM CORNER

Teacher Activities   (*continued*)

Recycle Everyday

Supplies

▶ boxes (the size that reams of paper come in); newspapers, chipboard boxes, magazines/catalogs; milk jugs and plastic bottles; cans (emptied out and clean; make sure cans don't have a sharp ring)

Learning Activities

▶ Read and discuss the books:
  - *Recycle Every Day* by Nancy Elizabeth Wallace
  - *Recycle* by Gail Gibbons
  - *The Adventures of a Plastic Bottle: A Story About Recycling* by Alison Inches

▶ Decorate each box so children will know which items need to go in it (picture of a milk jug, a water or soda bottle, newspaper, etc.). Children can help decorate the boxes ahead of time.

▶ Spread items out on the floor to show how much space discarded items take up. Talk about how items can be sorted and recycled and not thrown away.

▶ Demonstrate how items need to be sorted according to the pictures on the box.

▶ Have children come up and pick an item to place in the correct box. Sort all items. If possible, plan a field trip to a recycling center.

▶ Discuss what happens to items that are tossed in the garbage. Talk about where all of the garbage is taken. Ask children for their ideas about ways that families can reduce the amount of garbage they throw away.

Evaluation

▶ Children can sort items.

▶ Children will explain that items can be recycled and made into other items instead of thrown away as trash.

Additional lesson plans for grades 3-5 are available on CourseMate.

Summary

▶ Identifying high-quality early care and education programs that are available, affordable, and convenient can be challenging for families.
  - The environment affects all aspects of children's growth and development.

▶ Licensing regulations and procedures reflect minimal standards and vary from state to state. However, they provide some assurance that children's health and safety will be protected. Not everyone agrees about how much regulation is necessary.
  - Adhering to licensing regulations can help protect teachers from potential claims of negligence.

▶ Key indicators of high-quality programs include: small group size, low teacher/child ratios, and teachers' educational preparation and experience.

▶ Care attention must be given to planning and monitoring environments so they are safe for young children.

- Location, security, fire safety, plumbing, surfaces and furnishings, and air quality should be considered when planning children's indoor environments.
- Space, play equipment, vegetation, impact surface materials, adult supervision, and transportation must be addressed when planning outdoor play areas.

◖ Terms to Know

environment *p. 169*
cognitive *p. 169*
accreditation *p. 171*
licensing *p. 171*

regulations *p. 171*
compliance *p. 171*
registration *p. 172*

developmentally appropriate
practice (DAP) *p. 175*
notarized *p. 177*
cryptosporidiosis *p. 192*

◖ Chapter Review

A. By Yourself

1. Match the definition in **Column I** with the term in **Column II**.

Column I	Column II
1. local ordinance permitting specific types of facilities or businesses to operate in an area	a. regulation
2. legal standard that outlines procedures	b. minimal
3. child development credential	c. small group size
4. legally recognized signature	d. staff qualifications
5. indicator of a quality program	e. notarized
6. skills possessed by an employee	f. CDA
7. least restrictive requirements	g. zoning codes
	h. accreditation

2. Identify and describe eight features of a high-quality early childhood program.

3. Outline the steps involved in obtaining a license to operate an early childhood program?

4. What type of car seat or restraint is appropriate for a 3 years old? What about an 11-month-old infant who weighs 27 pounds?

B. As a Group

1. Locate and review the child care licensing regulations for your state posted online. Discuss the pros and cons of the following question: Should the quality of state child care licensing standards be raised?

2. In what ways does the environment influence a child's growth and development?

3. Describe several features that make an outdoor play yard safe for 2½- to 5-year-old children.

4. What steps can programs take to make their facilities secure from unwanted intrusions?

5. Discuss how a teacher's educational training affects the quality of a child's experiences in an early childhood program.

6. Brainstorm several ways that a school can "go green" and discuss what effect(s) this could potentially have on children's health.

◖ Case Study

Reya Gonzales has offered to help out her best friend Manuela by watching her three children several afternoons each week. Manuela has had difficulty finding child care because her new job requires her to work on different weekdays. Although she assured Reya this arrangement would only last a short time, two months have already passed. In the meantime, three of Manuela's coworkers have also asked Reya to watch their children on a regular basis. As a result, Reya now has seven children ranging in age from 15 months to 7 years who are in her care four days a week. Their parents are grateful and pleased with Reya's nurturing care. However, she fears the neighbors will report her to the local licensing agency or that the licensing authorities will soon discover her activities. Reya enjoys working with the children and has considered opening a child care business in her home. However, she is reluctant to contact the licensing agency because she has no formal training in early childhood and is unsure that her house and yard will pass the safety inspection. Reya also knows that her friends depend on her for child care and could lose their jobs if they are unable to locate an affordable program with openings.

1. What advice would you offer to Reya regarding her options?

2. What steps could Reya take to improve her success in becoming licensed?

3. Do you think family child care programs should be licensed or registered? Explain your position.

4. If Reya is unable to meet all of the state licensing standards during the initial inspection, should her child care activities be stopped? Why or why not?

5. How can the need to improve early childhood program quality be balanced with meeting increased demands for care?

◖ Application Activities

1. Develop a safety checklist that teachers and families can use when inspecting children's outdoor play areas for hazardous conditions. Use your list to conduct an inspection of two different play yards (for example, public vs. private), or the same play area on two separate occasions and summarize your findings. Repeat the process for indoor areas.

2. Contact your local child care licensing agency. Make arrangements to accompany licensing personnel on an on-site visit of a center-based program; be sure to review the state licensing regulations beforehand. Observe how the licensing inspection is conducted. Prepare a short paper in which you describe your reactions to this experience.

3. Licensing personnel are often viewed as unfriendly or threatening authority figures. However, their major role is to offer guidance and to help teachers create safer environments for children. Role-play how you would handle the following situations during a licensing visit. Keep in mind the positive role of licensing personnel (e.g., offering explanations, providing suggestions, and planning acceptable solutions and alternatives):
    - electrical outlets not covered
    - all children's toothbrushes found stored together in a large plastic bin
    - open boxes of dry cereals and crackers in kitchen cabinets
    - an adult-sized toilet and wash basin in the only bathroom
    - a swing set located next to a cement patio
    - incomplete information on children's immunization records
    - a teacher who prepares snacks without first washing his or her hands

4. Create a PowerPoint presentation to help families identify quality features to look for in an early childhood program. Include photographs of actual programs to illustrate your points. Prepare a modified version for families in your community who may not speak English as their predominant language. Make presentations to several parent groups and have them evaluate the effectiveness of your program.

5. Learn more about the CDA credential by searching online (http://www.cdacouncil.org) or contacting the Council for Professional Recognition (800-424-4310). After reading through the materials, prepare a brief summary describing the program and its requirements.

6. Locate and read through the *Public Playground Safety Handbook* (http://www.cpsc.gov /CPSCPUB/PUBS/325.pdf ; CPSC, 2010). Summarize the recommended safety standards for at least six different outdoor play equipment items. Prepare a safety checklist that families can use when they take children to public parks or playground areas. Test and revise your checklist before distributing it to families.

Helpful Web Resources

Canadian Child Care Federation	http://www.cccf-fcsge.ca
Child Care Aware	http://www.naccrra.org
Health Canada (Consumer Product Safety)	http://www.hc-sc.gc.ca
National Association for Family Child Care	http://www.nafcc.org
National Association for the Education of Young Children (NAEYC)	http://www.naeyc.org
National Network for Child Care	http://www.nncc.org
National Program for Playground Safety	http://playgroundsafety.org
U.S. Product Safety Commission	http://www.cpsc.gov
U.S. Product Safety Commission	http://www.cpsc.gov

 Visit the Education CourseMate for this textbook to access the eBook, Did You Get It? quizzes, Digital Downloads, TeachSource Video Cases, flashcards, and more. Go to CengageBrain.com to log in, register, or purchase access.

References

Allen, K. E., & Cowdery, G. (2012). *The exceptional child: Inclusion in early childhood education.* (7th ed.). Belmont, CA: Wadsworth Cengage Learning.

American Public Health Association (APHA) and American Academy of Pediatrics (AAP). (2011). *Caring for our children: National health and safety performance standards for out-of-home care.* (3rd ed.). Washington, DC. Available online at http://nrckids.org/CFOC3/index.html.

Belsky, J., & Pluess, M. (2012). Differential susceptibility to long-term effects of quality of child care on externalizing behavior in adolescence?, *International Journal of Behavioral Development*, 36(1), 2–10.

Bracy, N. (2011). Student perceptions of high-security school environments, *Youth & Society*, 43(1), 365–395.

Child Care Law Center. (2009). Questions and answers about the Americans with Disabilities Act: A quick reference for child care providers. Accessed on June 4, 2012 from http://www.childcarelaw.org/docs/ADA%20Q%20and%20A%202009%20Final%203%2009.pdf.

Consumer Product Safety Commission (CPSC). (2012a). Chromated copper arsenate (CCA) – Treated wood use in playground equipment. Accessed on June 6, 2012 from, http://www.cpsc.gov/phth/ccafact.html.

Consumer Product Safety Commission (CPSC). (2012b). *Public playground safety handbook.* Accessed on May 2, 2013 from http://www.cpsc.gov/PageFiles/116134/325.pdf .

Copeland, K., Sherman, S., Kendeigh, C., Kalkwarf, H., & Saelens, B. (2012). Societal values and policies may curtail preschool children's physical activity in child care centers, *Pediatrics*, 129(2), 265–274.

Dennis, S., & O'Connor, E. (2013). Reexamining quality in early childhood education: Exploring the relationship between the organizational climate and the classroom, *Journal of Research in Childhood Education*, 27(1), 74–92.

Dotterweich, A., Greene, A., & Blosser, D. (2012). Using innovative playgrounds and cross-circular design to increase physical activity, *Journal of Physical Education, Recreation, & Dance*, 83(5), 1–60.

Environmental Protection Agency (EPA). (2013). *America's children and the environment*. (3rd ed.). Accessed on May 3, 2013 from http://www.epa.gov/ace .

Environmental Protection Agency (EPA). (2012). Managing radon in schools. Accessed on June 9, 2012 from http://www.epa.gov/iaq/schools/managing_radon.html.

Essa, E. (2014). *Introduction to early childhood education*. 7th ed. Belmont, CA: Wadsworth Cengage.

Fults, R., & Harryl, B. (2012). Combining family centeredness and diversity in early childhood teacher training programs, *Exceptional Children*, 35(1), 27–48.

Green, B., Malsch, A., Kothari, B., Busse, J., & Brennan, E. (2012). An intervention to increase early childhood staff capacity for promoting children's social-emotional development in preschool settings, *Early Childhood Education Journal*, 40(2), 123–132.

Hayward, D., Lebow, S., & Brooks, K. (2011). *Methods for mitigating the environmental risks associated with wood preservatives*. Accessed on June 6, 2012 from http://www.fpl.fs.fed.us/documnts/pdf2011/fpl_2011_hayward001.pdf.

Hebbeler, K., Spiker, D., & Kanhn, L. (2012). Individuals with Disabilities Act's early childhood programs powerful vision and pesky details, *Topics in Early Childhood Special Education*, 31(4), 199–207.

Hillemeier, M., Morgan, P., Farkas, G., & Maczuga, S. (2012). Quality disparities in child care for at-risk children: Comparing Head Start and non-Head Start settings, *Maternal & Child Journal*. Advanced online publication. DOI: 10.1007/s10995-012-0961-7.

Hong, J., & Eamon, M. (2012). Student's perceptions of unsafe schools: An ecological systems analysis, *Journal of Child & Family Studies*, 21(3), 428–438.

Kim, S., Yang, J., Kim, H., Yeo, I., Shin, D., & Lim, Y. (2012). Health risk assessment of lead ingestion exposure by particle sizes in crumb rubber on artificial turf considering bioavailability, *Environmental Health & Toxicology*, 27. DOI: 10.5620/eht.2012.27.e2012005.

Lin, S., Kielb, C., Reddy, A., Chapman, B., & Hwang, S. (2012). Comparison of indoor air quality management strategies between the school and district levels in New York State, *Journal of School Health*, 82(3), 139–146.

Lovejoy, S., Weiss, J., Epps, H., Zionts, L., & Gaffney, J. (2012). Preventable childhood injuries, *Journal of Pediatric Orthopedics*, 32(7), 741–747.

Ma, X., Shen, J., Lu, X., Brandi, K., Goodman, J., & Watson, G. (2013). Can quality improvement system improve childcare site performance in school readiness?, *The Journal of Educational Research*, 106(2), 146–156.

Milteer, R., & Ginsburg, K. (2012). The importance of play in promoting healthy child development and maintaining strong parent-child bond: Focus on children in poverty, *Pediatrics*, 129(1), e204–e213.

National Association for the Education of Young Children (NAEYC). (2012). Accreditation of programs for young children. Accessed on June 4, 2012 from http://www.naeyc.org/academy.

Nicholson, S., & Reifel, S. (2011). Sink or swim: Child care teachers' perceptions of entry training experiences, *Journal of Early Childhood Teacher Education*, 32(1), 5–25.

Rhodes, H., & Huston, A. (2012). *Building the workforce our youngest children deserve, Social Policy Report*, 26(1), 1–32. Available online at http://www.naccrra.org/sites/default/files/default_site_pages/2012/srcdworkforcerept2012.pdf.

Safe Kids USA. (2011). Playground safety fact sheet. Accessed on June 5, 2012 from http://www.safekids.org/our-work/research/fact-sheets/playground-safety-fact-sheet.html.

Sripada, K. (2012). Neoscience in the Capital: Linking brain research and Federal early childhood policies, *Early Education & Development*, 23(1), 120–130.

Tran, H., & Winsler, A. (2011). Teacher and center stability and school readiness among low-income ethnically diverse children in subsidized, center-based child care, *Child & Youth Services Review*, 33(11), 2241–2252.

Tucker-Drob, E. (2012). Preschools reduce early academic achievement gaps: A longitudinal twin approach, *Psychological Science*, 23(3), 310–319.

U.S. Department of Justice. (1997). Commonly asked questions about child care centers and the Americans with Disabilities Act. Accessed on June 10, 2012 from http://www.ada.gov/childq&a.htm.

Veitch, J., & Galasiu, A. (2012). The physiological and psychological effects of windows, daylight, and view at home: Review and research agenda. NRC-IRC Research Report RR-325. Accessed on June 4, 2012 from http://www.nrc-cnrc.gc.ca/obj/irc/doc/pubs/rr/rr325.pdf.

Vidoni, C. & Ignico, A. (2011). Promoting physical activity during early childhood, *Early Child Development & Care*, 181(9), 1261–1269

Wen, X., Bulotsky-Shearer, R., Hahs-Vaughn, D., & Korfmacher, J. (2012). Head Start program quality: Examination of classroom quality and parent involvement in predicting children's vocabulary, literacy, and mathematics achievement trajectories, *Early Childhood Research Quarterly*. Advanced online publication. http://dx.doi.org/10.1016/j.ecresq.2012.01.004.

Whitebook, M., & Ryan, S. (2011). *Degrees in context: Asking the right questions about preparing effective teachers of young children*, Preschool Policy Brief Vol. 22. New Brunswick, NJ: National Institute for Early Education Research.

Woolley, H., & Lowe, A. (2012). Exploring the relationship between design approach and play value of outdoor play spaces, *Landscape Research*. Advanced online publication. DOI:10.1080/01426397.2011.640432.

chapter 9

Management of Injuries and Acute Illness

- **1 a and b:** Promoting child development and learning
- **#2 a and b:** Building family and community relationships
- **#3 a, c and d:** Observing, documenting, and assessing to support young children and families
- **#3 c:** Knowing about and using observation, documentation, and other assessment tools and approaches
- **#6 b:** Becoming a professional

Learning Objectives

After studying this chapter, you should be able to:

LO 9-1 Discuss the steps schools should take to prepare for medical emergencies.

LO 9-2 Describe how emergency care and first aid differ.

LO 9-3 Name six life-threatening conditions and demonstrate the emergency treatment for each.

LO 9-4 Identify six non-life-threatening conditions and describe the first aid treatment for each.

Prevention of unintentional childhood injuries is a major responsibility of families and teachers. This goal is best achieved by creating safe environments, providing health and safety education for children and first aid training for teachers, and establishing procedures for handling illness and injury emergencies (Copeland et al., 2012).

9-1 Responding to Medical Emergencies

High-quality programs have policies and procedures in place so they can respond to children's health emergencies quickly and efficiently. They have supplies available and provide advanced training to ensure that staff are ready to address emergencies in a prompt and knowledgeable manner (Figure 9–1). Points that should be addressed in a school's comprehensive emergency response plan include:

- training of personnel in infant and child CPR and basic first aid techniques
- designating staff who are responsible for administering emergency care
- obtaining contact information and notarized permission from each child's parent or guardian that authorizes emergency medical treatment (Note: Most medical facilities will not treat minor children without the notarized consent of their legal parent or guardian.)
- having an accessible telephone
- posting emergency telephone numbers (e.g., families and their designated emergency contacts, hospital emergency room, fire department, emergency medical technicians [EMTs], law enforcement, local poison control) next to the telephone
- making arrangements for emergency transportation
- providing a fully equipped first aid kit that is stored in a central location (Teacher Checklist 9-1); modified kits can be prepared for individual classrooms and for taking along on field trips (Teacher Checklist 9-2)

FIGURE 9–1   Planning guidelines for serious injury and emergency illness.

1. Remain with the child at all times. Keep calm and reassure the child that you are there to help. Your presence can be comforting to the child, especially when faced with unfamiliar surroundings or pain.
2. Do not move a child who has a serious injury unless there is immediate danger from additional harm, such as fire or electrical shock.
3. Begin appropriate emergency care procedures immediately. Meanwhile, send for help. Have another adult or child alert the person designated to handle such emergencies in your school or program.
4. Do not give food, fluids, or medications unless specifically ordered by the child's physician or Poison Control Center.
5. Call 911 for emergency medical assistance if in doubt about the child's condition. Don't attempt to handle difficult situations by yourself. A delay in contacting emergency authorities could make the difference in saving a child's life. If you are alone, have a child dial the emergency number in your community (911).
6. If the child is transported to a medical facility before parents arrive, a teacher should accompany, and remain with the child until a family member is present. You are able to provide medical personnel with valuable information about events preceding the injury or illness, symptoms the child exhibited, and any treatment administered.
7. Contact the child's family. Inform them of the illness or injury and the child's general condition. If the child's condition is not life-threatening, discuss plans for follow-up care (e.g., contacting the child's physician, observing for signs of infection). If the family cannot be reached, call the child's emergency contact person or physician.
8. Record all information concerning serious injury or illness on appropriate forms within 24 hours; place in the child's folder and provide the family with a copy. If required, notify local licensing authorities.

TeachSource Digital Download Download from CourseMate.

TEACHER CHECKLIST 9-1

Basic First Aid Supplies for Schools

adhesive tape, 1/2- and 1-inch widths	safety pins
antibacterial soap or cleanser	scissors, blunt tipped
bandages, assorted sizes	soap, preferably liquid
space blanket (Mylar)	spirits of ammonia
bulb syringe	SAM rolled splints (small)
thermometer	cotton balls
flashlight and extra batteries	plastic bags (sealable)
gauze pads, sterile, 2×2s, 4×4s	tongue blades
instant cold packs or plastic bags for ice cubes	towels, large and small
needle (sewing type)	triangular bandages for slings
roller gauze, 1- and 2-inch widths	tweezers
disposable gloves	first aid book or reference cards
pen and small notepad	emergency telephone numbers
saline eye wash solution	

TeachSource Digital Download Download from CourseMate.

TEACHER CHECKLIST 9-2
Modified First Aid Kits

For in the Classroom	To Take on Field Trips
(Assemble in a child's plastic lunchbox)	(Assemble in a "fanny pack")
antibacterial soap	alcohol wipes or antibacterial soap
assorted gauze pads	adhesive bandages (non-latex)
adhesive bandages (non-latex)	cotton balls
a glaring oversight	disposable gloves
cotton balls	plastic bags
flashlight and batteries	safety pins
instant ice packs	tweezers
non-allergenic tape	emergency telephone numbers
plastic bags	
disposable gloves	
safety pins	
saline contact solution	
scissors	
thermometer	
tweezers	
emergency telephone numbers	

TeachSource Digital Download   Download from CourseMate.

Copies of a program's emergency response plans should be made available to families and reviewed on a regular basis with staff members.

Information about universal precautions must be addressed in a program's emergency policies and procedures. Universal precautions are special infection-control guidelines that have been developed to prevent the spread of diseases transmitted via blood and other body fluids, such as hepatitis B and C, and AIDS/HIV. (See Chapter 5.) These guidelines include several areas of precaution—barrier protection (including the use of disposable gloves and hand washing), environmental disinfection, and proper disposal of contaminated materials—that must be strictly followed when caring for children's injuries.

Despite careful planning and supervision, childhood injuries and illnesses are inevitable. For this reason, it is important that teachers learn the fundamentals of emergency care and first aid (APHA & AAP, 2011). Appropriate training and continued participation in refresher courses enable personnel to handle emergencies with skill and confidence (Banghart & Kreader, 2012).

Teachers are responsible for administering initial and urgent care to children who are seriously injured or acutely ill. These measures are considered to be temporary and aimed at saving lives, reducing pain and discomfort, and preventing complications and additional injury. Once

TABLE 9–1 Initial Injury Assessment

Take a deep breath, survey the situation, and consider the following points before taking action:

- Safety – Determine if it is safe to proceed or if precautions must first be taken to protect you and or the child from additional risks (e.g., traffic, electricity, chemical fumes, glass).

- Location – Note whether the child may have fallen from play equipment, had access to toxic chemicals, been stung by an insect, or cut on a sharp object.

- Child's appearance – Observe the child for breathing, bleeding, choking, skin color (e.g., pallor, blue-grey, flushed), seizures, lying in an unusual position, and so on.

- Child's reaction – Note whether the child is crying and inconsolable, lethargic, confused, unresponsive, or able to respond appropriately.

the child has been stabilized, responsibility for obtaining further medical treatment can be transferred to the child's family (Marotz, 2000).

9-2   Emergency Care vs. First Aid

Emergency care refers to immediate treatment administered for life-threatening conditions. It includes a quick assessment of the child and conditions that may have contributed to the emergency (Table 9–1). First aid refers to treatment administered for injuries and illnesses that are not considered life-threatening. Emergency care and first aid treatments are based on principles that should be familiar to anyone who works with children:

1. Call 911 to summon emergency medical assistance for any injury or illness that requires more than simple first aid.
2. Stay calm and proceed cautiously.
3. Always remain with the child. If necessary, send another adult or child for help.
4. Don't move the child until the extent of injuries or illness can be determined. If in doubt, have the child remain in the same position and await emergency medical help.
5. Quickly evaluate the child's condition, paying special attention to signs of respiratory distress and significant bleeding.
6. Carefully plan and administer appropriate emergency care. Improper treatment can lead to other injuries.
7. Don't give any medications unless they are prescribed for certain lifesaving conditions.
8. Don't offer diagnoses or medical advice. Refer the child's family to seek professional health care.
9. Contact the child's family and inform them of the child's injury and any first aid care that has been administered.
10. Record all facts concerning the injury and treatments administered on the appropriate forms; file in the child's permanent folder.

All states grant legal protection to individuals who do not have medical training but volunteer to administer emergency treatment to an injured person. The **Good Samaritan Law** protects individuals from liability as long as they provide reasonable care to the best of their ability and without intentional harm. Teachers are also protected by this law and should not hesitate to give emergency care to an injured child.

▼ **Teachers should know the fundamentals of emergency and first aid care.**

© Cengage Learning

Good Samaritan Law – *legal protection afforded to an individual who renders emergency or first aid care in a reasonable manner.*

9-3 Life-Threatening Conditions

Did You Know...
that after the heart stops, the human brain can live only 4 minutes without oxygen before irreversible brain damage occurs?

Situations that require emergency care to prevent death or serious disability are discussed in this section. The emergency techniques and suggestions included here are not intended as substitutes for certified first aid and cardiopulmonary resuscitation (CPR) training. Rather, they are provided as a review of basic instruction and to enhance the teacher's ability to respond to children's emergencies. A course involving hands-on practice is necessary to master these skills. It is also important to complete a refresher course every few years.

9-3a Absence of Breathing

Breathing emergencies accompany many life-threatening conditions, such as asthma, drowning, electrical shock, convulsions, poisoning, severe injuries, suffocation, choking, cardiac arrest, and Sudden Infant Death Syndrome (SIDS). For this reason, adults who work with children should complete certified training in basic first aid and CPR. This training is available from most chapters of the American Red Cross and the American Heart Association (AHA) or from a local ambulance service, rescue squad, fire department, high school, or community parks and recreation departments.

The current AHA guidelines for administering CPR recommend a single compression-to-ventilation rate of 30:2 for persons of all ages (with the exception of newborns) (Berg et al., 2010). A rescue breath is defined as being one second in length and sufficient to cause the chest to rise and fall. The CPR sequence of chest compressions and rescue breaths should be delivered as follows: Compressions first, open Airway, give Breaths (C-A-B) (Figure 9–2). The AHA continues to stress the slogan, "push hard and push fast," to convey the critical importance of administering high-quality chest compressions (approximately 100 per minute) sufficient to maintain adequate blood flow to vital organs. An adequate compression should depress the chest cavity by approximately one-third of its depth or 1.5 inches (3.8 cm) in infants and 2 inches (5.1 cm) in children.

It is important to remain calm while administering emergency lifesaving procedures and to perform them quickly and with confidence (Figure 9–3). Have someone call for an ambulance or emergency medical assistance while you begin chest compressions. If

FIGURE 9–2 **Using C-A-B to perform CPR.**

CPR is as easy as

C-A-B

Compressions
Push hard and fast on the center of the victim's chest

Airway
Tilt the victim's head back and lift the chin to open the airway

Breathing
Give mouth-to-mouth rescue breaths

American Heart Association
Learn and Live

Reprinted with permission. www.heart.org. Copyright©2010, American Heart Association, Inc.

American Heart Association

you are alone, administer five cycles (30 chest compressions, 2 breaths) for approximately 2 minutes before leaving the victim to call 911 for emergency assistance.

To perform CPR:

1. ***For an infant*** (0–12 months):

   a. Have someone call 911 to summon emergency assistance.

   b. Check for a response. Shake the infant and shout, "(Child's name), are you sleeping?" or "Are you okay?" to determine if he is conscious. If the infant responds, check for injuries. If the infant isn't breathing and doesn't respond, begin CPR immediately.

FIGURE 9–3 Cardiopulmonary resuscitation (CPR) for infants and children.

(A)   Have someone call 911. If you are alone, perform CPR for approximately 2 minutes before calling 911 for emergency medical service (EMS).

(B)   Position child on a hard surface on his/her back and check for a response.

(C)   Remove vomitus or foreign objects from the mouth *only* if they are clearly visible.

(D)   Administer 30 chest compressions (100 per minute rate). Place two fingers just below the nipple line and compress (for infants); or, link fingers together and place heel of hand over lower half of breast bone (for child). Push hard enough to depress the chest 1.5 inches for infants, or 2 inches for a child.

(E)   Open airway. *For an infant*: Place your mouth over the infant's nose and mouth to create a tight seal. Give 2 small puffs of air (1–1 ½ seconds each), pausing between breaths. *For a child*: Place your mouth over the child's mouth forming a tight seal. Gently pinch the nostrils closed. Give 2 small breaths of air (1–1 ½ seconds each). Reposition if air does not go in.

(F)   Continue the cycles of 30 chest compressions and 2 breaths until the child begins to breath or EMS help arrives.

c. Position the infant on her back on a hard surface. Remove vomitus or foreign object from the mouth only if it is clearly visible.

d. Immediately administer 30 quick chest compressions by placing two fingers just below the nipple line; each compression should depress the chest by one-third of its depth (1.5 inches [3.8 cm]). Let the chest return to its normal position between each compression by lifting your hand slightly.

e. Use the head tilt-chin lift to open the airway. Do not tip the head back too far to avoid obstructing the airway. Keep your fingers on the jawbone, not on the soft tissue under the chin.

f. Place your mouth over the infant's nose and mouth to create a tight seal. Give 2 small puffs of air (one second per breath with a short pause in between). Observe the chest (rise and fall) to be sure air is entering the lungs.

g. Continue cycles of 30 chest compressions (100 per minute) followed by 2 breaths (30:2) until the infant resumes breathing or emergency help arrives.

> ⚠️ **CAUTION**
>
> *Too much air forced into an infant's lungs may also fill the stomach (causes vomiting and an increased the risk of **aspiration**). Always remember to use small, gentle puffs of air from your cheeks.*

2. ***For a child*** (1 year to puberty):

a. Have someone call 911 to summon emergency medical assistance.

b. Check the child for a response (i.e., shake, shout).

c. Remove any vomitus or foreign objects from the mouth only if clearly visible.

d. Position the child on his back on a hard surface.

e. Immediately administer 30 quick chest compressions by placing the heel of your hand over the lower half of the breast bone; each compression should depress the chest by approximately one-third of its depth (2 inches [5.1 cm]). Allow the chest to return to its normal position between compressions.

f. Open the airway using the head tilt-chin lift. Gently pinch the nostrils closed and place your open mouth over the victim's open mouth, forming a tight seal. Give 2 breaths of air (1 second per breath), pausing between breaths to make sure air is going into the child's lungs.

g. Continue cycles of 30 chest compressions followed by 2 breaths (30:2) until the child resumes breathing or emergency help arrives.

DO NOT STOP OR GIVE UP! Continue administering CPR (30 compressions, 2 breaths) until the infant or child is breathing or emergency medical service personnel arrive. If air does not appear to be entering the lungs or the chest does not rise and fall while administering CPR, check the mouth and airway for foreign objects. Only remove the object if it is clearly visible and easy to reach. (Refer to section 9.3b, Foreign Body Airway Obstruction.) If the child resumes breathing, keep her lying down and roll (as a unit) onto one side; this is called the **recovery position** (Figure 9–4). Placing a child in the recovery position helps keep the airway open and decreases the risk of aspiration and choking. Maintain body temperature by covering with a light blanket, and continue to monitor the child's breathing closely until medical help arrives.

FIGURE 9–4 Placing a child in the recovery position prevents aspiration and choking.

---

aspiration – *accidental inhalation of food, fluid, or an object into the respiratory tract.*
recovery position – *placing an individual in a side-lying position*

TEACHER CHECKLIST 9-3

Teacher Checklist: Foods Commonly Linked to Childhood Choking

raw carrots	seeds (sunflower), peanuts,
hot dogs	and other nuts
pieces of raw apple	chewy cookies
grapes (whole)	cough drops
fruit seeds and pits	chewing gum
gummy or hard candies	hard pretzels
peanut butter sandwich	popcorn

TeachSource Digital Download Download from CourseMate.

Occasionally, families of children with special medical problems or life-threatening conditions make a decision not to have their child resuscitated and will obtain a Do Not Attempt to Resuscitate (DNAR) order from their physician. A copy of this document should be kept on file and honored in the event of a breathing emergency. School personnel should be made aware of the family's request.

9-3b Foreign Body Airway Obstruction

Children under 5 years of age account for nearly 90 percent of deaths due to airway obstruction (Kaushal et al., 2011). More than 66 percent of these deaths occur in infants. Certain foods (Teacher Checklist 9-3) and small objects (Teacher Checklist 9-4) are the most common causes of aspiration and should not be accessible to children under age 5 without supervision (Sih et al., 2012). However, developmental delays and disabilities may place some older children at higher risk for choking and the need for close supervision.

In most instances, children will be successful in coughing out an aspirated object without requiring emergency intervention. It is best not to interfere as long as the child continues to cough. However, emergency lifesaving measures must be started immediately if:

- Breathing is labored or absent.
- Lips and nail beds turn blue.
- Cough is weak or ineffective.
- The child is unable to speak.
- The child becomes unresponsive.
- A high-pitched sound can be heard when the child inhales.

Respiratory infections can sometimes cause swelling and obstruction of children's airway. If this occurs, call immediately for emergency medical assistance. Time should not be wasted on attempting

TEACHER CHECKLIST 9-4

Objects Commonly Linked to Childhood Choking

latex balloons (uninflated or pieces)
small batteries (calculator, hearing aid)
magnets
marker or pen caps
paper clips
small objects (less than 1.5 inches [3.8 cm]) in diameter
toys with small pieces
coins
marbles
small balls, blocks, beads, or vending machine toys
plastic film on toys and packages

TeachSource Digital Download Download from CourseMate.

FIGURE 9-5 **The infant's head should be positioned lower than the chest.**

FIGURE 9-6 **Location of fingers for chest compressions on an infant.**

techniques for clearing an airway obstruction (foreign body). They are not effective and may actually cause the child more harm. Emergency techniques to relieve an airway obstruction should be attempted only if a child is known to be choking on an object or is unconscious and not breathing after attempts have been made to open the airway and to breathe for the child.

Different emergency techniques are used to treat infants, toddlers, and older children who are choking (AHA, 2010). Attempts to retrieve the object from the child's mouth should be made only if the object is clearly visible. Extreme care must be taken not to push the object further back into the airway.

For an infant: If the object cannot be removed easily and the infant is conscious, quickly:

⫸ Have someone call 911 to summon emergency medical assistance.
⫸ Position the infant face down over the length of your arm, with the child's head lower than her chest and the head and neck supported in your hand (Figure 9–5). The infant can also be placed (face down) in your lap with the head lower than the chest.
⫸ Use the heel of your hand to give five quick back blows between the infant's shoulder blades.
⫸ Support and turn the infant over, face up, with the head held lower than the chest.
⫸ Give five chest thrusts. Place two fingers just below the nipple line (Figure 9–6). Rapidly compress the infant's chest approximately 1/2–1 inch (1.3–2.5 cm); release pressure completely between thrusts, allowing the chest to return to its normal position.
⫸ Look inside the child's mouth for the foreign object. If clearly visible and reachable, remove it.
⫸ Repeat the steps, alternating five back blows and five chest thrusts until the object is dislodged and the infant begins to cry or lose consciousness.

> ⚠ **CAUTION**
>
> *Do not use excessive force as this could injure the infant.*

For the child: If the object cannot be removed easily and the child is conscious, quickly:

⫸ Call 911 to summon emergency medical assistance.
⫸ Administer the Heimlich maneuver. Stand or kneel behind the child with your arms around the child's waist (Figure 9–7).
⫸ Make a fist with one hand, thumbs tucked in.
⫸ Place the fisted hand (thumb-side) against the child's abdomen, midway between the base of the rib cage (xiphoid process) and the navel.
⫸ Press your fisted hand into the child's abdomen with a quick, inward and upward thrust.
⫸ Continue to repeat abdominal thrusts until the object is dislodged or the child regains consciousness.
⫸ If the child loses consciousness and is still breathing, lower him to the floor and continue to administer abdominal thrusts until the object is dislodged (Figure 9–8).

If the infant or child LOSES CONSCIOUSNESS AND IS NOT BREATHING:

⫸ Have someone call 911 for emergency medical assistance (if this has not already been done).
⫸ Place the child on the floor or other hard surface on his back and begin CPR immediately (30 chest compressions, open the airway, and give 2 rescue breaths).

FIGURE 9-7 The Heimlich maneuver.

Stand or kneel behind the child with your arms around the child's waist.

Make a fist with one hand. Place the fisted hand against the child's abdomen below the tip of the rib cage, slightly above the navel.

Grasp the fisted hand with your other hand. Press your fists into the child's abdomen with a quick upward thrust.

▶ Continue the cycle of chest compressions and rescue breaths until emergency help arrives.

The AHA suggests that CPR chest compressions alone are sufficient to dislodge an object in the airway. Look inside of the child's mouth (for the foreign object) before each cycle of breaths is given and remove only if the object is visible.

If the infant or child begins to breathe on her own, stop CPR and continue to monitor the child closely until emergency medical personnel arrive. Roll the child (as a unit) onto his side (recovery position). Always be sure the child receives follow-up medical attention after the object has been dislodged and breathing is restored.

FIGURE 9-8 Heimlich maneuver with child lying down.

9-3c Anaphylaxis: Life-Threatening Allergic Reaction

A severe allergic reaction to an allergen such as food, medication, insect bite, or latex can cause some children (and adults) to experience a life-threatening condition known as anaphylaxis or anaphylactic shock. It is essential that teachers be aware of children who are predisposed to this condition and work closely with their families to establish emergency plans (Ercan et al., 2012). The symptoms of an anaphylactic reaction usually develop within minutes of exposure to the offending allergen and include:

▶ difficulty breathing, talking, and/or swallowing
▶ wheezing and/or cough
▶ hives
▶ swelling of the lips, tongue, eyes, and/or face
▶ abdominal pain, nausea, and/or vomiting
▶ dizziness, confusion
▶ slurred speech
▶ unusual restlessness or agitation

Anaphylaxis requires immediate treatment:

▶ Lay the child down and keep her as quiet as possible. If breathing is difficult, allow the child to sit up.
▶ Call 911 at once.
▶ If the child has injectable epinephrine (EpiPen), administer it immediately.
▶ Do not give the child any food or fluids to drink.
▶ Monitor breathing closely; begin CPR if breathing stops.

The family should be contacted as soon as the child is stable so they can seek medical attention. In some cases, the child may require a second dose of epinephrine because the medication's effects will begin to wear off.

9-3d Shock

Shock frequently accompanies injuries, especially those that are severe, and should therefore be anticipated. However, it can also result from extreme emotional upset and injuries, such as bleeding, pain, heat exhaustion, poisoning, burns, and fractures. Shock is considered a life-threatening condition that requires prompt emergency treatment. Early indicators of shock include:

▶ skin that is pale, cool, and clammy
▶ confusion, anxiety, restlessness
▶ increased perspiration
▶ weakness
▶ rapid, shallow breathing

Signs of more serious shock may develop, and include:

▶ rapid, weak pulse
▶ bluish discoloration around lips, nails, and ear lobes
▶ dilated pupils
▶ extreme thirst
▶ nausea and vomiting
▶ unconsciousness

To treat a child in shock:

1. Have someone call 911 for emergency medical assistance.
2. Quickly assess the child to identify what may have caused the shock (e.g., bleeding, poisoning, broken bone) and treat the cause first.
3. Keep the child lying down.
4. **Elevate** the child's feet 8 to 10 inches, if there is no indication of back injuries or fractures to the legs or head.
5. Maintain body heat by covering the child lightly with a blanket.
6. Moisten a clean cloth and use it for wetting the lips and mouth if the child complains of thirst; do not give food or fluids.
7. Stay calm and reassure the child until emergency medical help arrives.
8. Observe the child's breathing closely; begin CPR if the child is unresponsive and stops breathing.

9-3e Asthma

Asthma is a chronic disorder of the respiratory system characterized by periods of wheezing, gasping, and labored breathing. Numerous factors are known to trigger an acute asthma attack, including allergic reactions, respiratory infections, emotional stress, air pollutants, and physical exertion (Pawankar et al., 2012; Price et al., 2012). Asthma attacks make breathing intensely difficult and, therefore, must be treated as a life-threatening event (Allen et al., 2012). Schools should have an action plan in place for any child with a known history of asthma. (See Chapter 4).

Remaining calm and confident during a child's asthmatic attack is crucial. To treat a child who is having an asthma attack:

> **Did You Know...**
> that every day approximately 36,000 children are absent from school due to asthma? In a given school year, it is estimated that children miss more than 14 million days because of an asthma attack. This makes asthma a major cause of school absenteeism.

1. Call 911 to summon emergency medical help immediately if the child shows signs of anxiety, wheezing, restlessness, loss of consciousness, or blue discoloration of the nail beds or lips. Fatigue, inability to recognize teachers, or loss of consciousness are dangerous signs of impending respiratory failure or cardiac arrest.
2. Reassure the child.
3. Administer any medications (such as an inhaler) prescribed for the child's acute asthmatic symptoms immediately.
4. Encourage the child to relax and breathe slowly and deeply. (Anxiety makes breathing more difficult.)
5. Have the child assume a position that is most comfortable. (Breathing is usually easier when sitting or standing up.)
6. Notify the child's family.

9-3f Bleeding

Occasionally, children receive injuries, such as a deep gash or head laceration, that will bleed profusely. Severe bleeding requires prompt emergency treatment. Again, it is extremely important that the teacher act quickly, yet remain calm. To stop bleeding:

1. Summon emergency medical assistance immediately if bleeding comes in spurts or is profuse and cannot be stopped.
2. Follow universal infection control precautions (wear disposable gloves, wash hands, seal and dispose of contaminated items, clean and disinfect surfaces).

elevate – to raise to a higher position.

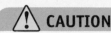 **CAUTION**

Tourniquets should be used only as a last resort and with the understanding that the extremity will probably need to be amputated.

3. Place a **sterile** gauze pad or clean material over the wound.
4. Apply firm pressure (5–10 minutes) directly over the site, using the flat parts of the fingers; do not let up, as bleeding may resume.
5. Place additional pads on top of the first bandage if blood soaks through. Do not remove the original gauze pad; bleeding may resume if the wound is disturbed.
6. Secure the gauze pad(s) in place with tape or an elastic bandage when bleeding has stopped.

Save all blood-soaked dressings. Doctors will use them to estimate the amount of blood loss. Contact the child's family when bleeding is under control and advise them to seek prompt medical attention.

9-3g Diabetes

Two potentially life-threatening emergencies associated with diabetes are hypoglycemia and hyperglycemia. Teachers must be able to quickly distinguish between these two conditions in order to determine appropriate emergency measures (American Diabetes Association, 2012). The causes and symptoms associated with these complications are often opposites of each other (Teacher Checklist 9-5).

✓✓ TEACHER CHECKLIST 9-5

Teacher Checklist: Signs and Symptoms of Hyperglycemia and Hypoglycemia

Hyperglycemia (diabetic coma)	Hypoglycemia (insulin reaction)
Causes	**Causes**
High blood sugar caused by too little available insulin, improper diet, illness, stress, or omitted dose of insulin	Low blood sugar caused by too much insulin, insufficient amounts of carbohydrates, increased activity, decreased food intake, and illness
Symptoms	**Symptoms**
• Slow, gradual onset • Slow, deep breathing • Increased thirst • Skin flushed and dry • Confusion • Staggering; appears as if drunk • Drowsiness • Sweet smelling, wine-like breath odor • Nausea, vomiting • Excessive urination	• Sudden onset • Skin cool, clammy, and pale • Dizziness • Shakiness • Nausea • Headache • Hunger • Rapid, shallow breathing • Confusion, abrupt moodiness • Seizures • Unconsciousness
Treatment	**Treatment**
Summon emergency medical assistance. Keep the child quiet and warm.	Summon emergency medical assistance if the child's state of consciousness is altered. If conscious and alert, quickly administer orange juice or a concentrated glucose source, such as glucose tablets or gel. If unconscious, maintain airway, summon emergency medical assistance, or rush the child to the nearest hospital.

sterile – *free from living microorganisms.*

Hypoglycemia, or insulin reaction, is caused by low glucose (blood sugar) levels. It can occur whenever a diabetic child either receives an excessive dose of insulin or an insufficient amount of food. Other causes may include illness, delayed eating times, or increased activity. Similar symptoms are experienced by nondiabetic children when they become overly hungry. Hypoglycemia can often be quickly reversed by administering a sugar substance. Orange juice is ideal for this purpose because it is absorbed rapidly by the body. Regular soda (not diet) or 1–2 tablespoons of honey mixed into a small amount of water will also work. Concentrated glucose gel or tablets can also be purchased and used for emergency purposes. Hard candies, such as Life Savers® or lollipops, should not be used because a child could easily choke.

Hyperglycemia (which can lead to diabetic coma), results when too much sugar is circulating in the blood stream, and is a potential complication for children who have diabetes. Illness, infection, emotional stress, poor dietary control, fever, or a dose of insulin that is too small or forgotten can lead to hyperglycemia. Local emergency medical assistance should be contacted immediately if a child who has diabetes develops symptoms of hyperglycemia. Emergency treatment usually requires medical personnel to administer intravenous (IV) insulin. The child's family should be notified so they can consult with their health care provider.

9-3h Drowning

Drowning is a leading cause of unintentional death among young children (Laosse, Gilchrist, & Rudd, 2012). For this reason, every parent and teacher should complete basic CPR training. Even small amounts of water, such as toilet bowls, buckets, wading pools, bathtubs, outdoor water features, and fish ponds pose a serious danger. Poor muscle coordination and large upper body proportion make it difficult for young children to escape from water hazards. Older children who drown often have overestimated their swimming abilities or engaged in unsafe water activities.

CPR must be started as soon as the child is removed from the water. If the rescuer is alone, she should complete five cycles of chest compressions and rescue breaths (30:2) before calling 911. The child may vomit during **resuscitation** attempts because large amounts of water are often swallowed.

CONNECTING TO EVERYDAY PRACTICE

Water Safety

Several times each month, the Arizona 5 o'clock news and local newspapers carry heartbreaking stories of childhood drownings. More often than not, the victim is a toddler who momentarily escapes a parent's watchful eye, wanders through an unlocked gate, and falls into a residential swimming pool. Although current regulations require new houses and pool installations to meet strict building codes, many existing homes do not have these safety features in place. However, pools and spas are not the only water hazards that contribute to childhood drowning.

Think About This:

- What water sources are present in and around most homes that could contribute to a potential childhood drowning?
- What characteristics place the toddler at greater risk for drowning?
- What safety measures should be taken to protect children from drowning in residential pools or spas?
- How would you care for a toddler who has just been pulled from the water and is unconscious?
- What safety rules and regulations are pool owners in your community required to follow?

resuscitation – *to revive from unconsciousness or death; to restore breathing and heartbeat.*

To reduce the risk of choking, the child should be placed in a recovery position (side-lying) and observed closely for signs of shock. Even if a child appears to have fully recovered from a near drowning incident, medical care should be obtained immediately. Complications, such as pneumonia, can develop from water, chemicals, or debris remaining in the lungs.

9-3i Electrical Shock

Exposure to electrical shock can be a life-threatening condition in children. Although it is a natural reaction to immediately want to grab the child, this must never be attempted until the main electrical source has been turned off or disconnected. This can be accomplished by unplugging the cord, removing the appropriate fuse from the fuse box, or turning off the main breaker switch. Always stand on something dry such as a board or cardboard while attempting to rescue the child (after the electrical source has been turned off) if there is water in the area.

Severe electrical shock can cause breathing to cease, surface burns, deep tissue injury, symptoms of shock, and the heart to stop beating (cardiac arrest). To treat an infant or young child who has received an electrical shock:

1. Have someone call 911while you attend to the child.
2. Check the child's breathing.
3. Begin CPR immediately if the child is not breathing.
4. Observe for, and treat, signs of shock and burns.
5. Have the child transported to a medical facility as quickly as possible.

9-3j Head Injuries

Head injury can occur from a bump, blow, or force that directly strikes the skull. Serious complications such as internal bleeding and swelling, can accompany any head injury, including those that may initially appear to be minor. These developments can occur within minutes, hours, or even several days following the initial injury (Bailey et al., 2012; Hockenberry & Wilson, 2012). Large-scale campaigns have recently been launched to increase public awareness and knowledge about the potential dangers of head injury and concussion. Early warning signs of mild to moderate head injury may include:

- repeated or forceful vomiting
- bleeding or clear fluid coming from nose or ears
- disorientation (e.g., confusion, aggressive behavior, apathy)
- loss of consciousness
- drowsiness
- severe headache

Symptoms associated with more severe head injury may appear immediately or several hours later, including:

- weakness or **paralysis**
- poor balance, coordination, or gait
- unequal size of the pupils of the eye (Figure 9–9)
- slurred speech
- blurred or double vision
- seizures
- an area of increasing swelling beneath the scalp
- unexplained restlessness or agitation

If any of these signs or symptoms are observed, call 911 to summon emergency medical services and contact the child's family immediately.

paralysis – *temporary or permanent loss of sensation, function, or voluntary movement of a body part.*

Children who receive even a minor blow or bump to the head should not be moved until it can be determined that there are no fractures or additional injuries. If the injury does not appear to be serious, the child should be encouraged to rest or play quietly for the next few hours. Always inform families of any blow or injury to a child's head regardless of how insignificant it may seem at the time. It is important to continue observing the child closely during the next 24 to 48 hours for any changes in behavior or appearance that may indicate the development of complications.

Scalp wounds have a tendency to bleed profusely, causing even minor injuries to appear more serious than they actually are. Therefore, when a child receives an injury to the scalp, it is important to avoid becoming overly alarmed at the sign of extensive bleeding. Pressure applied directly over the wound with a clean cloth or gauze dressing is usually sufficient to stop most bleeding. An ice pack can also be applied to the area to decrease swelling and pain. Families should be advised of the injury so they can continue to monitor the child's condition at home.

FIGURE 9-9 Unequal pupils may be a sign of serious head injury.

Did You Know...

that more than 1.7 million concussions are suffered in the United States each year? Children 0 to 14 years of age are at highest risk and account for nearly half a million annual emergency room visits for head injury.

9-3k Poisoning

Unintentional poisoning results when harmful substances have been inhaled, **ingested**, absorbed through the skin, or injected into the body. The majority of incidences occur in children under 6 and involve substances that have been swallowed (MMWR, 2012). Signs of poisoning may develop quickly or be delayed, and can include:

- nausea or vomiting
- abdominal cramps or diarrhea
- unusual odor to breath
- skin that feels cold and clammy
- burns or visible stains around the mouth, lips, or skin
- restlessness
- difficulty breathing
- convulsions
- confusion, disorientation, apathy, or listlessness
- loss of consciousness
- seizures

The emergency treatment for accidental poisoning is determined by the type of poison the child has ingested. For this reason, it is important to provide the name of the substance and time of exposure when contacting the Poison Control Center or emergency medical personnel. Poisons are divided into three basic categories: strong acids and **alkalis**, petroleum products, and all others. Examples are included in Table 9–2.

ingested – *the process of taking food or other substances into the body through the mouth.*
alkalis – *group of bases or caustic substances that are capable of neutralizing acids to form salts.*

TABLE 9–2 **Poisonous Substances**

Strong Acid and Alkalis	Petroleum Products	All Others
bathroom, drain, and oven cleaners	charcoal lighter	medicines
battery acid	cigarette lighter fluid	plants
dishwasher soaps	furniture polish and wax	berries
lye	gasoline	cosmetics
wart and corn remover	kerosene	nail polish remover
ammonia	naphtha	insecticides
bleach	turpentine	mothballs
	floor wax	weed killers
	lamp oil	

▶❙❙ **TeachSource** Video Connections

© 2015 Cengage Learning

Working with Children Who Have Physical Disabilities

Children's physical limitations may place them at higher risk for certain types of injuries and life-threatening conditions. For this reason, teachers who work in inclusive classrooms must be prepared to respond quickly in an emergency situation. As you watch the learning video, *Maddie: Positive Collaboration Between School Professionals and Parents to Serve a Student with Physical Disabilities* consider the following questions:

1. Which of the emergency conditions described in this chapter would you expect to encounter most often in an inclusive setting?

2. Why is a positive family-school partnership especially beneficially in these situations?

Watch on CourseMate.

If a child is suspected of swallowing a poisonous substance:

▶ Quickly check for redness or burns around the child's lips, mouth, and tongue. These are indications of a chemical burn, usually caused by strong acids or alkalis. Do not give the child anything to drink; do not make the child vomit.

▶ Smell the child's breath. If the poison is a petroleum product, the odor of gasoline or kerosene will be present. Do not give the child anything to drink; do not make the child vomit.

If the child is **conscious**:

▶ Quickly try to locate the container; it will provide clues about what the child has ingested. Also, try to estimate how much of the product the child may have swallowed and the approximate time when this incident may have occurred.

▶ If you cannot locate the container, do not delay in calling Poison Control.

▶ Call the nearest Poison Control Center (1-800-222-1222) or your city's emergency number (911) and follow their instructions.

▶ Observe the child closely for signs of shock and difficulty breathing.

▶ Do not give the child anything to eat or drink unless instructed to do so.

If the child is **unconscious**:

▶ Call 911 immediately to summon emergency medical assistance.

▶ Monitor the child's airway, breathing, and circulation; administer CPR if breathing stops or is absent.

▶ Do not give the child anything to eat or drink.

▶ Position the child in the recovery position (side-lying) to prevent choking on vomited material. Continue to observe the child for signs of breathing difficulty.

Always check with the Poison Control Center and follow their instructions before attempting to treat childhood poisoning. If the child begins to vomit, keep his head lowered to prevent aspiration and choking. Contact the child's family as soon as possible.

9-4 Non–Life-Threatening Conditions

The majority of children's injuries and illnesses are not life-threatening but may require first aid. Teachers who have received proper training can administer this type of care, but they are not qualified or expected to provide comprehensive medical treatment. Initial first aid treatment of children's injuries is important for reducing complications and making children feel more comfortable until their family arrives. The remainder of this chapter addresses conditions typically encountered by young children that may require first aid care.

Did You Know...
that cleaning scrapes and abrasions from the center outward with an increasingly larger circular motion reduces the risk of infection?

9-4a Abrasions, Cuts, and Minor Skin Wounds

Minor cuts, scrapes, and abrasions are among the most common types of injury young children experience. First aid care is concerned primarily with the control of bleeding and the prevention of infection. To care for the child who has received a simple skin wound:

1. Follow universal infection control precautions, including the use of disposable gloves.
2. Apply direct pressure to the wound, using a clean cloth or sterile pad to stop any bleeding.
3. Wash the wound under running water for at least 5 minutes or until all foreign particles have been removed.
4. Cover the wound with a sterile bandage. A thin layer of antibiotic ointment can be applied to superficial abrasions if permitted.
5. Apply a cold pack, wrapped in a disposable paper towel or plastic bag, to the area; this can help slow bleeding and reduce pain and swelling.
6. Inform the child's family of the injury. Advise them to check on the child's tetanus immunization and to watch for signs of infection (e.g., warmth, redness, swelling, drainage).
7. Record the incident.

Puncture-type wounds and cuts that are deep or ragged require medical attention because of the increased risk of infection. Stitches may be needed to close a gash greater than 1/2 inch (1.3 cm), especially if it is located on the child's face, chest, or back.

9-4b Bites

Human and animal bites are painful and can lead to serious infection (Boat, 2012). The possibility of rabies should be considered with any animal bite that is unprovoked, unless the animal is known to be free of the virus. A suspected animal should be confined and observed by a veterinarian. In cases where the bite was provoked, the animal is not as likely to be rabid. First aid care for human and animal bites includes the following:

1. Follow universal infection control precautions, including the use of disposable gloves.
2. Allow the wound to bleed for a short while if the skin is broken (to remove any saliva) before applying direct pressure to stop bleeding.

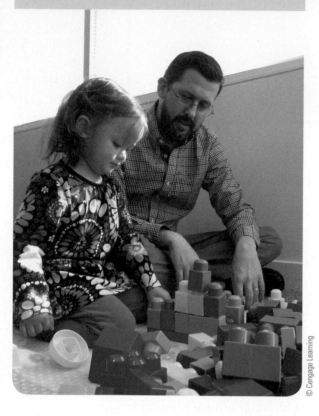

▼ **Families must always be informed of children's injuries.**

© Cengage Learning

3. Cleanse the wound thoroughly with soap and water or hydrogen peroxide and cover with a clean dressing.
4. Notify the child's family and advise them to have the wound checked by the child's physician.
5. Notify local law enforcement authorities immediately if the injury is due to an animal bite; provide a description of the animal and its location (unless it is a classroom pet).
6. Record the incident.

Most insect bites cause little more than local skin irritations. However, some children are extremely sensitive to certain insects, especially bees, hornets, wasps, and spiders. Signs of severe allergic reaction (anaphylaxis) include:

▶ sudden difficulty breathing
▶ joint pain (delayed reaction)
▶ abdominal cramps
▶ vomiting
▶ fever
▶ red, swollen eyes
▶ hives or generalized itching
▶ shock
▶ weakness or unconsciousness
▶ swollen tongue

Allergic reactions to insect bites can be life-threatening and require immediate emergency treatment. (See the "9.3c Anaphylaxis: Life-Threatening Allergic Reaction" section in this chapter for emergency procedures.) First aid treatment for insect bites is aimed at relieving discomfort and preventing infection. If a stinger remains in the skin, an attempt should be made to remove it by scraping the area with the back of a flatware knife or clean credit card (removing with a tweezers may inject more venom into the skin). The area should then be washed and a cold pack applied to decrease swelling and pain. Calamine lotion or a paste of baking soda and water applied to the area will also provide temporary pain relief.

9-4c Blisters

A blister is a collection of infection-fighting fluid (white blood cells) that builds up beneath the skin's surface. Blisters most commonly develop from rubbing or friction, burns, or allergic reactions.

First aid care of blisters is aimed at protecting the affected area from infection. Efforts should be made to avoid breaking a blister. However, if it does break, wash the area with soap and water and cover with a bandage.

9-4d Bruises

Bruises result when small blood vessels rupture beneath the skin. They are often caused by falls, bumps, and blows. Fair-skinned children tend to bruise more easily. First aid care is designed to control subsurface bleeding and swelling. Apply a cold pack to the bruised area for 15 to 20 minutes and repeat three to four times during the next 24 hours. Later, warm moist packs can be applied several times daily to improve circulation and healing. Alert the child's family to watch for signs of infection or unusual bleeding if the bruising is extensive or severe.

Teacher Checklist: Burns—When to Call for Emergency Medical Assistance (911)

Always call for emergency medical assistance if:

- A child or elderly person is involved.
- The victim experiences any difficulty breathing.
- Burned areas are located on the face, head, neck, feet, hands, or genitalia.
- Multiple areas of the body have been burned.
- Burned area is larger than 2 to 3 inches (5.1 to 7.6 cm).
- Chemicals, electrical current, smoke, or an explosion has caused the burn.

TeachSource Digital Download Download from CourseMate.

9-4e Burns

Burns occur when body surfaces come in contact with heat, electrical current, or chemicals. Several factors affect the severity of an accidental burn and the need to call for emergency medical assistance, including the source, temperature of the source, affected body part or area, length of exposure, and victim's age and size (Teacher Checklist 9-6).

Burns are always considered more serious when they are sustained by children due to their smaller body surface area (De Young et al., 2012; Hockenberry & Wilson, 2012). Burns caused by heat are classified according to the degree (depth and extent) of tissue damage:

- first degree – Surface skin is red with some pain and swelling.
- second degree – Surface skin is red and blistered with swelling and severe pain.
- third degree – Burn is deep; skin and underlying tissues may be brown, white, or charred. Pain is often minimal, but these burns require emergency medical attention—call for help immediately.

First aid care of minor burns (first and second degree) that cover less than 3 inches (7.6 cm) of surface area includes the following:

1. Use caution to protect yourself from the heat source.
2. Quickly **submerge** the burned areas in cool water, hold under running water, or cover with a cool, wet towel for 5 to 10 minutes. Cool water temperatures reduce the depth of a burn as well as lessen swelling and pain.
3. Cover the burn with a sterile gauze dressing and tape in place. Do not use greasy ointments because dirt and bacteria can collect in these creams and increase the risk of infection.
4. Elevate the burned extremity to relieve discomfort.
5. Burns that involve feet, face, hands, or genitals, cover a large area (greater than 2 to 3 inches/5.1 to 7.6 cm) or cause moderate blistering are critical and require immediate medical attention. Families should be advised to contact the child's health care provider.

In the case of third degree burns, stop the burning process but do not attempt to cool the burn or to remove burnt clothing. Cover any open areas with a dry, sterile dressing and call immediately for emergency medical assistance.

Chemical burns should be rinsed for 10 to 15 minutes under cool, running water. Put on gloves and gently remove any clothing that may still have the chemical on it. Call for emergency medical assistance or the nearest Poison Control Center for further instructions. The child's family should also be advised to contact their health care provider.

Burns caused by smoke or electrical current require immediate medical attention and should not be cooled with water.

submerge – *to place in water*

9-4f Eye Injuries

Most eye injuries are not serious and can be treated by teachers. However, because eyes are delicate structures, it is important to know how to properly care for different types of injuries. Families should always be informed of any injury to a child's eye(s) so they can continue to observe and consult with a physician if they have concerns.

A sudden blow to the eye from a snowball, wooden block, or other hard object can be quite painful. First aid treatment includes the following:

1. Keep the child quiet.
2. Apply a cold pack to the eye for 15 minutes if there is no bleeding.
3. Use direct pressure to control any bleeding around the eye. Do not apply pressure to the eyeball itself. Cleanse and cover skin wounds with a sterile gauze pad.
4. Summon emergency medical assistance at once if the child complains of inability to see or is seeing spots or flashes of light.
5. Inform the child's family about any blow to the eye so they can continue to monitor the child's condition.
6. Record the incident.

Foreign particles such as sand, cornmeal, or specks of dust frequently find their way into children's eyes. Although children may want to rub their eyes, this must be discouraged to prevent the eyeball from becoming scratched. Spontaneous tearing is often sufficient to wash out the object. If the particle is visible, it can also be removed with the corner of a clean cloth or by flushing the eye with saline eye wash solution or lukewarm water. If the particle cannot be removed easily, the eye should be covered and medical attention sought.

An object that penetrates the eyeball must never be removed (Kelly & Reeves, 2012). Place a paper cup, funnel, or small cardboard box over both the object and the eye. Cover the uninjured eye with a gauze pad and secure both dressings (cup and gauze pad) in place by wrapping an elastic roller bandage around the head. Movement of the injured eyeball should be kept to a minimum and can be achieved by covering both eyes. Seek immediate medical treatment.

A thin cut on the eye's surface can result from a piece of paper, toy, or child's fingernail. Injuries of this type cause severe pain and tearing. Both of the child's eyes should be covered with a gauze dressing and the child's family advised to seek immediate medical attention.

Chemical burns to a child's eye are very serious (Blackburn et al., 2012). Ask another staff member to call 911 immediately for emergency medical assistance so the child can be transported to the nearest medical facility. Begin immediately to flush the child's eye with lukewarm water or saline eye wash solution. Tip the child's head toward the affected eye and use a small bulb syringe or bottle to rinse the eye for at least 15 minutes. Meanwhile, contact the child's family.

Did You Know...

that picking up or swinging children by their arms can easily cause joints to dislocate? This is a painful injury that requires prompt medical treatment.

9-4g Fractures

A fracture is a break or crack in a bone. It is always best to treat an injured extremity as if it were broken until the child can be examined by a health care provider. A child who sustains a mild break may be able to move the injured part and present few notable symptoms. The only way to confirm a fracture is by X-ray. Signs of a potential fracture may include:

- particular areas of extreme pain or tenderness
- an unusual shape or deformity of the bone
- a break in the skin with visible bone edges protruding
- swelling
- a change in skin color around the injury site
- numbness or a tingling sensation

A child who complains of pain after falling should not be moved, especially if a back or neck injury is suspected.

1. Have someone call 911 immediately for emergency medical assistance.
2. Keep the child warm and observe carefully for signs of shock.
3. Do not give the child anything to eat or drink in the event that surgery is necessary.
4. Stop any bleeding by applying direct pressure.
5. Contact the child's family and record the incident.

If no emergency medical help is available, only persons with prior first aid training should attempt to splint a fracture before the child is moved. Splints can be purchased from medical supply stores or improvised from items such as a rolled-up magazine, pillow or blanket, a ruler, or a piece of board. Never attempt to straighten a fractured bone. Call 911 at once if the injured extremity turns blue or pale. Cover open wounds with a sterile pad but do not attempt to clean the wound. Elevate the splinted part on a pillow and apply an ice pack to reduce swelling and pain. Observe the child closely for signs of shock and contact the child's family immediately so they can notify their physician.

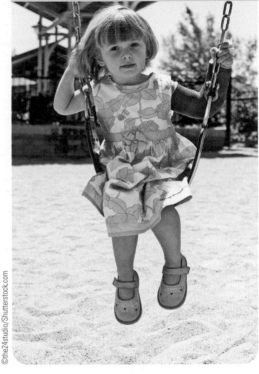

▼ **If a child shows any signs of a potential fracture, always treat the bone as if it were broken until ruled out by X-ray.**

©the24studio/Shutterstock.com

9-4h Frostbite and Hypothermia

Frostbite results when body tissues freeze from exposure to extremely cold temperatures. Exposed areas such as ears, nose, fingers, and toes are especially prone to frostbite, particularly if clothing or shoes become wet. Frostbite can develop within minutes, causing the skin to take on a hard, waxy, gray-white appearance with or without blisters. For this reason, infants and young children should be monitored closely during cold weather so they don't remove hats, boots, or mittens. Initially, the child may experience considerable pain or have no discomfort. However, when tissues begin to warm, there is often a tingling and painful sensation. First aid treatment for minor frostbite consists of the following:

- Bring the child indoors and into a warm room.
- Remove wet clothing; replace with dry clothing or wrap the child in blankets for warmth.
- Do not rewarm the affected part(s) unless medical care is unavailable.
- Handle the frostbitten part(s) with care; avoid rubbing or massaging the area as this could further damage frozen tissue.
- Elevate the affected area(s) to ease pain and prevent swelling.
- Contact the child's family and encourage them to seek medical care for the child.
- Record the incident.

Exposure to cold temperatures can also cause **hypothermia**, a drop in body temperature that slows heart rate, respirations, and metabolism. This slowing of body functions reduces the amount of available oxygen and can lead to shivering, drowsiness, loss of consciousness, and cardiac arrest. Emergency medical personnel should be summoned at once.

hypothermia – *below-normal body temperature caused by overexposure to cold conditions.*

9-4i Heat Exhaustion and Heat Stroke

First aid treatment of a heat-related illness requires the teacher to distinguish between heat exhaustion and heat stroke. A child who has lost considerable fluid through sweating and is overheated may be suffering from **heat exhaustion**. The following symptoms would be observed:

- skin is pale, cool, and moist with perspiration
- weakness, dizziness, or fainting
- thirst
- nausea
- abdominal or muscle cramps
- headache
- normal or below-normal body temperature

Heat exhaustion is not considered life-threatening, but can become a serious condition if it is not treated quickly. It usually occurs when a child has been playing vigorously in extreme heat or humidity. First aid treatment for heat exhaustion is similar to that for shock:

1. Have the child lie down in a cool place.
2. Elevate the child's feet 8–10 inches (20–25 cm).
3. Loosen or remove the child's clothing.
4. Sponge the child's face and body with tepid (lukewarm) water or spray with cool water.
5. Offer frequent sips of cool water.

Heat stroke is a life-threatening condition that requires immediate treatment. The child's temperature begins to rise quickly and dangerously as perspiration stops and the body's temperature-regulating mechanism fails (Mattis & Yates, 2011). For example, children left in a parked car with the windows rolled up on a warm day (70°F and over) can quickly develop heat stroke and die (Figure 9–10). Symptoms of heat stroke include:

- high body temperature (102–106°F; 38.8–41.1°C)
- dry, flushed skin
- headache or confusion
- seizures
- diarrhea, abdominal cramps
- loss of consciousness
- shock

Emergency treatment for heat stroke is aimed at cooling the child as quickly as possible:

1. Call 911 to summon emergency medical assistance at once.
2. Move the child to a cool place and remove outer clothing.
3. Place the child in a shallow tub of cold water or gently spray her with a garden hose. Do not leave child unattended!
4. Elevate the child's legs to decrease the potential for shock.
5. Offer small sips of cool water only if the child is fully conscious; do not force.
6. Notify the child's family and record the incident.

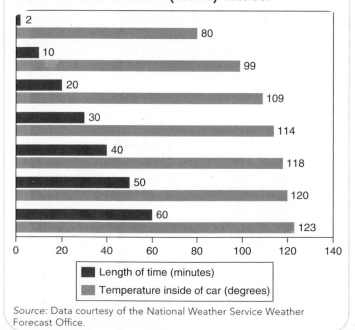

FIGURE 9–10 How quickly temperatures rise inside a closed car when it is 80°F (26.7°C) outside.

2	80
10	99
20	109
30	114
40	118
50	120
60	123

- Length of time (minutes)
- Temperature inside of car (degrees)

Source: Data courtesy of the National Weather Service Weather Forecast Office.

---

heat exhaustion – *overheating that occurs when a person is exposed to high outdoor temperatures. and humidity during vigorous activity*
heat stroke – *failure of the body's sweating reflex to function properly during exposure to high temperatures; causes body temperature to rise*

9-4j Nosebleeds

Accidental bumps, allergies, nose picking, or sinus congestion can all cause a child's nose to bleed. Most nosebleeds are not serious and can be stopped quickly. However, if a nosebleed continues for more than 30 minutes, get medical help. To stop a nosebleed, do the following:

▼ **Firmly grasp and squeeze the child's nostrils to stop a nosebleed.**

© Cengage Learning

1. Place the child in a sitting position, with his head tilted slightly forward, to prevent any swallowing of blood. Ask the child to breathe through her mouth.
2. Follow universal infection control precautions, including the use of disposable gloves.
3. Firmly grasp the child's nostrils (lower half) and squeeze together for at least 5 minutes before releasing the pressure.
4. If bleeding continues, pinch the nostrils together for another 10 minutes.
5. Once the bleeding has stopped, avoid nose-blowing and encourage the child to play quietly for the next hour or so to prevent the bleeding from resuming.
6. Advise parents to discuss the problem with the child's health care provider if nosebleeds occur repeatedly.
7. Record the incident.

9-4k Seizures

Infants and young children experience seizures for a variety of reasons. Simple precautionary measures can be taken during and immediately after a seizure to protect a child from injury and should include the following:

1. Call 911 for emergency medical assistance if this is the first time a child has experienced a seizure. If the child has a known seizure disorder, call for emergency help if the seizure lasts longer than 3 to 4 minutes or the child experiences severe difficulty breathing or stops breathing.
2. Encourage the other children and adults to remain calm.
3. Carefully lower the child to the floor. Protect the child's head from striking the floor or nearby objects by placing a small pillow or item of soft clothing under the child's head.
4. Move furniture and other objects out of the way.
5. Do not hold the child down.
6. Do not attempt to force any protective device into the child's mouth.
7. Loosen tight clothing around the child's neck and waist to make breathing easier.
8. Observe closely to make sure the child is breathing.
9. Place the child in the recovery position (side-lying) with head slightly elevated when the seizure ends. This prevents choking by allowing oral secretions to drain out of the mouth.
10. Inform the child's family and record the incident.

When the seizure has ended, move the child to a quiet area and encouraged him to rest or sleep. An adult should continue to monitor the child closely.

9-4l Splinters

Most splinters under the skin's surface can be easily removed with a sterilized needle and tweezers. (Only bleach or alcohol should be used to clean the instruments.) Clean the skin with soap and water or alcohol before and after removing the splinter. Cover the area with a bandage. If the splinter is very deep, do not attempt to remove it; inform the child's family to seek medical attention and to make sure the child's tetanus immunization is current.

9-4m Sprains

A sprain is caused by injury to the ligaments and tissue surrounding a joint and often results in pain and considerable swelling. In most cases, only an X-ray can confirm whether an injury is a sprain or fracture. If there is any doubt, it is always best to splint the injury and treat it as if it were broken. Elevate the injured part and apply ice packs intermittently for 15 to 20 minutes at a time for several hours. Notify the child's family and encourage them to have the child examined by a physician.

9-4n Tick Bites

Ticks are small, oval-shaped insects that generally live in wooded areas and on wild animals and dogs. On humans, ticks frequently attach themselves to the scalp or base of the neck. However, the child is seldom aware of the tick's presence. Diseases, such as Rocky Mountain spotted fever and Lyme disease, are rare but serious complications of a tick bite (Hamlen, 2012). If a child develops chills, fever, or rash following a known tick bite, medical treatment should be sought at once.

Ticks must be removed carefully. Grasp the tick closely to the skin with tweezers, pulling steadily and straight out to remove all body parts; do not squeeze or twist. Wash the area thoroughly with soap and water and apply a disinfectant such as alcohol. The child's family should be advised to observe the site closely for several days and to contact their health care provider if any signs of infection or rash develop.

9-4o Tooth Emergencies

The most common injuries to children's teeth involve chipping or loosening of a tooth. Blood may be involved, so universal infection control precautions must be followed when caring for the child or handling the tooth. A tooth that has been knocked loose by a blow or fall will often retighten itself within several days. Care should be taken to keep the tooth and gum tissue clean, avoid chewing on hard foods, and watch for signs of infection (redness, swelling).

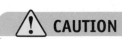

⚠ CAUTION

To avoid accidental choking, do not attempt to reinsert the tooth into the socket or have a child hold the tooth in place.

If a tooth has been completely dislodged, the child should be seen by a dentist and monitored for signs of infection. Although dentists will seldom attempt to replace a baby tooth, it is important to save the tooth and send it home with the child. Dentists are more apt to reimplant children's permanent teeth, but this process requires prompt emergency treatment to be successful.

- Rinse out the tooth socket (hole remaining in the gum); apply direct pressure to stop bleeding.
- Handle the tooth with care; do not to touch the root-end (part beneath the gum).
- Place the tooth in a small cup of milk or water; if this isn't available, wrap the tooth in a damp cloth.
- Get the child to a dentist or emergency room as quickly as possible (Turkistani & Hanno, 2011).

Did You Get It?

What is not a critical factor in determining whether or not to call for emergency assistance for burns?
 a. the size of the burns
 b. expressed pain associated with the burns (the amount of pain a child is experiencing)
 c. specific location of the burns
 d. degree of blistering associated with the burns

Take the full quiz on CourseMate.

PARTNERING with FAMILIES

Poison Prevention in the Home

Dear Families,

Children under the age of 6 are the most frequent victims of unintentional poisonings. Their curiosity and limited understanding often lead them unknowingly into risky situations. In many households, items such as cleaning products, garden chemicals, automobile waxes, charcoal lighter, lamp oil, and medications are commonly left in places accessible to young children. Often, simple precautions can be taken to make children's environments safe.

▶ Always place potentially dangerous substances in a locked cabinet. Don't rely on your child's ability to "know better."

▶ Supervise children closely whenever using harmful products. Take them with you if the doorbell rings or if you must leave the room.

▶ Teach children not to put anything into their mouths unless it is given to them by an adult.

▶ Test the paint on your house, walls, children's furniture, and toys to be sure it doesn't contain lead. Contact the National Lead Information Center for information (1-800-424-LEAD).

▶ Check before purchasing plants and flowers (indoor and outdoor) to make certain they are not poisonous.

▶ Insist that vitamins and medications, including those purchased over-the-counter, are in child-resistant containers. Store them in a locked cabinet.

▶ Post the number of the nearest Poison Control Center near the telephone.

▶ Caution visitors to keep purses, suitcases, and backpacks out of children's reach.

CLASSROOM CORNER

Teacher Activities

Preventing Burns

(**NHES** PreK–2; National Health Education Standards 5.2.1 and 5.2.2)

Concept: There are things that are safe to touch and play with and other things that can hurt you.

Learning Objectives

▶ Children will be able to identify items that are safe to touch and other items that are not safe.

▶ Children will explain what to do if they aren't sure that an item is safe to touch.

Supplies

▶ pictures of a stove, lighter, matches, campfire, candle, barbeque grill, ball, car, apple, crayons, a stuffed toy, and a block

▶ two pieces of string (long enough to make two big circles to sort the cards in)

▶ picture of a smiling face and a frowning face

Learning Activities

▶ Read and discuss one of the following books:

  • *Fire Fighters* by Robert Maass

(continued)

CLASSROOM CORNER

Teacher Activities *(continued)*

- *Tonka Fire Truck to the Rescue* by Ann Martin
- *What If There Is a Fire?* by Anara Guard

▸ Tell the children you are going to talk about some items that are safe to touch and play with and others that aren't safe and can hurt them.

▸ Hold up the picture cards and talk about each item.

▸ Tell the children they are to sort the picture cards according to items that are safe to touch and those that are not. Put the smiling face in the middle of one circle and the frowning face in the middle of the other.

▸ Call a child to come up and pick a card and tell the other children if it is a safe item to touch and play with or an unsafe item. Continue until all cards have been sorted.

▸ Tell the children if they are not sure an item is safe or not to ask a grownup.

Evaluation

▸ Children will name at least two items safe to touch and two items they should not touch.

▸ Children will state what to do when they aren't sure if an object is safe to touch.

Additional lesson plans for grades 3–5 are available on CourseMate.

Summary

▸ Written emergency policies and procedures enable teachers to respond quickly and effectively to children's injuries and illnesses.

- Plans should include: personnel who are trained in first aid and CPR and are available at all times when children are in attendance; emergency telephone numbers; and first aid supplies

▸ Emergency care is administered for life-threatening conditions. First aid treatment is provided for conditions not considered to be life-threatening.

- Teachers never diagnosis or offer medical advice.
- Families are responsible for obtaining follow-up medical treatment after initial emergency or first aid care has been administered.

▸ Life-threatening conditions, such as severe bleeding, absence of breathing, shock, and head injuries require immediate emergency treatment.

▸ Treatment for life-threatening conditions, such as abrasions, fractures, burns, and frost bite is aimed at alleviating pain and further complications.

◖ Terms to Know

Good Samaritan Law *p. 239*   resuscitation *p. 249*   hypothermia *p. 257*
aspiration *p. 242*   paralysis *p. 250*   heat exhaustion *p. 258*
recovery position *p. 242*   ingested *p. 251*   heat stroke *p. 258*
elevate *p. 247*   alkalis *p. 251*
sterile *p. 248*   submerge *p. 255*

◖ Chapter Review

A. By Yourself

1. Complete each of the statements with a word selected from the following list. Take the first letter from each answer and place it in the appropriate space following question (j) to spell out one of the basic principles of first aid.

activate	evaluate	emergency
breathing	plans	rescue breaths
diagnose	pressure	anaphylaxis
elevate	responsible	

   a. Always check to be sure the child is _____.

   b. The immediate care given for life-threatening conditions is called _____ care.

   c. Schools and early childhood programs should develop _____ for handling emergencies.

   d. If an infant is found unconscious and not breathing, immediately give 30 chest compressions followed by 2 _____.

   e. The first step in providing emergency care is to quickly _____ the child's condition.

   f. Bleeding can be stopped by applying direct _____.

   g. If a child is seriously injured, you would immediately _____ emergency medical services (EMS) by calling 911.

   h. Families are _____ for arranging follow-up medical treatment for a child's injuries.

   i. To treat a child for shock, you would _____ the child's legs 8 to 10 inches.

   j. Teachers never _____ or give medical advice.

   A basic principle of first aid is _ _ _ _ _ _ _ _ _ _.

2. Explain the Good Samaritan Law and the purpose it serves.

3. What clues would help you determine if a child has swallowed a petroleum-based liquid or an acid/strong alkali?

4. Describe the classification of burns and how each level should be treated.

B. As a Group

1. Explain why a child who has fallen and bumped his head must be closely monitored for the next 48 hours despite the fact that he appears to be okay.

2. Assume that you are the teacher in the following scenarios. Role-play how you would respond:
   a. Child is having a nose bleed.
   b. Child appears to be experiencing a seizure.
   c. Toddler is choking on a bead that she found on the floor.
   d. Child is having an acute asthma attack.
   e. Child was pushed off of a piece of playground equipment and fell several feet to the ground; child appears disoriented, is pale, and has cool, clammy skin.

3. Discuss why you wouldn't begin the Heimlich maneuver immediately on a child who was choking but still able to cough. At what point would you initiate this emergency measure?

4. Describe how a teacher would determine if a child who has diabetes was experiencing hypoglycemia or hyperglycemia. How does the treatment of each differ?

◖ Case Study

It was a beautiful spring morning and Myesha and Tyrell had taken their class of eager 4-year-olds outside to work in the school's newly established garden. The children had been reading books about flowers and vegetables for several weeks, purchased plants and seeds at a local market, and even helped to prepare the soil for planting. Today, they were going to weed and water the rows of lettuce, cucumbers, squash, and tomato plants that were beginning to grow. Myesha looked up from where she was working with the children and saw Jade running toward her with the watering can. Before Jade reached the garden gate, she suddenly dropped the can, fell to the sidewalk, and appeared to be having a seizure. Tyrell ran to check on Jade while Myesha tried to calm the other children.

1. What immediate measures should Tyrell take to care for Jade?

2. In what ways would his response differ if Jade had a known history of seizures or if she had never experienced a seizure prior to this one?

3. Should he notify Jade's family? At what point? Why?

4. If Jade's seizure continues longer than 3 to 4 minutes, what should the teachers do?

5. What information should Tyrell note during the seizure, observe afterwards, and record in Jade's file?

◖ Application Activities

1. Complete basic CPR and first aid courses. Volunteer to assist with first aid trainings at local school or early childhood program.

2. Design a poster or bulletin board illustrating emergency first aid for a young child who is choking. Offer your project to a local school or early childhood program where it can be displayed for families to read.

3. Divide the students into small groups. Discuss and demonstrate the emergency care or first aid treatment for each of the following situations. A child who:
   • burned several fingers on a hot plate
   • ate de-icing pellets
   • splashed turpentine in her eyes
   • fell from a climbing gym
   • is choking on popcorn
   • slammed fingers in a door
   • is found chewing on an extension cord

4. Learn how to use an EpiPen and know what precautions need to be taken.

5. Observe two to three teachers at five different schools or early childhood programs during recess or outdoor time. Record the number of children who experience an injury during this period, the type of injury sustained, and the nature of teacher supervision (i.e., proximity, attentiveness, response). Summarize your findings. Provide recommendations for measures that can be taken to prevent similar injuries in the future and for teacher inservice training.

Helpful Web Resources

Children's Safety Network (CSN)	http://www.childrenssafetynetwork.org
International Bicycle Fund (bicycle safety materials)	http://www.ibike.org/education
Learn CPR (children)	http://depts.washington.edu/learncpr/childrencpr.html
Learn CPR (infants)	http://depts.washington.edu/learncpr/infantcpr.html
Safe Kids Worldwide	http://www.safekids.org
National Safety Council	http://www.nsc.org
PoisonPrevention.org	http://www.poisonprevention.org

 Visit the Education CourseMate for this textbook to access the eBook, Did You Get It? quizzes, Digital Downloads, TeachSource Video Cases, flashcards, and more. Go to CengageBrain.com to log in, register, or purchase access.

References

Allen, K., Henselman, K., Laird, B., Quiñones, A., & Reutzel, T. (2012). Potential life-threatening events in schools involving rescue inhalers, epinephrine autoinjectors, and glucagon delivery devices: Reports from school nurses, *The Journal of School Nursing*, 28(1), 47–55.

American Public Health Association (APHA) and American Academy of Pediatrics (AAP). (2011). *Caring for our children: National health and safety performance standards for out-of-home care*. (3rd ed.). Washington, DC. Available online at http://nrckids.org/CFOC3/index.html.

American Diabetes Association. (2012). Safe at school. Accessed on June 21, 2012 from http://www.diabetes.org /living-with-diabetes/parents-and-kids/diabetes-care-at-school.

American Heart Association (AHA). (2010). 2010 American Heart Association guidelines for cardiopulmonary resuscitation and emergency cardiovascular care, *Circulation*, 122, S862–S875.

Bailey, B., Liesemer, K., Statler, K., Riva-Cambrin, J., & Bratton, S. (2012). Monitoring and prediction of intracranial hypertension in pediatric traumatic brain injury: Clinical factors and initial head computed tomography, *Journal of Trauma & Acute Care Surgery*, 72(1), 263–270.

Banghart, P. & Kreader, J. (2012). *What can CCDF learn from the research on children's health and safety in child care?* Urban Institute. Office of Planning, Research, and Evaluation. U.S. Department of Health & Human Services. Accessed June 21, 2012 from http://www.acf.hhs.gov/programs/opre/resource/what-can-ccdf-learn-from-the-research-on-childrens-health-and-safety-in-child.

Berg, M., Schexnayder, S., Chamceides, L., Terry, M., Donoghue, A., Hickey, R., Berg, R., Sutton, R., & Hazinski, M. (2010). Pediatric basic life support: 2010 American Heart Association guidelines for cardiopulmonary resuscitation and emergency cardiovascular care, *Pediatrics*, 126(5), e1345–e1360.

Blackburn, J., Levitan, E., MacLennan, P., Owsley, C., & McGwin, G. (2012). The epidemiology of chemical eye injuries, *Current Eye Research*, 37(9), 787–793.

Boat, B., Dixon, C., Pearl, E., Thieken, L., & Bucher, S. (2012). Pediatric dog bite victims, *Clinical Pediatrics*, 51(5), 473–477.

Copeland, K., Sherman, S., Kendeigh, C., Kalkwarf, H., & Saelens, B. (2012). Societal values and policies may curtail preschool children's physical activity in child care centers, *Pediatrics*, 129(2), 265–274.

De Young, A., Kenardy, J., Cobham, V., & Kimble, R. (2012). Prevalence, comorbidity, and course of trauma in young burn-injured children, *Journal of Child Psychology & Psychiatry*, 53(1), 56–63.

Ercan, H., Ozen, A., Karatepe, H., Berber, M., & Cengizlier, R. (2012). Primary school teacher's knowledge about and attitudes toward anaphylaxis, *Pediatric Allergy & Immunology*. Advanced online publication. DOI:10.1111/j.1399-3038.2012.01307.x.

Hamlen, R. (2012). Tick-borne infections—A growing public health threat to school-age children. Prevention steps that school personnel can take, *NASN School Nurse*, 27(2), 94–100.

Hockenberry, M., & Wilson, D. (2012). *Wong's essentials of pediatric nursing*. (9th ed.). New York: Mosby.

Kaushal, P., Brown, D., Lander, L., Brietzke, S., & Shah, R. (2011). Aspirated foreign bodies in pediatric patients, 1968–2010: A comparison between the United States and other countries, *International Journal of Pediatric Otorhinolaryngology*, 75(10), 1322–1326.

Kelly, S., & Reeves, G. (2012). Penetrating eye injuries from writing instruments, *Clinical Ophthalmology*, 6, 41–44.

Laosse, O., Gilchrist, J., & Rudd, R. (2012). Drowning — United States, 2005–2009, *Morbidity & Mortality Weekly Report (MMWR)*, 61(19), 344–347.

Marotz, L. (2000). Childhood and classroom injuries. In J. L. Frost (ed.), *Children and injuries*. Tuscon, AZ: Lawyers & Judges Publishing Co.

Mattis, J., & Yates, A. (2011). Heat stroke: Helping patients keep their cool, *Nurse Practitioner*, 36(5), 48–52.

Morbidity & Mortality Weekly Report (MMWR). (2012). Vital signs: Unintentional injury deaths among persons aged 0–19 years — United States, 2000–2009. Accessed on June 21, 2012 from http://www.cdc.gov/mmwr/preview /mmwrhtml/mm61e0416a1.htm.

Pawankar, R., Canonica, G., Holgate, S., & Lockey, R. (2012). Allergic diseases and asthma: A major global health concern, *Current Opinion in Allergy & Clinical Immunology*, 12(1), 39–41.

Price, K., Plante, C., Goudreau, S., Boldo, E., Perron, S., & Snargiassi, A. (2012). Risk of childhood asthma prevalence attributable to residential proximity to major roads in Montreal, Canada, *Canadian Journal of Public Health*, 103(2), 113–118.

Sih, T., Bunnag, C., Ballali, S., Lauriello, M., & Bellussi, L. (2012). Nuts and seed: A natural yet dangerous foreign body, *International Journal of Pediatric Otorhinolaryngology*, 76(Suppl.1), S49–S52.

Turkistani, J., & Hanno, A. (2011). Recent trends in the management of dentoalveolar traumatic injuries to primary and young permanent teeth, *Dental Traumatology*, 27(1), 46–54.

chapter 10

Maltreatment of Children: Abuse and Neglect

Juanmonino/Getty Images

naeyc Standards Chapter Links

▸ **#1 a, b, and c:** Promoting child development and learning
▸ **#2 a, b, and c:** Building family and community relationships
▸ **#3 a, c, and d:** Observing, documenting, and assessing to support young children and families
▸ **#4 a and c:** Using developmentally effective approaches to connect with children and families
▸ **#5 c:** Using content knowledge to build meaningful curriculum
▸ **#6 a, b, c, and e:** Becoming a professional

Learning Objectives

After studying this chapter, you should be able to:

LO 10-1 Explain the significance of Public Law 93-247.

LO 10-2 Describe how discipline and punishment differ.

LO 10-3 Provide an example of each form of abuse (physical, emotional/verbal, sexual) and neglect (physical and emotional/psychological).

LO 10-4 Describe factors that may perpetuate abusive or neglectful acts.

LO 10-5 Discuss the protective steps programs can take to avoid allegations of abuse.

LO 10-6 Identify individuals who are mandated by law to report abuse and neglect.

LO 10-7 Explain how teachers can help children who have been maltreated.

For many reasons, the true extent of **abuse** and **neglect** may never be known. Although an estimated three million cases are reported to investigative authorities in the United States each year, many more incidences are unreported. An average of four children die each day from maltreatment, but the actual number may be considerably higher than the data reveal (Child Welfare Information Gateway, 2013). Thousands of additional children are known to suffer serious and sometimes permanent physical and emotional injuries that are also never reported (Leventhal, Martin, & Gaither, 2012).

Did You Know...

that hospital emergency rooms in the United States treat more than 84 abused children with injuries (many uninsured) every hour?

Child maltreatment creates significant emotional and economic burdens for the individuals involved as well as for their communities and society at large. Researchers have estimated the lifetime costs, based on 1,740 confirmed cases for one year, to be approximately $124 million, or $210,012 per victim (significantly more than the costs associated with stroke or diabetes 2) (Fang et al., 2012). State and local agency resources are strained by the number of reported cases (more than six cases every minute) they must investigate. Community expenditures for prevention programs, interventions, and court costs continue to consume a significant portion of their annual budgets.

Although numbers are helpful for understanding the magnitude of child maltreatment, they overlook the enormous human toll and impact this problem creates. Witnessing or experiencing violence affects children's brain development and wires it for survival rather than for

abuse – *to mistreat, attack, or cause harm to another individual.*
neglect – *failure of a parent or legal guardian to properly care for and meet the basic needs of a child under 18 years of age.*

learning. These changes cause children who have been abused to have long-term difficulty with attention, recall, forming positive social relationships, and understanding emotions (Hart & Rubia, 2012). Researchers have also discovered that children who are abused develop permanent changes in their DNA that increase the risk for illness and chronic disease (Keeshin, Cronholm, & Strawn, 2012).

10-1 Historical Developments

Accounts of child abuse date from ancient times to the present. Throughout history, young children, especially those who have developmental disabilities, have suffered abusive and neglectful treatment. They have also been subjected to cultural practices that by today's standards would be considered inhumane. In many societies, children had no rights or privileges whatsoever, including the right to live.

One of the first child abuse cases in this country to attract widespread public attention involved a young girl named Mary Ellen. Friends and neighbors were concerned about the regular beatings Mary Ellen received from her adoptive parents. However, in 1874, there were no organizations responsible for dealing with the problems of child abuse and neglect. Consequently, Mary Ellen's friends contacted the New York Society for the Prevention of Cruelty to Animals on the basis that she was a human being and, therefore, also a member of the animal kingdom. Her parents were found guilty of cruelty to animals and eventually Mary Ellen was removed from their home. This incident brought gradual recognition to the need for establishing some form of protection for the many maltreated and abandoned children in this country.

It wasn't until 1961 that the subject of child abuse once again received national attention despite the fact that it continued to occur. For a period of years, Dr. C. Henry Kempe studied various aspects of child abuse and was concerned about children whose lives were endangered. He first introduced the phrase "battered child syndrome" in 1961 during a national conference that he organized to address problems related to the harsh treatment of children (Kempe & Helfer, 1982).

The passage of Public Law (PL) 93-247, the Child Abuse Prevention and Treatment Act (CAPTA), on January 31, 1974, signified a turning point in the history of child abuse and neglect. For the first time, national attention was drawn to the issue of childhood maltreatment. This law created the National Center on Child Abuse and Neglect, and required individual states to establish a central agency with legal authority to investigate and prosecute incidences of abuse and neglect. PL 93-247 also mandated states to develop policies, procedures, definitions, and laws that addressed maltreatment. In October 1996, CAPTA was reauthorized and amended to more clearly define circumstances related to the withholding of medical treatment in life-threatening situations. Changes in the 2003 reauthorization required states to expand their services to include adoption, foster care, abandoned infants, and family violence prevention. Additional funding was also appropriated for child protective worker training and efforts to strengthen collaboration among community agencies (Child Welfare Information Gateway, 2011). CAPTA was last reauthorized and amended in December 2010.

Although child abuse and neglect have occurred throughout history, it is only recently that public attention has acknowledged the magnitude of this problem. And, only now are professionals realizing the full impact and prolonged effects that maltreatment has on children's development.

Did You Get It?

The Child Abuse Prevention and Treatment Act (CAPTA) authorized and mandated that _____ establish centralized agencies tasked to investigate and prosecute instances of child maltreatment.

a. the federal government
b. individual states
c. local governments
d. counties

Take the full quiz on CourseMate.

10-2 Discipline vs. Punishment

The term **discipline** is derived from the word disciple and refers to the act of teaching or guiding. When used appropriately, discipline can be effective for helping children learn socially acceptable behavior. However, when it is used improperly or involves threats, fear, or harsh physical **punishment**, it teaches children only anger and violence.

For decades, the right to punish or discipline children as families saw fit was considered a parental privilege. Consequently, outsiders often overlooked or ignored incidences of cruelty to children so as not to interfere in a family's personal affairs. However, public attitudes regarding family privacy and the rights of families to discipline children as they wished began to change. Educators, health and law enforcement professionals, neighbors, and concerned friends grew intolerant of the abusive and neglectful treatment of young children. They began to speak out against such behavior and to serve as advocates for innocent children who were being victimized by adults.

One of the most difficult aspects of this problem is deciding at what point discipline or punishment becomes maltreatment. For example, when does a spanking or verbal **reprimand** constitute abuse? Is sending a child to his room without dinner neglect? In an attempt to establish clear guidelines, federal legislation forced states to define abuse and neglect and to establish policies and procedures for addressing individual cases.

Did You Get It?

One of the most difficult aspects involved in identifying and prosecuting child maltreatment cases is:
a. why these acts occur
b. at what point the line between reasonable discipline and abuse is crossed
c. when, where, and how often these acts occur
d. whether there is sufficient evidence to prosecute and convict the perpetrator

Take the full quiz on CourseMate.

10-3 Abuse and Neglect

Child maltreatment refers to any situation or environment in which a child is not safe due to inadequate protection, exposure to hazardous conditions, exploitation, or harm intentionally inflicted by adults. For legal purposes, a child is defined as an individual under 18 years of age. The most commonly recognized categories of maltreatment include:

▼ **A child is legally defined as an individual under the age of 18 years.**

© Cengage Learning

- physical abuse
- emotional or verbal abuse
- sexual abuse
- physical neglect
- emotional or psychological neglect

Physical abuse is the most common form of abuse and is characterized by a range of visible, non-accidental injuries, such as cuts, burns, welts, fractures, scratches, and missing hair (Figure 10–1). The explanations families provide for these injuries are often inconsistent or unreasonable based

---

discipline – *training or enforced obedience that corrects, shapes, or develops acceptable patterns of behavior.*
punishment – *a negative response to what the observer considers to be wrong or inappropriate behavior; may involve physical or harsh treatment.*
reprimand – *to scold or discipline for unacceptable behavior.*
physical abuse – *injuries, such as welts, burns, bruises, or broken bones, that are caused intentionally.*

on the child's age or developmental stage (Petska, Sheets, & Knox, 2013; Debelle, 2012). A combination of new and older or untreated injuries may suggest repeated abuse. In almost every instance, observable changes in the child's behavior, including shyness, fearfulness, passiveness, anger, aggression, or apprehension will accompany physical injuries (Teacher Checklist 10-1).

Abusive head trauma, formerly known as **shaken baby syndrome**, is a form of physical abuse most often observed in infants and young children. It is caused by vigorously shaking or tossing a child into the air, often because of persistent crying (Figure 10–2). The whiplash motion causes internal bleeding and trauma to the infant's brain that can result in blindness, deafness, fractures, learning disabilities, seizures, and death (Vitale et al., 2012). Prevention of this senseless tragedy requires adults to understand that shaking a child can have devastating effects and that crying is normal because it is an infant's primary mode of communication.

Physical abuse frequently begins as an innocent act of frustration or punishment. In other words, most adults do not set out to intentionally harm a child. However, in the process of disciplining the child, quick tempers and uncontrollable anger may lead to punishment that is severe and sufficiently violent to cause injuries and sometimes even death. In some cases, this outburst represents a one-time, regrettable incidence of poor judgment, while in others maltreatment may become a repetitive pattern. Regardless of the circumstances, the hurtful treatment of children is never considered acceptable.

Emotional or **verbal abuse** occurs when caregivers repeatedly and unpredictably criticize, verbally assault, ignore, or belittle a child's behavior or achievements. In many cases, adult demands and expectations are unrealistic given the child's age and developmental abilities. Chronic exposure to negative statements, such as "Why can't you ever do things right?" or "I knew you were too stupid" have lifelong effects on children's emotional and intellectual development (Rosenkranz, Muller, & Henderson, 2012). Verbal assaults frequently turn into physical abuse over time. Toddlers and preschoolers are the most frequent victims of emotional abuse because they trust adults, do not always fully understand adult expectations, and are relatively defenseless.

Notable changes in a child's behavior are often an early indicator of verbal abuse

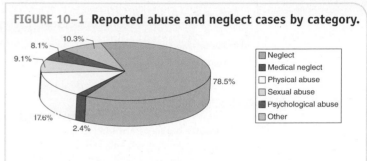

FIGURE 10–1 Reported abuse and neglect cases by category.

- Neglect — 78.5%
- Medical neglect
- Physical abuse
- Sexual abuse
- Psychological abuse
- Other

10.3%
8.1%
9.1%
17.6%
2.4%

Source: U.S. Department of Health and Human Services, Administration for Children and Families, Administration on Children, Youth and Families, Children's Bureau. (2012). *Child Maltreatment 2011.* Retrieved from http://www.acf.hhs.gov/sites/default/files/cb/cm11.pdf.

Did You Know...

the rate of arrest for juvenile crime is nearly 60 percent higher among children who have experienced abuse or neglect?

FIGURE 10–2 Tossing or shaking young children can cause permanent brain injury.

---

shaken baby syndrome – *forceful shaking of a baby that causes head trauma, internal bleeding, and sometimes death.*
Emotional abuse – *repeated humiliation, ridicule, or threats directed toward another individual.*
verbal abuse – *to attack another individual with words.*

TEACHER CHECKLIST 10-1

Identifying Signs of Abuse and Neglect

Physical Abuse

- has frequent or unexplained injuries (e.g., burns, fractures, bruises, bites, eye, or head injuries)
- complains frequently of pain
- wears clothing to hide injuries; clothing may be inappropriate for weather conditions
- reports harsh treatment
- is often late or absent; arrives too early or stays after dismissal from school
- seems unusually fearful of adults, especially parents
- appears malnourished or dehydrated
- avoids logical explanations for injuries
- is withdrawn, anxious, or uncommunicative or may be outspoken, disruptive, and aggressive
- lacks affection, both giving and seeking
- receives inappropriate food, beverages, or drugs

Emotional/Verbal Abuse

- seems generally unhappy; seldom smiles or laughs
- is aggressive and disruptive or unusually shy and withdrawn
- reacts without emotion to unpleasant statements and actions
- displays behaviors that are unusually adult-like or child-like
- has delayed growth or emotional and intellectual development

Sexual Abuse

- wears underclothing that may be torn, stained, or bloody
- complains of pain or itching in the genital area
- has symptoms of venereal disease
- has difficulty getting along with other children, e.g., withdrawn, infant-like, anxious
- has rapid weight loss or gain
- experiences sudden decline in school performance
- engages in delinquent behaviors, including prostitution, running away, alcoholism, or drug abuse
- is fascinated with body parts, uses sexual terms and talks about sexual activities that are unfamiliar to children of this age

Physical Neglect

- has a bad odor from dirty clothing, body, or hair; repeatedly arrives unclean
- is in need of medical or dental care; may have untreated injuries or illness
- is often hungry; begs or steals food while at school
- dresses inappropriately for weather conditions; shoes and clothing often sized too small or too large
- is chronically tired; falls asleep at school, lacks the energy to play with other children
- has difficulty getting along with other children; spends much time alone

Emotional/Psychological Neglect

- performs poorly in school
- appears apathetic, withdrawn, and inattentive
- is frequently absent or late to school
- uses any means to gain teacher's attention and approval
- seldom participates in extracurricular activities
- engages in delinquent behaviors, e.g., stealing, vandalism, sexual misconduct, abuse of drugs or alcohol

TABLE 10–1 **Tips for Determining If Children Are Ready to Be Left Home Alone**

- Has your child expressed interest in staying home alone?
- Does your child typically understand and abide by family rules?
- Is your child reliable and able to handle responsibility in a mature manner?
- Does your child handle unexpected events in a positive way?
- Is your child able to entertain herself for long periods of time or does she require constant supervision?
- Have you rehearsed safety and emergency procedures so your child knows how to respond in the event of a fire, an unwanted telephone call, or someone knocking at the front door?
- Does your child know how to reach you if necessary? Is there another adult your child can contact if you are not available?
- Has your child experienced being left home alone for short periods?
- Does your child have any fears that would be problematic if he were left alone?

Teacher Checklist 10-1. Careful observation and documentation of adult-child interactions can be useful for identifying the potential signs of emotional maltreatment. Unlike the immediate harm caused by an act of physical abuse, the effects of verbal abuse may not appear until years later. This fact makes it difficult to identify and treat the problem before the abuse has left permanent scars on the child's personality and development. Sadly, many children who have endured emotional abuse will go on to engage in antisocial behaviors and to experience serious psychiatric disorders later in life (Gray & Montgomery, 2012; Jonson-Reid, Kohl, & Drake, 2012).

Sexual abuse involves any sexual involvement between an adult and a child, including fondling, exhibitionism, rape, incest, child pornography, and prostitution. Such acts are considered abusive regardless of whether or not the child agreed to participate. This belief is based on the assumption that children are incapable of making a rational decision or may not be able to refuse because of adult pressure. For this reason, the incidence of sexual abuse is probably much greater than reported and often not discovered until years later. Girls are sexually abused at a rate nearly twice that of boys (APA, 2012). More often, the perpetrator is male and not a stranger to the child, but rather someone the child knows and trusts, such as a babysitter, relative, caretaker, parent, stepparent, coach, teacher, or neighbor. Victims may be exposed to sexually transmitted diseases (STDs) and should be observed for characteristic symptoms (Teacher Checklist 10-2). Children who have been sexually abused also suffer a high rate of adult-onset mental health disorders (Nelson, Baldwin, & Taylor, 2012). Many sexually abused adolescents become runaways or prostitutes, or engage in a range of violent or dependency behaviors (Oshri, Tubman, & Burnette, 2012).

Did You Know...

that teen pregnancy is 25–30 percent higher among children who have been abused?

Physical neglect is defined as a family's abandonment of a child or their failure to provide for the child's basic physical needs and care. More than half of all substantiated maltreatment cases involve some form of neglect, including inadequate or inappropriate food, shelter, clothing, or cleanliness. Medical neglect is also considered a form of physical neglect that places a child at risk for disability or death (USLegal, Inc., 2012). Parents may be prosecuted if they fail to obtain appropriate medical treatment (e.g., immunizations, surgery, medications, dental care) necessary to address children's health needs. Charges are also being brought against families for educational neglect if they fail to enroll children in school, allow them to drop out prematurely, or permit children to be truant from school.

Failure to protect children's safety can also result in prosecution for criminal neglect and endangerment. For example, adults who supply drugs or alcohol to underage children or knowingly permit children to have access to, or use, illegal substances are considered guilty of exposing children to extreme risk. Parents who leave children alone and unsupervised are also being

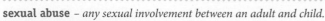

sexual abuse – *any sexual involvement between an adult and child.*
physical neglect – *failure to meet children's fundamental needs for food, shelter, medical care, and education, including abandonment.*

TEACHER CHECKLIST 10-2

Identifying Symptoms of Common Sexually Transmitted Diseases (STDs)

Gonorrhea	May cause painful or burning discomfort when urinating, increased vaginal discharge (yellow, green), or vaginal bleeding. Discharge, anal itching, soreness, bleeding, or painful bowel movements are characteristic of rectal infections. May cause sore throat (oral sex). Many victims have no symptoms, but are contagious; serious complications can develop if left untreated.
Chlamydia trachomatis	May cause abnormal vaginal discharge or burning discomfort when urinating 5 to 7 days following infection. Victims may not have any immediate symptoms; however, if left untreated infection can damage reproductive organs.
Syphilis	Symptoms appear in stages following infection. Initial stage: within 10 days to 3 months a chancre (painless sore) appears at the point of contact (vagina, rectum, mouth, penis) and heals. Second stage: 6 weeks to 6 months after sore heals a generalized rash appears along with fever and enlarged lymph glands. Curable with antibiotics.
Trichomoniasis	The most common and curable STD. Symptoms appear within 5 to 28 days and typically include a frothy, yellow-green, foul-smelling vaginal discharge, burning during urination, irritation, and itching around the genital area.
Genital herpes	Many victims have no symptoms. Others may develop painful blister-like sores (around vagina, rectum, penis, mouth), fever, flu-like symptoms, and swollen glands several days following infection; sores heal in 2 to 4 weeks. Reoccurrence of sores is common.
Condyloma (genital warts)	Caused by the human papilloma virus (HPV); single or clusters of warts may develop around the genital area within weeks or months following infection. Not everyone will develop symptoms. A vaccine is currently available.
HIV/AIDS	Infected persons usually have no initial symptoms. Blood tests can detect the HIV virus 6 weeks after exposure.

TeachSource Digital Download) Download from CourseMate.

charged with neglect and endangerment. The term **latch-key** has been used to describe children who are consistently left home alone during the hours before and after school. A shortage of programs, lack of trained personnel, and cost has made it difficult for many working families to secure adequate before- and after-school care for school-aged children. Questions remain unanswered about when it is appropriate for children of any age to be left home alone and if they are at greater risk for injury or emotional distress as a result (Table 10–1) (Ruiz-Casares et al., 2012).

Emotional or psychological neglect is perhaps the most difficult form of maltreatment to recognize and document. For this reason, not all states include this category in their reporting laws. Emotional neglect reflects a basic lack of parental interest or responsiveness to a child's psychological needs and development (Spratt et al., 2012) (Teacher Checklist 10-1). They fail to understand the need for affection, nurturing, and conversing with their child. The absence of any emotional connection, such as hugging, kissing, touching, conversation, or facial expressions, can result in developmental delays and stunted growth (Moxley, Squires, & Linstrom, 2012). The term **failure to thrive** describes this condition when it occurs in infants and young children. A lack of measurable gains in weight or height is often one of the first indications of psychological neglect.

latch-key – *a term that refers to school-age children who care for themselves without adult supervision before and after school hours.*
emotional or psychological neglect – *failure to meet a child's psychological needs for love and attention.*
failure to thrive – *a term used to describe an infant whose growth and mental development are severely slowed due to lack of nurturing or mental stimulation.*

CONNECTING TO EVERYDAY PRACTICE

Cultural Practices and Child Abuse

Members of a local Vietnamese community were irate following the arrest of a boy's 23-year-old parents for child abuse. Teachers had noted purple "bruises" on the little boy's back and chest when he arrived at school one day. The couple denied any wrongdoing, insisting they were merely performing "cao gio," a traditional Vietnamese practice used to cure fever. Following the application of medicated oil to the skin, a warm coin or spoon is scraped along the spine and chest until reddened patches appear. The boy's parents believed this would eliminate "bad winds" that had caused his fever.

Think About This:

▶ Is this practice a form of abuse?

▶ How do cultural differences affect parental practices and values?

▶ Should families be expected to give up traditional cultural practices related to healing and medicine when they immigrate to this country?

▶ Why is it important for teachers to acquire an understanding of cultural differences?

Did You Get It?

Which of the following forms of abuse and/or neglect is the most difficult to detect, document, report, and potentially prosecute?
   a. emotional/psychological abuse or neglect
   b. child exploitation
   c. physical abuse
   d. sexual abuse

Take the full quiz on CourseMate.

10-4 Understanding the Risk Factors for Maltreatment

Abusive adults come from all levels of social, economic, educational, ethnic, religious, and occupational backgrounds (Children's Bureau, 2011). They live in rural areas, as well as small towns and large cities. Some are well-educated professionals, whereas others dropped out of school early. Also, not all abusive adults are poor, alcoholics, or drug abusers, as is often believed. Although the incidence tends to be significantly higher among these groups, such generalizations are overly simplistic and do not address the complex social and economic issues that are involved.

One explanation for why the incidence of child abuse or neglect appears to be greater among disadvantaged families may relate to their increased reliance on public and social service programs. Frequent communication and visits with these families allow agency personnel to more closely monitor their actions. Furthermore, families living in poverty often face circumstances that make daily living more stressful and limit their options (Leventhal, Martin, & Gaither, 2012). Simply finding adequate food, clothing, housing, and transportation can prove to be overwhelming. In contrast, families with greater financial resources may have more choices available to them and can afford private medical care, move from doctor to doctor, and even seek treatment in neighboring cities. This flexibility limits their contact with a single health care provider and makes it easier for families to avoid immediate suspicion.

Researchers continue to study childhood maltreatment in an effort to better understand the complex nature of this problem. To date, they have identified three major risk factors:

▶ characteristics of adults who have a potential for committing maltreatment
▶ vulnerable children
▶ family and environmental stressors

It is believed that for abuse and neglect to take place, all three risk factors must occur at approximately the same time.

10-4a Characteristics of Abusive or Neglectful Adults

Certain adult behaviors and predispositions are commonly associated with abusive tendencies, including:

- a history of repeated fear, anger, and rejection
- low self-esteem
- difficulty in forming long-term relationships (e.g., friendships, marriage) that leads to social isolation and loneliness; depending on a child for love
- lack of trust
- early marriage and pregnancy
- maternal depression, post-traumatic stress disorder (PTSD), and other mental health conditions (Feldman, McConnell, & Aunos, 2012)
- belief in, and use of, harsh punishment to "discipline" children (Lansford et al., 2012)
- impulsive; poor anger control
- low stress tolerance
- drug and alcohol addictions
- poor problem-solving abilities

▶❙❙ TeachSource Video Connections

© 2015 Cengage Learning

0–2 Years: Observation Module for Infants and Toddlers

Caring for infants and toddlers is a demanding and, at times, stressful responsibility. Many adults are overwhelmed by the experience and may unintentionally harm a young child out of frustration. Linking families to informational and supportive resources is critical to reducing the risk of childhood maltreatment. As you watch the learning video, *0–2 Years: Observation Module for Infants and Toddlers*, consider the following questions:

1. Why do you think infants and toddlers experience a high rate of maltreatment?

2. What behaviors did you observe in this video that some parents might find frustrating or difficult to handle?

3. What resources would you recommend to help these parents cope and to enjoy their child's early years?

Watch on CourseMate.

Although not every adult who exhibits these characteristics is abusive or neglectful, likewise not every abusive or neglectful caregiver will necessarily display all of these behaviors. In many cases, adults simply lack the knowledge and skills needed to be successful parents. Their lack of understanding can lead to expectations that may be unrealistic and developmentally inappropriate based on the child's age and abilities. For example, a parent may become upset because a 15-month-old wets the bed, a toddler spills milk, or a 7-year-old loses a mitten despite the fact that these behaviors are typical and to be expected. Intolerance, frustration, and uncontrolled anger can, in turn, lead to a subsequent lashing out of abusive behavior. Drugs and alcohol addictions may further reduce an adult's ability to be nurturing or to respond appropriately to children's needs. Evidence also suggests that adults who grew up in abusive families are more likely to treat their own children in a similar manner.

10-4b Vulnerable Children

Victims of child maltreatment include an almost equal number of boys and girls. Children under age 4 years and those who have developmental delays or disabilities, especially autism, are at highest risk for physical abuse (Leeb et al., 2012; Stalker & McArthur, 2012). Infants under 12 months and children over the age of 6 years are more likely to suffer from neglect, whereas adolescents experience the highest rate of sexual abuse. Although age and disability increase children's risk for abuse and neglect, additional factors can include:

- difficult temperament (e.g., fussy, defiant, overly active)
- living in a single parent family (especially with father absent)
- poverty
- gender (sexual abuse)

▶ frequent or chronic illness

▶ gender nonconformity (Roberts et al., 2012)

Occasionally an abusive or neglectful caregiver will single out a child who does not live up to their expectations. This child may be perceived as being physically unattractive, disobedient, clumsy, weak, unintelligent, or similar to someone else whom the adult dislikes. These qualities may be real or imagined; in either case, the adult is convinced that they truly exist.

The risk of maltreatment is also greater for children who are born outside of marriage, from unwanted or unplanned pregnancies, stepchildren, or living in a foster home. Researchers have also established a strong connection between domestic violence and child abuse. Children living in households where domestic violence is also occurring are at significantly greater risk for abuse and neglect (Miller et al., 2012).

> **Did You Know...**
>
> that 80 percent of young adults who were abused as children will suffer from at least one psychological disorder?

10-4c Family and Environmental Stresses

All individuals and families face conflict and crises from time to time. However, the economic recession, frequent military deployments, natural disasters, and incarcerations have caused extraordinary hardships for many families with children (Valentino et al., 2012; Waliski et al., 2012). Some are able to cope with these stressful events. Others are unable to handle the pressures or to maintain emotional control during difficult times. In many maltreatment cases, stress is identified as the **precipitating** factor. That is, the perceived conflict is sufficient to push an adult to action (abuse) or withdrawal (neglect) as a caretaker (Easterbrooks et al., 2011).

Adults who mistreat children often have difficulty discriminating between events that are significantly stressful and those that are not. Instead, they find all crises equally threatening, overwhelming, and difficult to manage (Schneiderman et al., 2012). The following examples illustrate the range of personal and environmental stressors that can potentially lead to a loss of control, especially when they occur in combination with other challenging events:

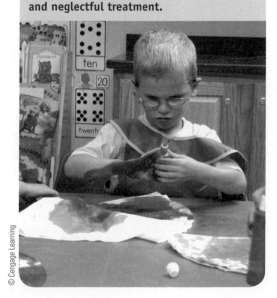

▼ **Children who have developmental disabilities are at greater risk for abusive and neglectful treatment.**

© Cengage Learning

▶ flat tire, lost keys, clogged sink, or broken window

▶ unemployment or underemployment

▶ illness, injury, or death

▶ poverty, financial pressures, home foreclosure

▶ partner violence, divorce, or marital conflict

▶ moving

▶ birth of another child

▶ single parenting

▶ military deployment (James & Countryman, 2012)

Some events may seem trivial in comparison to others. Yet, any one may become the "straw that breaks the camel's back" and trigger abusive behavior. The level of an adult's anger may be inappropriate and out of proportion to the actual event and ultimately be directed toward a child.

> ### Did You Get It?
>
> Poverty, disability, living in a household where domestic violence is occurring, and _____ increase a child's risk for maltreatment.
> - **a.** being the youngest child
> - **b.** having older parents
> - **c.** residing in a rural community
> - **d.** living in a single-parent household
>
> Take the full quiz on CourseMate.

precipitating – *factors that trigger or initiate a reaction or response.*

10-5 Protective Measures for Programs and Teachers

It is essential that early childhood programs and school personnel take steps to protect themselves from potential accusations of child maltreatment. Special attention should be given to careful hiring practices, policy development, and ongoing personnel training, including:

- conducting background checks on potential employees for any prior record of child abuse or felony convictions (These are mandated in most states and performed by state law enforcement agencies.)
- hiring individuals who have formal training in early education and child development
- contacting an applicant's references (nonrelative) and requesting information about the applicant's prior work performance
- reviewing an employee's past employment record, including reasons for leaving previous jobs
- establishing a code of conduct regarding appropriate child-teacher behavior
- providing continued inservice training, especially on topics related to identification of abuse or neglect, effective behavior management strategies, and teaching children self-protection skills (Teacher Checklist 10-3)
- establishing a program policy of nontolerance regarding any form of abusive behavior, including harassment, bullying, or harsh discipline

Teachers can take additional measures to protect themselves against the possibility of false allegations. Conducting daily health checks upon a child's arrival and documenting all findings can protect teachers from being blamed for a bruise or scratch that may have occurred elsewhere. Teachers should also maintain thorough records of children's injuries so there is factual evidence that describes the circumstances and treatment administered. It is also preferable not to leave a teacher alone with children. A second teacher who serves as an eyewitness can eliminate any suspicions of wrongdoing. Teachers should also participate in inservice training opportunities to improve their understanding of child maltreatment and their role in successful identification and intervention. Finally, teachers may want to purchase their own professional liability insurance unless they are covered by their employer's policy.

TEACHER CHECKLIST 10-3

Strategies for Positive Behavior Management

- **Reinforce** desirable behaviors. Give lots of hugs and pats, adult attention, and verbal acknowledgment for things the child is doing appropriately; reinforcement should be given often and immediately following the appropriate behavior. For example: "I really like the way you are sharing your toys" or "That was nice of you to let Mat have a turn on the bike."
- **Redirect** the child's attention to another activity or area when he is behaving inappropriately; don't comment on the inappropriate behavior. "Juan, could you come and help me set the table?" or "Let's go to the block area and build a zoo together."
- **Consistent expectations** help children understand their limits and the way in which adults expect them to behave. Expectations should be realistic and state behavior that is considered appropriate. Keep explanations simple and brief. "Mika, you need to sit on the sofa; feet go on the floor" or "We need to walk in the hallways."
- **Consequences** can be used together with other management strategies. Most children understand consequences from an early age on. "When your hands are washed we can eat" or "I will have to take the ball away if you throw it at the window again."
- **Ignoring** undesirable behaviors, such as tantrums or throwing things can be effective for decreasing the attention-getting response children may be seeking. Don't look at the child or discuss the behavior with the child.
- **Practice** desirable behaviors when the child behaves inappropriately. For example, if the child scatters crayons across the floor, she needs to pick them up and then be acknowledged for doing what was asked. An adult may also model the desired behavior by helping the child to pick up the crayons.

10-5a Inservice Training

Teachers are morally, professionally, and legally responsible for reporting children whom they suspect are being maltreated (Feng et al., 2012; Goldman & Grimbeek, 2011). However, to be effective, they must know what signs to look for, to whom a report should be made, and what community resources are available to help families. These topics make ideal subjects for inservice training, in addition to:

- relevant state laws
- teachers' rights and responsibilities
- physical and behavioral signs of maltreatment
- development of school policies and procedures for handling suspected cases
- teacher and staff management of abuse and neglect
- community resources and services
- classroom strategies for helping children who have been maltreated
- stress reduction and time management skills.

Teachers also play a valuable role advocating for laws, policies, and programs that protect children's rights and well-being.

Did You Get It?

Teachers, administrators, and school counselors have the authority to assess children for signs of physical and/or sexual abuse without an eyewitness present.
- **a.** Never
- **b.** Yes, but doing so is not recommended
- **c.** Yes, but only with prior written consent of authorities
- **d.** Only if witnessed by the child's parent or legal guardian

Take the full quiz on CourseMate.

10-6 Reporting Laws

Reporting laws support the philosophy that parenthood carries with it certain obligations and responsibilities toward children. Therefore, punishment of abusive adults is not the primary objective. Rather, the purpose of these laws is to protect children from maltreatment and exploitation. Every attempt is made to preserve family unity by helping parents find solutions to problems that may be contributing to the abuse or neglect. Contrary to common belief, removing children from their homes is not always the best solution. Alternative placements and frequent moves may not improve the stability or quality of a child's life. Criminal action against parents is usually reserved for cases in which they are unwilling or unable to cooperate with prescribed educational and treatment programs.

Each case of maltreatment involves a unique and complex set of conditions such as home environments, economic obligations, individual temperaments, cultural differences, and parenting skills that must be taken into consideration. For this reason, states have intentionally written their child maltreatment laws to address the basic federal mandates established by CAPTA while remaining somewhat open-ended. This approach allows the legal system and social agencies flexibility in determining, on a case-by-case basis, whether or not an adult has acted irresponsibly.

Laws in every state identify specific groups and professionals who are required to report suspected incidences of maltreatment, including:

- teachers, assistants, paraprofessionals, and student teachers
- center directors and principals
- health care providers (e.g., doctors, nurses, dentists, pharmacists, psychologists, mental health counselors)
- law enforcement personnel
- social workers
- clergy

TEACHER CHECKLIST 10-4

What to Include in a Written Child Abuse/Neglect Report

1. The child and parents' or caretakers' name(s) and address (if known).
2. The child's age.
3. The nature and extent of the child's injuries or description of neglect including any evidence of previous injuries or deprivation.
4. The identity of the offending adult (if known).
5. Any additional information the reporting person believes may be helpful in establishing the cause of injuries or neglect.
6. The name, address, telephone number, and professional title of the individual making the report.

TeachSource Digital Download Download from CourseMate.

10-6a Program Policy

Schools and early childhood programs should have a written action plan for addressing suspected incidences of abuse and neglect (Moxley, Squires, & Lindstrom, 2012). These policies and procedures should be reviewed frequently with staff to ensure their understanding and compliance. In larger programs, teachers may report directly to the director, principal, head administrator, or health consultant who, in turn, contacts appropriate local authorities and files a report. However, if at any time teachers are not satisfied that their concerns have been properly acted upon, they are obligated by law to personally report the incident. In home-based programs or smaller centers, an individual staff member may be responsible for filing a report. Failure to do so may prolong a potentially harmful situation for the child, and result in criminal prosecution and monetary fines for the teacher.

Initial reports are usually made by telephone and followed up with a written report that is completed several days later (Teacher Checklist 10-4). All information is kept strictly confidential, including the identity of the person making the report. State laws protect anyone who reports abuse or neglect from liability and criminal charges as long as the information provided is not intended to deliberately harm another individual.

It is not the teacher's role to prove suspicions of abuse and neglect before making a report. Local child protective services or the National Child Abuse Hotline (800-422-4453) should be contacted immediately if there is reason to believe that a child is being inadequately cared for or mistreated. As long as a report is made in good faith, the teacher is merely indicating that a family may be in need of help. The law does not require the family or adult in question to be notified when a report is filed. In some cases, doing so could place the child in additional danger, especially if sexual or harsh physical abuse is involved. Some families may actually experience relief when their problems are finally recognized. Therefore, the decision about whether or not to inform the family or adult in question may depend on the particular circumstances.

Reporting a family, colleague, or acquaintance can be difficult. However, as advocates for children's rights, teachers must always be concerned about children's safety and welfare. Unless the child is in immediate danger, trained personnel will generally meet with the family or caregiver within days to evaluate circumstances surrounding the incident. Legal action may be taken depending on the seriousness of the situation or arrangements may be made to provide family-centered support services.

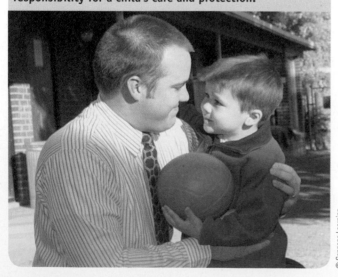

Parenthood implies that an adult is willing to accept responsibility for a child's care and protection.

© Cengage Learning

Did You Get It?

Teachers play a multifaceted role in dealing with potential instances of child abuse and/or neglect. What is not the teacher's responsibility?

a. detecting signs of maltreatment
b. documenting findings
c. reporting findings
d. proving allegations

Take the full quiz on CourseMate.

10-7 The Teacher's Role

A teacher may be one of the few adults children can turn to when they are being mistreated. Teachers serve as important child advocates by establishing effective communication, providing emotionally supportive and accepting environments, identifying and reporting suspicions of abuse or neglect, and helping children to learn socially appropriate behaviors.

10-7a Early Identification and Reporting

Teachers are in an ideal position to identify and help children who are being mistreated (Katz et al., 2012). Daily health checks and frequent interactions with children enable teachers to recognize early changes in children's behavior or appearance. (See Teacher Checklist 10-1 and Chapter 2). Patterns of non-accidental injury or neglect often become apparent when these observations are documented. This information may also be used by child protective services and the courts to determine if maltreatment is occurring. Therefore, it is important that teachers include the following information in their reports:

▶ a precise description of the nature, location, color, size, and severity of any suspected injury (Figure 10–3)

FIGURE 10–3 Form for reporting location, size, and nature of suspected abuse-related injuries.

Child's Name: _____
Date: _____
Comments: _____
Description of Injury: _____
Location and Size of Injury: _____
Color of Injury: _____
Description of Child's Behavior: _____
Additional Comments/Concerns: _____
Reported by: _____

- ❱ the child's explanation of how the injury occurred
- ❱ the family's or caretaker's explanation for the incident
- ❱ obvious signs of neglect (e.g., malnutrition, uncleanliness, inappropriate dress, excessive fatigue, lack of medical or dental care)
- ❱ recent or significant changes in the child's behavior
- ❱ nature of parent/child interactions

Comprehensive documentation provides child protective authorities with supporting evidence and also aids in determining the services and intervention programs most appropriate for the child and family.

Teachers must not ignore their professional and legal responsibilities to protect children's safety. In many cases, a teacher may be the only adult whom a child trusts enough to reveal maltreatment. Teachers must be able to identify the signs of abuse and neglect and know when and how to report suspected cases to the appropriate authorities. They must also be aware of cultural differences in parenting skills, expectations, and practices so as not to misinterpret what they may observe (Lilly & Kundu, 2012; Raman & Hodes, 2012).

10-7b Providing a Supportive Environment for Children

Teachers play an important role in helping children to understand and cope with the effects of abusive and neglectful treatment. They must be positive role models and accept children for who they are, listen to their concerns without judgment, encourage their efforts, and acknowledge their successes. For many children, teachers may be the only adult in their lives who accepts them unconditionally and shows a sincere interest in their well-being without making threatening demands or causing them harm.

Establishing a trusting relationship with children who have suffered maltreatment is a critical step in helping them begin to open up and to verbalize their feelings. This process takes time and cannot be forced or hurried. It often requires teachers to initially meet children on their own terms. For example, a teacher might start out by offering several books to the child who is reluctant to join a group story-time. Later, the teacher might sit alone with the child and read a story together. Finally, the child may be gently coaxed to participate with her peers in a group activity.

Play therapy can also be beneficial for drawing children out and allowing them safe opportunities for expressing anger, fears, and anxieties related to abusive treatment (Mishna et al., 2012; Thompson & Trice-Black, 2012). Activities such as housekeeping, puppets, and doll play are ideal for this purpose. For example, talking about how the puppet or doll (child) feels when it is mistreated may encourage children to talk about their true feelings. At the same time, teachers can model effective parenting skills for children, such as appropriate ways of talking to, treating, and caring for the puppets or dolls.

Artwork and story-telling can also be effective means for encouraging children to talk about their feelings, anxieties, and concerns related to traumatic events. For example, self-portraits may reveal an exaggeration of certain body parts or circumstances that children have experienced. Pictures may also depict unusual practices that children have been subjected to, such as being tied up, locked in a closet, or struck with an object. However, extreme caution must be exercised whenever attempting to interpret children's artwork. A child's immature drawing skills and lack of perspective can easily cause an inexperienced observer to misinterpret or reach false conclusions. Therefore, it is best to view unusual items in children's drawings as additional clues, rather than as absolute indicators of abusive or neglectful treatment. Small group discussions and story-telling (verbal, child-written, or dictated to a teacher) also provide valuable outlets for articulating feelings and helping children to explore effective solutions.

Teachers can be instrumental in helping children learn how to manage anger and to express emotions in ways that are positive and appropriate (Kim-Spoon et al., 2012). For example, a teacher might say, "Rosa, if you want another cracker, you need to say 'Please can I have another cracker.' We can't understand when you whine or cry." Or, "I can't let you hit Rodney. You need to ask him, 'May I please have a turn on the bike?'" Children can also be taught strategies that will help them to regain self-control when tension begins to escalate.

10-7c Building Children's Resilience

Teachers have many unique opportunities to help children develop and practice developmental skills that also promote **resilience** (see Chapter 1, Table 1–3) (Bruster & Foreman, 2012; Lee, Cheung, & Kwong, 2012). Victims of child abuse and neglect often have poor self-esteem and blame themselves for the way they have been treated. Letting children know they are safe, accepted, and loved is an important first step in helping them to overcome their fears and to regain trust. Teachers can facilitate this process by:

- responding to children in a consistent and supportive manner
- providing private space that children can call their own
- establishing gradual limits for acceptable behavior; following predictable routines and schedules to create order in children's lives
- letting children know you are available whenever they need someone, whether it be for companionship, extra attention, or reassurance
- taking time to prepare children for new experiences; informing children of expectations in advance enhances the "safeness" of their environment
- accepting children's initial fears and reluctance to participate; gradually involving them in activities
- encouraging children to talk about their feelings, fears, and concerns

Educational programs and materials are available to improve children's awareness and ability to respond to maltreatment (Table 10–2). Many excellent resources can be accessed on the Internet or through local public libraries, schools, and pediatric and mental health clinics. Materials should be selected and reviewed carefully so they are developmentally appropriate, instructive, and not frightening to young children. Social workers, nurses, doctors, mental health specialists,

TABLE 10–2   Children's Books about Maltreatment

Bentrim, W. (2009). *Mommy's black eye: Children dealing with domestic violence.* USA: CreateSpace.

Dietzel, M. (2000). *My very own book about me: A personal safety book.* Spokane, WA: ACT for Kids.

Federico, J. (2009). *Some parts are not for sharing.* Mustang, OK: Tate Publishing & Enterprises (also available in Spanish).

Foltz, L. (2003). *Kids helping kids break the silence of sexual abuse.* Lighthouse Point, FL: Lighthouse Point Press (for older children).

Girard, L. (1992). *My body is private.* Morton Grove, IL: Albert Whitman & Co.

Gross, P. (1996). *Stranger safety.* Southfield, MI: Roo Publishing.

Guard, A. (2011). *What if a stranger approaches you?* Mankato, MN: Picture Window Books.

Holmes, M. (2000). *A terrible thing happened: A story for children who have witnessed violence or trauma.* Washington, DC: Magination Books.

Kehoe, P. (1987). *Something happened and I'm scared to tell: A book for young victims of abuse.* Seattle, WA: Parenting Press.

King, K., & Rama, S. (2008). *I said no! A kid-to-kid guide to keeping your private parts private.* Weaverville, CA: Boulden Publishing.

Kleven, S., & Bergsma, J. (1998). *The right touch.* Bellevue, WA: Illumination Arts.

Kraizer, S. (1996). *The safe child book: A commonsense approach to protecting children and teaching children to protect themselves.* New York: Fireside Press.

Loftis, C. (1997). *The words hurt: Helping children cope with verbal abuse.* New York: Horizon Press.

Pendziwol, J. (2006). *Once upon a dragon: Stranger safety for kids (and dragons).* Tonawanda, NY: Kids Can Press.

Saltz, G. (2008). *Amazing you! Getting smart about your private parts.* New York: Puffin.

Schor, H. (2002). *A place for Starr: A story of hope for children experiencing family violence.* Charlotte, NC: Kidsrights Press.

Spelman, C., & Weidner, T. (1997). *Your body belongs to you.* Morton Grove, IL: Albert Whitman & Co.

Susewitt, L. (2011). *Is there love after abuse? The story of Kobe.* USA: CreateSpace.

Wachter, O. (2002). *No more secrets for me.* London: Little Brown & Co.

resilience – *the capacity to endure or overcome difficult conditions.*

Caring adults provide children with much needed companionship, reassurance, and individualized attention.

© Cengage Learning

teachers, and public service groups can also be called upon to provide educational programs for children and families.

It is also important to help children develop effective communication, problem-solving, conflict resolution, and self-protection skills. Although children may not fully comprehend the complexity of abuse or neglect, these skills improve children's ability to recognize "uncomfortable" situations, how and when to tell a trusted adult, and how to assert themselves by saying no when someone attempts an inappropriate behavior. Informed children can be the first line of defense against abuse and neglect if they know that being beaten, forced to engage in sexual activity, or left alone for long periods is not normal or the type of treatment they deserve.

10-7d Reaching Out to Families

Raising young children is a challenging and demanding task. Many adults today have not had the same opportunities to learn parenting skills that past generations once had. They have often grown up in smaller families and had fewer opportunities to practice parenting firsthand until their own children arrive. Employment opportunities may require relocation to distant cities and result in the loss of extended family contact and support. And, more often than not, today's parents are holding down full-time jobs in addition to raising children. As a result, daily stress levels and economic worries may challenge some parents' ability to be patient, nurturing, and responsive to children's developmental needs. These circumstances in no way excuse the harsh or neglectful treatment of children. However, they signal the importance of early recognition and intervention.

There are many ways teachers can assist families who may be struggling (Haskett et al., 2012). Daily contacts provide opportunities for identifying families in crises and directing them to community services and programs, such as:

- child protective services
- day care and "crisis" centers
- family counseling
- help or "hot" lines
- temporary foster homes
- homemaker services
- transportation
- financial assistance
- parenting classes
- employment assistance
- home visitors
- self-help or support groups

Partnerships can be formed and strengthened when teachers also reach out to support families and encourage their involvement in children's education. Information can be shared about many topics that will enhance parents' confidence and child-rearing skills, including:

- child growth and development
- positive behavior management
- nutritious meals and snacks; how to manage feeding problems
- meeting children's social and emotional needs at different stages
- preventive health care
- activities that promote children's learning
- locating and utilizing community resources
- stress and tension relievers for parents
- creating safe environments; injury prevention
- financial planning

▶ time management

▶ organizing a family support group

Teachers must always be sensitive to cultural differences when providing families with information. Although most parents do their best to raise children, they may not share the same values and practices that teachers' consider to be important. Maintaining open communication with families promotes mutual understanding and lessens the risk of misinterpreting parenting ideas and behaviors as potentially abusive.

Legislation creating **safe havens** for unwanted infants has been passed in every state in an effort to eliminate maltreatment and abandonment. Although the laws vary somewhat from state to state, they basically allow a parent(s) to relinquish custody of an unharmed infant to authorities without fear of criminal prosecution. The laws typically declare a time/age limit and identify facilities such as hospitals, police precincts, or fire stations where infants can be safely left. The concept of safe havens is not without controversy, but has proven successful in saving the lives of many infants who might otherwise have been harmed or abandoned.

Did You Get It?

Laws creating "safe havens" have been passed in all 50 states and have paved the way for parents to more easily:

a. gain or regain lost custody of a child

b. relinquish custody of a child

c. find round-the-clock support services for themselves and their infant

d. locate community shelter for themselves and their child(ren)

Take the full quiz on CourseMate.

PARTNERING with FAMILIES

Anger Management

Dear Families,

Being a parent has many positive rewards, but it can also be a challenging and stressful role to fulfill. At times, children are likely to behave in ways that we find upsetting and cause us to react in anger. Although this behavior is understandable, it does not teach children how to handle their feelings of frustration or disappointment in a positive manner. Instead, our actions may teach children how to shout, say hurtful words, and respond in an emotional or physical manner, rather than in ways that are thoughtful and constructive. When adults practice effective anger management strategies, they become positive role models for children. The next time your child makes you angry, try several of the following techniques:

▶ Take a deep breath. Thoroughly assess the situation before you react.

▶ Leave the room. Take a brief "time out" and regain control of your emotions.

▶ Consider whether the situation or the child's behavior is actually worth your becoming upset. Could the outcome affect the long-term relationship you have with your child?

▶ Tell children what has upset you and why.

▶ Avoid lengthy explanations and arguments with your child. Children understand statements when they are brief and to the point.

▶ Learn to recognize your tolerance limits and what behaviors are most likely to make you upset.

▶ Always find something good to say about your child soon afterward. This helps children to understand that you still love them despite their unacceptable behavior.

---

safe haven – *a designated place, such as a hospital or fire station, where parents can leave their infant and give up parental rights without fear of criminal charges.*

CLASSROOM CORNER

Teacher Activities

We Have Many Kinds of Feelings

(PreK–2; National Health Education Standards 4.2.1)

Concept: We all have feelings and it is important to talk about our feelings.

Learning Objectives

▶ Children will learn that there are many different types of feelings.

▶ Children will learn that it is important to talk about their feelings.

Supplies

▶ large piece of paper to write down comments from the children

▶ marking pen

▶ two puppets (any kind)

▶ small pile of blocks

▶ three small cars

▶ box of crayons

▶ two pieces of paper

Learning Activities

▶ Read and discuss the following books (see Appendix D for additional titles):
  • *The Way I Feel* by Janan Cain
  • *What to Do When You Worry Too Much* by Dawn Huebner
  • *How to Take the Grrrrr Out of Anger* by Elizabeth Verdick
  • *Big Feelings* by Talaris Institute

▶ Ask children if they have felt the same as the children in the story. Ask children to talk about what makes them feel scared, happy, angry, and so on.

▶ Next, role-play with the puppets. Have puppet 1 playing with three cars and have puppet 2 come over to play. Have puppet 1 ask puppet 2 if she would like to play with a car. Ask the children how they think puppet 2 feels when she got to play with a car.

▶ Next, have puppet 1 stacking and playing with blocks. Then have puppet 2 come over and knock down his blocks. Ask the children how they think puppet 1 is feeling after his block building was knocked down. Talk about what puppet 2 should have done differently (asked to play, asked a teacher for other blocks, and so on).

▶ Finally, have puppet 1 drawing with paper and crayons. Have puppet 2 come over and ask puppet 1 if she can play. Have puppet 1 say, "No, I am playing with these." Ask children how puppet 2 is feeling, and talk about what puppet 2 can do to get some crayons and paper (grab them–not appropriate; ask a teacher to get them some crayons and paper–appropriate).

Evaluation

▶ Children will name several different kinds of feelings.

▶ Children will describe behaviors that evoke specific feelings.

Additional lesson plans for grades 3–5 are available on the Education CourseMate website for this book.

Summary

▶ Public Law 93-247, the Child Abuse Prevention and Treatment Act (CAPTA):
  - was the first national law that addressed the problems of child abuse and neglect
  - provides legal protection to children who are maltreated
  - requires states to pass laws, designate an investigative and enforcement agency, and establish policies
  - has addressed contemporary maltreatment issues, including adoption, foster care, abandoned infants, family violence, and improved interagency collaboration in recent reauthorizations.

▶ Discipline involves guiding or teaching children how they should behave.
  - Punishment teaches children negative behaviors, including anger and violence.

▶ Children under 18 years are protected by law from harm, exploitation, and inadequate care.
  - Most states recognize four categories of abuse/neglect, including physical abuse, sexual abuse, emotional abuse, and physical neglect; emotional/psychological neglect is recognized in some states.

▶ The potential for abuse or neglect is thought to be greatest when three factors exist at approximately the same time: an adult who has abusive tendencies, a child who is vulnerable because of certain characteristics (e.g., age, disability, temperament), and family or environmental stressors.

▶ Programs and schools must take steps to protect themselves against potential abuse or neglect allegations by implementing thorough hiring practices and inservice training.

▶ Teachers are required to report suspected incidences of abuse or neglect and are protected by the law if reports are made in good faith.
  - Programs should have a procedure in place for handling incidences of abuse and neglect.

▶ Teachers play an important role in the prevention and treatment of child abuse/neglect through early identification and reporting, providing emotional support to children, reaching out to families, helping children develop skills to improve resilience (e.g., communication, social, problem-solving, conflict resolution), and advocating on behalf of children.

Terms to Know

abuse p. 268	shaken baby syndrome p. 271	emotional or/pychological
neglect p. 268	emotional p. 271	neglect p. 274
discipline p. 270	verbal abuse p. 271	failure to thrive p. 274
punishment p. 270	sexual abuse p. 273	precipitating p. 277
reprimand p. 270	physical neglect p. 274	resilience p. 283
physical abuse p. 270	latch-key p. 274	safe havens p. 285

Chapter Review

A. By Yourself:

1. Define each of the *Terms to Know*.

2. Select a word from the list below to complete each of the following statements.

teachers	definition	childhood
trust	expectations	safe haven
physical	neglect	reported
psychological	identify	
sexual	confidential	

  1. A child's excessive fascination with body parts and talk about sexual activities may be an indication of _____ abuse.

2. Public Law 93-247 requires states to write a legal _____ of child abuse and neglect.

3. Injury that is intentionally inflicted on a child is called _____ abuse.

4. Malnutrition, lack of proper clothing, or inadequate adult supervision are examples of physical _____.

5. Verbal abuse sometimes results because of unrealistic parent demands and _____.

6. Emotional or _____ neglect is one of the most difficult forms of neglect to identify.

7. Reporting laws usually require _____ to report suspected cases of child abuse and neglect.

8. Information contained in reports of child abuse or neglect is kept _____.

9. Many abusive adults were abused during their own _____.

10. Lack of _____ makes it difficult for many abusive and neglectful adults to form friendships.

11. Daily contact with children helps teachers to _____ children who are maltreated.

12. Suspected abuse or neglect does not have to be proven before it should be _____.

B. As a Group:

1. Describe five observable clues that might suggest a child is being physically maltreated.

2. Discuss what teachers should do if they suspect that a child is being abused or neglected.

3. Describe what information should be included in both an oral and written report.

4. Discuss four ways that teachers can help abused and neglected children in the classroom.

5. Why does the incidence of child abuse and neglect appear to be higher among disadvantaged families?

6. Discuss how you would respond to a parent or teacher who believes that families have a right to discipline children as they wish to in their own home.

◖ Case Study

When it was time to go outdoors, 3-year-old Casandra said she didn't want to play and headed for her locker. At the teacher's gentle insistence, Casandra reluctantly joined the other children on the playground. Tears rolled down her cheeks when the teacher boosted Casandra onto a swing seat and began to push her. The teacher stopped the swing and helped Casandra off. She held her closely for a few minutes and then asked why she was crying. Casandra initially denied that anything was wrong. However, when the teacher persisted, said she "had fallen the night before and hurt her bottom."

The teacher took Casandra inside and asked to see where she had been hurt. When Casandra pulled down her shorts, the teacher noted what appeared to be a large burn with blisters approximately 2 inches in length by 1 inch in width on her left buttock. Several small bruises were also evident along one side of the burn. Again, the teacher quietly asked Casandra how she had been hurt, and once again she replied that she "had fallen."

1. What actions should Casandra's teacher take?

2. Would you recommend that the teacher report the incident right away or wait until she gathered more evidence? Why?

3. Would your feelings and responses be different if this was a first-time versus a repeated occurrence?

4. How can the teacher begin to help Casandra cope with this experience?

5. What would you suggest the teacher do if this happens again?

Application Activities

1. Gather statistics on the incidence of child abuse and neglect for your city, county, and state. Compare your numbers to the national rates.

2. Write an incident report using the information presented in the Case Study.

3. Develop a pamphlet that illustrates self-protection skills for young children. Use it with a group of 3- to 4-year-olds. Evaluate their response.

4. Identify local agencies that assist abusive or neglectful families in your community. Collect materials from each. Prepare a resource list that includes contact information and a brief description of the services each agency provides. Offer your list to local schools and early childhood programs.

5. Conduct an Internet search to learn about the CASA (Court Appointed Special Advocates) program. What role do they play in helping abused and neglected children? Is there a CASA program in your area? What qualifications are required of volunteer participants?

Helpful Web Resources

American Professional Society on the Abuse of Children	http://www.apsac.org
Boys and Girls Clubs of America	http://www.bgca.org
Child Welfare Information Gateway	http://www.childwelfare.gov
Child Welfare League of America (CWLA)	http://www.cwla.org
Futures Without Violence	http://www.futureswithoutviolence.org/
Prevent Child Abuse America	http://www.preventchildabuse.org
Shaken Baby Alliance	http://www.shakenbaby.com

Visit the Education CourseMate for this textbook to access the eBook, Did You Get It? quizzes, Digital Downloads, TeachSource Video Cases, flashcards, and more. Go to CengageBrain.com to log in, register, or purchase access.

References

American Psychological Association (APA). (2012). Child sexual abuse: What parents should know. Accessed on June 30, 2012 from http://www.apa.org/pi/families/resources/child-sexual-abuse.aspx.

Bruster, B., & Foreman, K. (2012). Mentoring children of prisoners: Program evaluation, *Social Work in Public Health*, 27(1–2), 3–11.

Child Welfare Information Gateway. (2013). *Child abuse and neglect fatalities 2011: Statistics and interventions.* Washington, DC: U.S. Department of Health & Human Services (HHS), Children's Bureau. Accessed on May 6, 2013 from https://www.childwelfare.gov/pubs/factsheets/fatality.cfm.

Child Welfare Information Gateway. (2011). *About CAPTA: A legislative history.* Washington, DC: U.S. Department of Health & Human Services, Children's Bureau.

Debelle, G. (2012). Interpreting physical signs of child maltreatment: 'grey cases' and what is 'reasonably possible', *Paediatrics & Child Health*, 22(11), 470–475.

Easterbrooks, M., Chaudhuri, J., Bartlett, J., & Copeman, A. (2011). Resilience in parenting among young mothers: Family and ecological risks and opportunities, *Children & Youth Services*, 33(1), 42–50.

Fang, X., Brown, D., Florence, C., & Mercy, J. (2012). The economic burden of child maltreatment in the United States and implications for prevention, *Child Abuse & Neglect*, 36(2), 156–165.

Feldman, M., McConnell, D., & Aunos, M. (2012). Parental cognitive impairment, mental health, and child outcomes in a child protection population, *Journal of Mental Health Research in Intellectual Disabilities*, 5(1), 66–90.

Feng, J., Chen, Y., Fetzer, S., Feng, M., & Lin, C. (2012). Ethical and legal challenges of mandated child abuse reporters, *Children & Youth Services Review*, 34(1), 276–280.

Goldman, J., & Grimbeek, P. (2011). Sources of knowledge of departmental policy on child sexual abuse and mandatory reporting identified by primary school student-teachers, *Educational Review*, 63(1), 1–18.

Gray, C., & Montgomery, M. (2012). Links between alcohol and other drug problems and maltreatment among adolescent girls: Perceived discrimination, ethnic identity, and ethnic orientation as moderators, *Child Abuse & Neglect*, 36(5), 449–460.

Hart, H., & Rubia, K. (2012). Neuroimaging of child abuse: A critical review, *Frontiers in Human Neuroscience*, 6, 52. Retrieved from http://www.ncbi.nlm.nih.gov/pmc/articles/PMC3307045/.

Haskett, M., Stelter, R., Proffit, K., & Nice, R. (2012). Parent emotional expressiveness and children's self-regulation: Associations with abused children's school functioning, *Child Abuse & Neglect*, 36(4), 296–307.

James, T., & Countryman, J. (2012). Psychiatric effects of military deployment on children and families, *Innovations in Clinical Neuroscience*, 9(2), 16–20.

Jonson-Reid, M., Kohl, P., & Drake, B. (2012). Child and adult outcomes of chronic child maltreatment, *Pediatrics*, 129(5), 839–845.

Katz, C., Hershkowitz, I., Malloy, L., Lamb, M., Atabaki, A., & Spindler, S. (2012). Non-verbal behavior of children who disclose or do not disclose child abuse in investigative interviews, *Child Abuse & Neglect*, 36(1), 12–20.

Keeshin, B., Cronholm, P., & Strawn, J. (2012). Physiologic changes associated with violence and abuse exposure, *Trauma, Violence & Abuse*, 13(1), 41–56.

Kempe, C. H., & Helfer, R. (Eds.). (1982). *The battered child*. Chicago: University of Chicago Press.

Kim-Spoon, J., Haskett, M., Longo, G., & Nice, R. (2012). Longitudinal study of self-regulation, positive parenting, and adjustment problems among physically abused children, *Child Abuse & Neglect*, 36(2), 95–107.

Lansford, J., Wager, L., Bates, J., Dodge, K., & Pettit, G. (2012). Parental reasoning, denying privileges, yelling, and spanking: Ethnic differences and associations with child externalizing behavior, *Parenting: Science & Practice*, 12(1), 42–56.

Lee, T., Cheung, C., & Kwong, W. (2012). Resilience as a positive youth development construct: A conceptual review, *Scientific World Journal*. Retrieved from http://www.ncbi.nlm.nih.gov/pmc/articles/PMC3353472.

Leeb, R., Bitsko, R., Merrick, M., & Armour, B. (2012). Does childhood disability increase risk for child abuse and neglect?, *Journal of Mental Health Research in Intellectual Disabilities*, 5(1), 4–31.

Leventhal, J., Martin, K., & Gaither, J. (2012). Using US data to estimate the incidence of serious physical abuse in children, *Pediatrics*, 129(3), 458–464.

Lilly, E., & Kundu, R. (2012). Dermatoses secondary to Asian cultural practices, *International Journal of Dermatology*, 51(4), 372–382.

Miller, L., Grabell, A., Thomas, A., Bermann, E., & Graham-Bermann, S. (2012). The associations between community violence, television violence, intimate partner violence, parent–child aggression, and aggression in sibling relationships of a sample of preschoolers, *Psychology of Violence*, 2(2), 165–178.

Mishna, F., Morrison, J., Basarke, S., & Cook, C. (2012). Expanding the playroom: School-based treatment for maltreated children, *Psychoanalytic Social Work*, 19(1), 70–90.

Moxley, K., Squires, J., & Lindstrom, L. (2012). Early intervention and maltreated children: A current look at the Child Abuse Prevention and Treatment Act and Part C, *Infants & Young Children*, 25(1), 3–18.

Nelson, S., Baldwin, N., & Taylor, J. (2012). Mental health problems and medically unexplained physical symptoms in adult survivors of childhood sexual abuse: An integrative literature review, *Journal of Psychiatric & Mental Health Nursing*, 19(3), 211–220.

Oshri, A., Tubman, J., & Burnette, M. (2012). Childhood maltreatment histories, alcohol and other drug use symptoms, and sexual risk behavior in a treatment sample of adolescents, *American Journal of Public Health*, 102(S2), S250–S257.

Petska, H., Sheets, L., & Knox, B. (2013). Facial bruising as a precursor to abusive head trauma, *Clinical Pediatrics*, 52(1), 86–88.

Raman, S., & Hodes, D. (2012). Cultural issues in child maltreatment, *Journal of Paediatrics & Child Health*, 48(1), 30–37.

Roberts, A., Rosario, M., Corliss, H., Koenen, K., & Austin, S. (2012). Childhood gender nonconformity: A risk indicator for childhood abuse and posttraumatic stress in youth, *Pediatrics*, 129(3), 410–417.

Rosenkranz, S., Muller, R., & Henderson, J. (2012). Psychological maltreatment in relation to substance use problem severity among youth, *Child Abuse & Neglect*, 36(5), 438–448.

Ruiz-Casares, M., Rousseau, C., Currie, J., & Heymann, J. (2012). 'I hold on to my teddy bear really tight': Children's experiences when they are home alone, *American Journal of Orthopsychiatry*, 82(1), 97–103.

Schneiderman, J., Hurlburt, M., Leslie, L., Zhang, J., & Horwitz, S. (2012). Child, caregiver, and family characteristics associated with emergency department use by children who remain at home after a child protective services investigation, *Child Abuse & Neglect*, 36(1), 4–11.

Spratt, E., Friedenberg, S., LaRosa, A., De Bellis, M., Macias, M., Summer, A., Hulsey, T., Runyan, D., & Brady, K. (2012). The effects of early neglect on cognitive, language, and behavioral functioning in childhood, *Psychology*, 3(2), 175–182.

Stalker, K., & McArthur, K. (2012). Child abuse, child protection and disabled children: A review of recent research, *Child Abuse Review*, 21(1), 24–40.

Thompson, E., & Trice-Black, S. (2012). School-based group interventions for children exposed to domestic violence, *Journal of Family Violence*, 27(3), 233–241.

USLegal, Inc. (2012). Medical neglect law and legal definition. Accessed on June 30 2012 from http://definitions.uslegal.com/m/medical-neglect.

Valentino, K., Nuttall, A., Comas, M., Borkowski, J., & Akai, C. (2012). Intergenerational continuity of child abuse among adolescent mothers: Authoritarian parenting, community violence, and race, *Child Maltreatment*, 17(2), 172–181.

Vitale, A., Vicedomini, D., Vega, G., Greco, N., & Messi, G. (2012). Shaken baby syndrome: Pathogenetic mechanism, clinical features, and preventive aspects, *Minerva Pediatrica*, 64(6), 641–647.

Waliski, A., Bokony, P., Edlund, C., & Kirchner, J. (2012). Counselors called for service: Impact of parental deployment on preschool children, *The Family Journal*, 20(2), 157–163.

Nutrition Guidelines

▶ **#1 a, b, and c:** Promoting child development and learning
▶ **#2 a and c:** Building family and community relationships
▶ **#3 a, b, c, and d:** Observing, documenting, and assessing to support young children and families
▶ **#6 b, c, and e:** Becoming a professional

Learning Objectives

After studying this chapter, you should be able to:

LO 12-1 Calculate the nutrient content of a meal.

LO 12-2 Use the *Dietary Guidelines for Americans* to achieve your personal nutritional goals.

LO 12-3 Identify the five MyPlate food groups and the major nutrient contributions of each.

LO 12-4 Evaluate the nutritional quality of a food item from its package label.

Diet has a direct effect on the quality of a person's health and well-being. Foods contain **nutrients** that play important roles in supporting and maintaining normal body functions. They:

▶ supply energy
▶ provide materials for growth and maintenance of body tissue
▶ regulate body processes

It is important to note that all persons require the same nutrients throughout their lifetime, but in different amounts. Factors such as age, activity, gender, health status, and lifestyle determine how much of a particular nutrient is needed. For example, young children have a significant need for nutrients that support growth and provide energy; older children and adults require nutrients to maintain and repair body tissue and to provide energy.

Approximately 50 nutrients are known to be essential for humans. **Essential nutrients** can be obtained only from food because they are not produced in the body in adequate amounts. An inadequate intake or poor utilization of nutrients can lead to **malnutrition** or **undernutrition** and disrupt normal body functions that support good health. Malnutrition can also develop from an excessive intake (supplementation) of one or more nutrients to the exclusion of others. This, too, can interfere with normal body functions and cause health problems. Information about the nutrient contributions of specific foods can be accessed online (http://ndb.nal.usda.gov) and in many books.

Nutrition is the study of food and how nutrients are used in the body—from the time food is ingested, digested, nutrients are absorbed and distributed throughout the body, and waste is eliminated. Table 12–1 shows the relationship between nutrients and their primary functions. Note that most nutrients serve one or two main purposes, whereas protein plays a critical role in all three.

nutrients – *the chemical substances in food that the body requires to function properly.*
essential nutrient – *nutrient that must be provided in food because it cannot be synthesized by the body at a rate sufficient to meet its needs.*
malnutrition – *prolonged inadequate or excessive intake of nutrients and/or calories required by the body.*
undernutrition – *an inadequate intake of one or more required or essential nutrients.*
nutrition – *the study of food and how it is used by the body.*

TABLE 12–1   **Nutrients and Their Roles**

	Calories per Gram	Energy	Build/Maintain Body Tissues	Regulators
Carbohydrates	4	×		
Fats	9	×		
Proteins (needed for every function)	4	×	×	×
Minerals			×	×
Water			×	×
Vitamins				×*

*required in a regulatory role only.

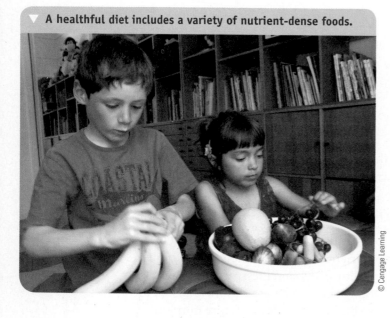

▼ **A healthful diet includes a variety of nutrient-dense foods.**

© Cengage Learning

A healthful diet is based on a daily intake of nutritious foods and meals. Consuming a wide variety of foods ensures that all essential nutrients will be obtained. Some foods contain many nutrients; others yield few. No single food supplies all of the nutrients in amounts adequate to support life. What should we eat? What should we not eat? How much should we eat? The answers to these important questions have led to the development of several nutrition tools and guidelines. Each provides information that promotes healthy eating habits. However, it is up to the individual to make the right choices.

12-1 Dietary Reference Intakes

The "master guideline" for nutrition planning in the United States and Canada is the **Dietary Reference Intakes (DRIs)**. The current DRI guidelines reflect major philosophical and format changes from the original 1941 plan previously known as the Recommended Daily Dietary Allowances (RDAs). DRI recommendations now emphasize the critical relationship that exists between dietary intake, health, and the reduced risk of chronic disease. Table 12–2 illustrates the first two sections of the DRI document, which consists of four basic components:

▶ Recommended Daily Allowance (RDA) – the ideal nutrient intake goals for individuals.
▶ Adequate Intake (AI) – goals for nutrient intake when an RDA has not been determined.
▶ Estimated Average Requirement (EAR) – the amount of a nutrient that is estimated to meet the requirements of 50 percent of the individuals in a given life-stage or gender group; this number is used to establish the RDAs.
▶ Tolerable Upper Intake Level (UL) – the highest intake level that is likely to pose no health risk; exceeding this limit could cause potential toxicity and health risks.

The DRIs are used to set national nutritional policy as well as for planning diets and assessing the nutrient intakes of individuals or groups. They are also used for determining

Dietary Reference Intake (DRI) – *a plan that presents the recommended goals of nutrient intakes for various age and gender groups.*

TABLE 12–2   Dietary Reference Intakes: RDA and AI for Vitamins and Elements

Food and Nutrition Board, Institute of Medicine, National Academies

Life Stage Group	Vitamin A (µg/d)[a]	Vitamin C (mg/d)	Vitamin D (µg/d)[bc]	Vitamin E (mg/d)[d]	Vitamin K (µg/d)	Thiamin (mg/d)	Riboflavin (mg/d)	Niacin (mg/d)[e]	Vitamin B_6 (mg/d)	Folate (µg/d)[f]	Vitamin B_{12} (µg/d)	Pantothenic Acid (mg/d)	Biotin (µg/d)	Choline (mg/d)[g]
Infants														
0 to 6 mo	400*	40*	10	4*	2.0*	0.2*	0.3*	2*	0.1*	65*	0.4*	1.7*	5*	125*
6 to 12 mo	500*	50*	10	5*	2.5*	0.3*	0.4*	4*	0.3*	80*	0.5*	1.8*	6*	150*
Children														
1–3 y	300	15	15	6	30*	0.5	0.5	6	0.5	150	0.9	2*	8*	200*
4–8 y	400	25	15	7	55*	0.6	0.6	8	0.6	200	1.2	3*	12*	250*
Males														
9–13 y	600	45	15	11	60*	0.9	0.9	12	1.0	300	1.8	4*	20*	375*
14–18 y	900	75	15	15	75*	1.2	1.3	16	1.3	400	2.4	5*	25*	550*
19–30 y	900	90	15	15	120*	1.2	1.3	16	1.3	400	2.4	5*	30*	550*
31–50 y	900	90	15	15	120*	1.2	1.3	16	1.3	400	2.4	5*	30*	550*
51–70 y	900	90	15	15	120*	1.2	1.3	16	1.7	400	2.4[h]	5*	30*	550*
>70 y	900	90	20	15	120*	1.2	1.3	16	1.7	400	2.4[h]	5*	30*	550*
Females														
9–13 y	600	45	15	11	60*	0.9	0.9	12	1.0	300	1.8	4*	20*	375*
14–18 y	700	65	15	15	75*	1.0	1.0	14	1.2	400[i]	2.4	5*	25*	400*
19–30 y	700	75	15	15	90*	1.1	1.1	14	1.3	400[i]	2.4	5*	30*	425*
31–50 y	700	75	15	15	90*	1.1	1.1	14	1.3	400[i]	2.4	5*	30*	425*
51–70 y	700	75	15	15	90*	1.1	1.1	14	1.5	400	2.4[h]	5*	30*	425*
>70 y	700	75	20	15	90*	1.1	1.1	14	1.5	400	2.4[h]	5*	30*	425*
Pregnancy														
14–18 y	750	80	15	15	75*	1.4	1.4	18	1.9	600[j]	2.6	6*	30*	450*
19–30 y	770	85	15	15	90*	1.4	1.4	18	1.9	600[j]	2.6	6*	30*	450*
31–50 y	770	85	15	15	90*	1.4	1.4	18	1.9	600[j]	2.6	6*	30*	450*
Lactation														
14–18 y	1,200	115	15	19	75*	1.4	1.6	17	2.0	500	2.8	7*	35*	550*
19–30 y	1,300	120	15	19	90*	1.4	1.6	17	2.0	500	2.8	7*	35*	550*
31–50y	1,300	120	15	19	90*	1.4	1.6	17	2.0	500	2.8	7*	35*	550*

Note: This table (taken from the DRI reports, see www.nap.edu) presents Recommended Dietary Allowances (RDAs) in **bold type** and Adequate Intakes (AIs) in ordinary type followed by an asterisk (*). An RDA is the average daily dietary intake level; sufficient to meet the nutrient requirements of nearly all (97–98 percent) healthy individuals in a group. It is calculated from an Estimated Average Requirement (EAR). If sufficient scientific evidence is not available to establish an EAR, and thus calculate an RDA, an AI is usually developed. For healthy breastfed infants, an AI is the mean intake. The AI for other life stage and gender groups is believed to cover the needs of all healthy individuals in the groups, but lack of data or uncertainty in the data prevent being able to specify with confidence the percentage of individuals covered by this intake.

[a]As retinol activity equivalents (RAEs). 1 RAE = 1 µg retinol, 12 µg β-carotene, 24 µg α-carotene, or 24 µg β-cryptoxanthin. The RAE for dietary provitamin A carotenoids is two-fold greater than retinol equivalents (RE), whereas the RAE for preformed vitamin A is the same as RE.

[b]As cholecalciferol. 1 µg cholecalciferol = 40 IU vitamin D.

[c]Under the assumption of minimal sunlight.

[d]As α-tocopherol. α-Tocopherol includes *RRR*-α-tocopherol, the only form of α-tocopherol that occurs naturally in foods, and the 2*R*-stereoisomeric forms of α-tocopherol (*RRR*-, *RSR*-, *RRS*-, and *RSS*-α-tocopherol) that occur in fortified foods and supplements. It does not include the 2*S*-stereoisomeric forms of α-tocopherol (*SRR*-, *SSR*-, *SRS*-, and *SSS*-α-tocopherol), also found in fortified foods and supplements.

[e]As niacin equivalents (NE). 1 mg of niacin = 60 mg of tryptophan; 0–6 months = preformed niacin (not NE).

[f]As dietary folate equivalents (DFE). 1 DFE = 1 µg food folate = 0.6 µg of folic acid from fortified food or as a supplement consumed with food = 0.5 µg of a supplement taken on an empty stomach.

[g]Although AIs have been set for choline, there are few data to assess whether a dietary supply of choline is needed at all stages of the life cycle, and it may be that the choline requirement can be met by endogenous synthesis at some of these stages.

[h]Because 10 to 30 percent of older people may malabsorb food-bound B₁₂, it is advisable for those older than 50 years to meet their RDA mainly by consuming foods fortified with B₁₂ or a supplement containing B₁₂.

[i]In view of evidence linking folate intake with neural tube defects in the fetus, it is recommended that all women capable of becoming pregnant consume 400 µg from supplements or fortified foods in addition to intake of food folate from a varied diet.

[j]It is assumed that women will continue consuming 400 µg from supplements or fortified food until their pregnancy is confirmed and they enter prenatal care, which ordinarily occurs after the end of the periconceptional period—the critical time for formation of the neural tube.

Sources: Dietary Reference Intakes for Calcium, Phosphorous, Magnesium, Vitamin D, and Fluoride (1997); Dietary Reference Intakes for Thiamin, Riboflavin, Niacin, Vitamin D, Folate, Vitamin B₆, Pantothenic Acid, Biotin, and Choline (1998); Dietary Reference Intakes for Vitamin C, Vitamin E, Selenium, and Carotenoids (2000); Dietary Reference Intakes for Vitamin A, Vitamin K, Arsenic, Boron, Chromium, Copper, Iodine, Iron, Manganese, Molybdenum, Nickel, Silicon, Vanadium, and Zinc (2001); Dietary Reference Intakes for Water, Potassium, Sodium, Chloride, and Sulfate (2005); and Dietary Reference Intakes for Calcium and Vitamin D (2011). These reports may be accessed via www.nap.edu.

Did You Get It?

The Dietary Reference Intakes (DRI) has replaced which of the following previously looked-to source for nutritional intake?

a. Recommended Daily Dietary Allowances

b. The Food Pyramid Groups

c. The Essential Nutrients Chart

d. The Dietary Reference Values of the United Kingdom.

Take the full quiz on CourseMate.

the nutrient information provided on food labels (Batada et al., 2012). It is suggested that RDAs, AIs, and ULs be used in planning diets for individuals, whereas the EAR is more effectively used for planning and assessing the nutrient intake of individuals and groups (Bucholz, Desai, & Rosenthal, 2011).

The DRI can be used to evaluate the nutrient contributions of an individual's 24-hour food intake. This can be determined by:

1. Listing the amounts of all foods and beverages consumed during one 24-hour period.
2. Looking up the nutrients in each food item and beverage consumed.
3. Totaling the values for each nutrient (e.g., calcium, sodium, protein).
4. Comparing each nutrient total with the DRIs (for the correct age and gender) (Table 12–2) to determine if it is deficient or adequately meets recommendations.

12-2 Dietary Guidelines for Americans

The National Nutrition Monitoring and Related Research Act of 1990 requires the Secretaries of Health and Human Services (HHS) and the U.S. Department of Agriculture (USDA) to issue a joint report, called the *Dietary Guidelines for Americans*, at least every 5 years. This document reflects the Advisory Committee's efforts to establish recommendations based on latest scientific evidence regarding nutrition's role in health maintenance and disease prevention. The current edition is available online (http://www.cnpp.usda.gov/DGAs2010-PolicyDocument.htm). A new document, *Dietary Guidelines for Americans, 2015*, is scheduled to be released in the fall of 2015.

Did You Know...

that salt occurs naturally in many foods, but added salt in restaurant, fast food, and processed foods accounts for nearly 80 percent of a person's total daily intake?

The *Dietary Guidelines* have come to serve as the basis for nearly all nutrition information in the United States (USDA, 2010). Whereas the DRIs focus on specific nutrients and age groups, the *Dietary Guidelines* assume a broader approach and provide advice about healthy eating, weight management, and increasing physical activity for persons 2 years of age and older. The document includes 23 health-promoting recommendations, which are summarized in Table 12–3.

Canada has developed similar guidelines in a document entitled, *Canada's Food Guide*. Citizens are encouraged to achieve good health by choosing nutritious foods and limiting foods that are

---

FIGURE 12–1 Physical activity recommendations for children.

The American Academy of Pediatrics (AAP), National Association for Sport & Physical Education (NASPE), and Canadian Academy of Sport Medicine (CASM) encourage daily physical activity for children of all ages:

— *infants* should have ample opportunities to explore their environment and should not be confined to a stroller or carrier for longer than 60 minutes/day.

— *toddlers* should accumulate at least 30 minutes of structured, vigorous physical activity and at least 60 minutes or more of free play.

— *preschoolers and school-age children* should participate in at least 60 minutes of structured physical activity during the day. They should also be given opportunities to engage in several hours of unstructured physical activity.

Dietary Guidelines for Americans – *a report that provides recommendations for daily food choices, to be balanced with physical activity, to promote good health and reduce certain disease risks.*

TABLE 12–3   Dietary Guidelines for Americans 2010: Key Recommendations

Balancing calories to manage weight:

- Prevent or reduce overweight and obesity through improved eating and physical activity behaviors during each stage of life.
- Control total calorie intake to manage body weight; consume fewer calories from foods and beverages if currently overweight.
- Increase physical activity and reduce time spent in sedentary behaviors.

Foods and food components to increase:

Recommendations for healthy eating should be made while staying within calorie needs.

- Increase vegetable and fruit intake. Eat a variety of vegetables, especially dark green, red, and orange vegetables, beans, and peas.
- Consume at least half of all grains as whole grains.
- Increase intake of fat-free or low-fat milk and dairy products (e.g., yogurt, cheese, or fortified soy beverages).
- Choose a variety of lean protein foods (e.g., seafood, meat and poultry, eggs, beans, peas, soy products, and unsalted nuts and seeds).
- Replace solid fats with oils where possible.
- Choose foods that provide potassium, dietary fiber, calcium, and vitamin D (often low in American diets): vegetables, fruits, whole grains, milk, and milk products.

Foods and food components to reduce:

- Reduce sodium to 2,300 milligrams (mg); African Americans, persons 51 and older, or anyone who has high blood pressure, diabetes, or chronic kidney disease should further reduce this level to 1,500 mg (Figure 12–2).
- Consume less than 10 percent of calories from saturated fatty acids; replace them with monounsaturated and polyunsaturated fats.
- Consume less than 300 mg per day of dietary cholesterol.
- Keep trans-fatty acid consumption as low as possible.
- Reduce intake of calories from solid fats, added sugars, and refined grains.
- If alcohol is consumed, it should be done in moderation (1 drink per day for women, 2 for men).

Building healthy eating patterns:

- Select an eating pattern that meets nutrient needs over time and within an appropriate calorie level.
- Follow food safety recommendations when preparing and eating foods to reduce the risk of foodborne illnesses.

Source: Adapted from, *Dietary Guidelines for Americans 2010: Executive Summary.* Accessed online from http://www.cnpp. usda.gov/Publications/DietaryGuidelines/2010/PolicyDoc/ExecSumm.pdf.

high in sodium, sugar, fats, and calories. A companion document, *Canada's Physical Activity Guide to Healthy Active Living*, stresses the importance of maintaining an active lifestyle.

Early childhood programs have an obligation to promote healthy eating and physical activity behaviors given the significant increase in childhood obesity. Excessive weight and sedentary lifestyles have been linked to the development of many chronic diseases and, thus, pose a serious public health concern. Schools must take an active role in addressing this problem by adhering to Dietary Guideline recommendations when serving food to children and by incorporating more physical activity throughout the day (AHA, 2012; NASPE, 2012).

12-2a Additional Nutrition Guidelines

The U.S. Public Health Service continues to update the original *Healthy People* guidelines. Several statements in the *Healthy People 2020* document that specifically address children's nutritional needs are:

- eliminating very low food insecurity among children in U.S. households
- reducing the proportion of children who are overweight or obese

▶ǀǀ TeachSource Video Connections

Young Children's Stages of Play: An Illustrated Guide

Children are inherently active individuals and express this behavior through their lively play. Nutrition guidelines urge all of us to maintain a healthy weight by balancing calorie intake with physical activity. As you watch the learning video, *Young Children's Stages of Play: An Illustrated Guide,* consider the following questions:

1. Why do you think children become more sedentary as they get older?

2. How can teachers and parents use play to help children maintain a physically active lifestyle?

3. What activities could you plan to keep children physically active during each stage of play described in this video?

Watch on CourseMate.

▶ increasing the contribution of fruits, vegetables, whole grains, and calcium to the diets of children 2 years and older

▶ reducing the consumption of calories from solid fats and added sugars in the population aged 2 years and older

▶ increasing the number of states and school districts that require regularly scheduled elementary school recess

▶ increasing the proportion of consumers who follow key food safety practices

Several non-profit organizations, including the American Heart Association and the National Cancer Institute, also advise similar healthy eating and physical activity behaviors. Their guidelines call for reducing dietary fat, cholesterol, sodium, and alcohol and increasing vegetable, fruit, low-fat dairy, and whole grain consumption.

© 2015 Cengage Learning

Did You Get It?

The Dietary Guidelines for Americans report recommends that all individuals reduce their sodium intake, especially those of which race or ethnicity?

a. Hispanic-American

b. Asian-American

c. Native-American

d. African-American

Take the full quiz on CourseMate.

12-3 MyPlate

The new MyPlate model replaces the Food Guide Pyramid and provides a graphic representation of the Dietary Guidelines for Americans (Figure 12–2). The Food Pyramid proved to be confusing for many consumers and presented information in a way that had limited appeal and functionality. The simplified MyPlate format presents critical dietary recommendations in a concise manner that is easier for the public to understand and to implement. It also conveys a strong preventive message and emphasizes the importance of balancing caloric intake with physical activity, consuming a greater variety of foods from each food group, and limiting foods high in sugar, fats, and calories. MyPlate also encourages consumers to incorporate more low-fat dairy products into their diet, and to fill half of their plate with fruits and vegetables, one-fourth with whole grains, and the remaining fourth with a lean protein food.

The ChooseMyPlate website (http://www.choosemyplate.gov) has also been improved and now offers comprehensive food charts, portion sizes (based on age), nutrient contributions and health benefits, and preparation suggestions for each food category. Separate sections address the specific health and nutrition needs of young children, children over 5 years, pregnant and breastfeeding women (locate by clicking on "Site Map"). The site also gives consumers access to extensive resource information about calories, weight management, physical activities, healthy eating suggestions (e.g., vegetarian, food safety, recipes, sample menus), and tips for eating out. The SuperTracker

Did You Know...

studies have shown that eating a diet rich in a variety of fruits and vegetables can reduce a person's risk of developing some cancers?

?

feature provides an opportunity for individuals to plan and monitor their food calorie intake and expenditures, as well as offering menu plans and information about portion sizes and reading food labels. The ChooseMyPlate website is easy to navigate and provides consumers with sound nutritional information for making healthy choices. It also offers extensive resources that teachers can use and incorporate into health and nutrition lessons.

FIGURE 12–2 The MyPlate model presents extensive nutrition and physical activity information in a clear and easy-to-use manner.

12-3a Vegetables

The Vegetable group is composed of food items in an array of colors and flavors. Vegetables contribute notable amounts of minerals, vitamins, and fiber to a person's diet and are low in fat and calories (Table 12–4). The vegetable group is organized into five subgroups according to their nutrient strengths: dark green; starchy; red and orange; beans and peas; and other. Daily food selections should include dark green vegetables such as broccoli and leafy greens, which are rich in vitamins A and C, as well as orange-red foods such as sweet potatoes, squash, tomatoes, and carrots, which are rich in vitamin A (Table 12–4). Adults should consume 2½–3 cups of vegetables daily (based on a 2,000-calorie intake); children 2 to 3 years old require 1 cup and 4- to 8-year-olds should have 1½ cups.

Dietary fiber continues to receive attention for its health-promoting benefits, yet many children's (and adults') intake is deficient because their diet lacks fruits and vegetables (Osborne & Forestell, 2012; Pabayo et al., 2012). Efforts to increase children's acceptance of different vegetables is an important issue to address (see Chapter 17). However, too much fiber in a child's diet can interfere with the absorption of essential vitamins and minerals. A practical recommendation for fiber intake for children over 2 years of age is the "age plus 5" rule. For example, Tasha, age 3 years, would require 8 grams of fiber per day. A sampling of food sources and their fiber contribution is presented in Table 12–5.

12-3b Fruits

The Fruit group is a major contributor of vitamins, especially vitamins A, C, potassium, folate (folic acid), and dietary fiber. Choosing a variety of fruits that are of different colors improves nutrient intake. Children are usually more receptive to eating fruit because it is sweet. Fruit can be prepared and served in many ways to increase its appeal to children (e.g., frozen, in smoothies, in muffins, with a nutritious yogurt dip). Adults are encouraged to consume the equivalent of 2 cups of fruit daily, whereas children 2 to 3 years old need 1 cup and 4- to 8-year-olds require 1 to 1 1/2 cups. At least one vitamin C–rich and one vitamin A–rich selection should be included in a child's diet every day (Table 12–4 and Table 12–6).

TABLE 12–4 Good to Excellent Vitamin A Sources

cantaloupe	winter squash
carrots	greens
pumpkin	apricots
sweet potatoes	watermelon*
spinach	broccoli

*May cause allergic reactions.

TABLE 12–5   **Dietary Fiber in Common Foods**

Food	Amount	Fiber (gram)
Cheerios®	1/2 cup	1.5
Raisin bran	1/2 cup	2.5
oatmeal	1/4 cup	1.9
macaroni, enriched	1/2 cup	1.3
bread, whole wheat	1/2 slice	0.9
bread, white	1/2 slice	0.6
graham crackers	1 square	0.5
orange sections	1/2 cup	2.2
banana, sliced	1/2 cup	1.9
apple with skin	1/2 cup	1.3
acorn squash	1/4 cup	2.3
green peas	1/4 cup	2.2
corn, frozen	1/4 cup	1.0
pinto beans	1/2 cup	5.5
black beans	1/2 cup	7.5

12-3c Grains

Foods such as breads, breakfast cereals, pastas, and a variety of whole grains make up the Grains group. Items from this group provide complex carbohydrates, B vitamins, minerals, and dietary fiber and are known to decrease the risk of chronic diseases, such as diabetes, heart disease, and hypertension. The Grains group is divided into two subcategories: whole grains and refined grains. Recommendations suggest that at least half of the grains an individual consumes each day should be whole grain. Whole grain products retain all of their original nutrients and are an ideal source of dietary fiber. Some grains are refined to improve their texture and shelf-life but the process removes important vitamins and minerals. Manufacturers are required to restore these nutrients so they are equivalent to the original whole grain. Breads and cereals are examples of foods that must be fortified or enriched with iron, calcium, thiamin, riboflavin, and niacin. Most grain products today are also fortified with folacin (folic acid), which reduces the incidence of spina bifida, cleft lip, and cleft palate birth defects (Colapinto et al., 2012).

A typical serving from the Grain group consists of one slice of bread, 1 cup of dry, ready-to-eat cereal, or 1/2 cup (1 ounce) of cooked rice, cereal, or pasta. A child's serving size is approximately one-half that of an adult's. Adults should consume the equivalent of 6 ounces of grains daily; children 2 to 3 years require 3 ounces, and 4- to 8-year-olds should have 5 ounces.

TABLE 12–6   **Good to Excellent Vitamin C Sources**

orange*	tomatoes*
orange juice*	grapefruit*
strawberries*	mustard greens
cauliflower	spinach
broccoli	cabbage
sweet peppers, red or green	tangerine*

*May cause allergic reactions.

12-3d Protein Foods

The Protein Foods group consists of meats (e.g., beef, veal, pork, lamb, wild game), seafood, poultry, eggs, beans and peas, nuts and seeds (nut butters), and soy products. Food items in this group play an important role in promoting children's growth. They provide critical nutrients, including **protein**, B vitamins, iron, zinc, and magnesium. Foods from this group should be selected carefully to avoid those high in calories, fat, and cholesterol. Consumers are encouraged to include more non-meat protein sources (e.g., beans, peas, nuts and seeds, soy products) in their diet to lower fat and cholesterol intake (Akbaraly et al., 2011). Information to help individuals make healthier choices is offered on the ChooseMyPlate website.

The recommended daily intake from the Protein Foods group, as with the other groups, varies according to age, gender, and level of physical activity. Children 2 to 3 years old require approximately 2 ounces of protein equivalents daily; children 4 to 8 should receive 4 ounces; adults should consume between 5 and 6 1/2 ounces. The following foods contain protein that is approximately equivalent to 1 ounce of meat, poultry, or fish:

1 egg
1/4 cup cooked dried peas or beans
2 tablespoons peanut butter
1/2 ounce nuts or seeds
1/4 cup tofu
2 tablespoons hummus

12-3e Dairy

This group includes milk and milk-based products that retain their **calcium** content, such as home-made pudding, frozen yogurt, ice cream; hard cheeses such as Swiss and cheddar; soft cheeses such as ricotta and cottage cheese; yogurt; and calcium-fortified soy milk. This group is a major supplier of the mineral calcium, which is essential for healthy bone development and tooth formation. Dairy products that provide little or no calcium include butter, cream cheese, and cream and are not considered part of the Dairy group. Food examples that provide the amount of calcium equivalent to one cup of milk include:

1 1/2 ounces cheddar, mozzarella,	2 cups cottage cheese or Swiss cheese
1 cup pudding or frozen yogurt	1 cup plain yogurt
1 1/2 cups ice cream	1 cup calcium-enriched soy milk

The Dairy group is a primary source of dietary calcium, potassium, and vitamin D, but also a poor source of iron and vitamins A and C. Children 2 to 3 years old should consume 2 cups of milk daily or the equivalent from this group; 4- to 8-year-olds require 2 1/2 cups; adults should have 3 cups. Servings may be divided into 1/2-cup portions in consideration of children's smaller appetites and stomach capacity. The number of servings reflects new recommendations that have been increased for calcium and vitamin D intake. Whenever possible, low-fat or fat-free items should be selected because foods in the Dairy group tend to be high in fat and cholesterol. However, children should not be given low-fat milk and dairy products prior to the age of 2. Infants and toddlers require the critical fats and fat-calories contained in whole milk and milk products to meet their high energy needs and to support healthy nervous system development (Parletta, Milte, & Meyer, 2013).

12-3f Oils

Oils are not considered a food group but they are present in many food items. The Oils group consists of two subgroups: oils and solid fats. Oils, such as canola, corn, cottonseed, olive, and

---

protein – *class of nutrients used primarily for structural and regulatory functions.*
calcium – *mineral nutrient; a major component of bones and teeth.*

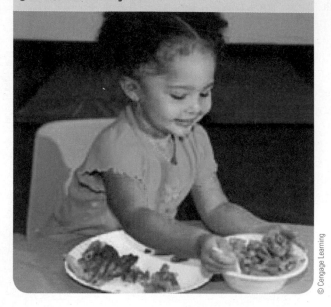

▼ **Children's nutrient needs are influenced by age, gender, and activity level.**

© Cengage Learning

sunflower, are liquid at room temperature and are often used in cooking. Some oils, such as walnut oil and sesame oil, are used primarily for flavoring. Plant oils contain no cholesterol and are considered beneficial. Foods such as nuts, olives, avocados, and fish have a high oil content that also offers health benefits. Mayonnaise, certain salad dressings, and soft (tub or squeeze) margarines that do not contain trans-fats are considered oils.

Solid fats are food products, such as butter, that have been prepared from animal sources. Stick and soft margarines are also classified as solid fats because they are made by converting liquid oil to a solid form through a process called hydrogenation. In general, the nutrient contribution of this group is low and the calorie content is high. Adults should limit their daily oil intake to a maximum equivalent of 5 to 7 teaspoons; young children should have no more than 3 to 4 teaspoons.

12-3g   Empty Calories

Foods from each of the MyPlate groups yield calories for energy. How many calories an individual requires varies according to age, gender, and level of physical activity. The new interactive SuperTracker feature on the ChooseMyPlate website allows individuals to monitor their food intake, record calories burned, and use the information to make healthier decisions.

Many foods also include empty calories, primarily sugars and fats. They are called "empty" because they contribute only calories to a person's diet and few other nutrients. Empty calories add up quickly and can lead to weight gain. They also dilute the quality of a person's healthy diet when too many food items with empty calories are included (Isoldi et al., 2012). For example, the potassium and vitamin C contribution of a banana are significantly altered when sugars, fats, and flour are added (Table 12–7).

Did You Get It?

Citrus fruits, strawberries, and tomatoes are all excellent sources of vitamin C and share what other trait that should be considered when preparing a classroom snack?

a. They all promote healthy teeth and bones
b. They can all cause allergic reactions
c. They improve memory
d. They can help prevent osteoporosis

Take the full quiz on CourseMate.

TABLE 12–7   How Added Sugar and Fats Alter a Food's Calories and Nutrient Contribution

	Calories	Potassium	Vitamin C
Banana, 1/2 cup sliced	67	211 mg	5.0 mg
Banana chips, 1 ounce	147	152 mg	1.8 mg
Banana pudding, 1/2 cup	72	62 mg	0.3 mg
Banana bread, 1 slice	196	80 mg	1.0 mg
Banana cream pie, 1/8 pie	387	238 mg	2.3 mg
Banana waffle, 1 small round	212	140 mg	1.1 mg

CONNECTING TO EVERYDAY PRACTICE

Eat Locally Campaign

Consumers are increasingly being encouraged to purchase and eat more locally grown foods. Concerns about sustainability practices, energy costs, and food safety have contributed significantly to this recent movement. Produce grown within a 100 mile radius retains more of its nutrients and is often more affordable. Eating locally also supports the farmers and has economic benefits for communities.

Think About This:

▶ In what ways does the MyPlate nutrition guide support this trend?

▶ What key recommendations in the *Dietary Guidelines for Healthy Americans* would be reinforced by eating locally?

▶ How might this trend contribute to lower obesity rates and improve children's intake of vitamins A and C?

12-4 Food Labels

The Nutritional Labeling and Education Act of 1990 led to significant changes in food product labeling. The food label, regulated by the U.S. Food and Drug Administration (FDA) and the U.S. Department of Agriculture (USDA), underwent further revision in 1994 (Figure 12–3) and resulted in the current label format that appears on all packaged food products. The redesign makes it easier for consumers to locate, understand, and use nutrient information when purchasing foods (Miller & Cassady, 2012). Labels provide:

▶ Manufacturer's name and contact information (e.g., address, telephone number) and country of origin.
▶ Product net weight.
▶ Standardized serving sizes that are consistent for similar foods (e.g., cereals, crackers, canned/frozen vegetables) and in amounts that are typically consumed. This prevents manufacturers from basing nutrient information on a smaller serving size in order to make their food product appear healthier than that of competing brands.
▶ A list of all ingredients– in descending order according to weight.
▶ **Percent Daily Values (%DV)** that show how a serving of food fits into a person's daily diet.
▶ **Nutrition and health claims** that are regulated and based on proven scientific findings (Figure 12–4).
▶ Warnings about any potentially allergenic substances that might be included.

Food allergens (milk, eggs, tree nuts [such as almonds, walnuts], peanuts, shellfish [such as shrimp, crab, lobster], fish, wheat, and soy) that could potentially cause life-threatening reactions for some individuals must be clearly identified (U.S. FDA, 2013a). Manufacturers may include health claims, such as "reduces the risk of heart disease," as long as there is scientific evidence to support the statement.

Laws have been proposed by the FDA that would require nutrient labels on foods sold in vending machines and in chain restaurants (with more than twenty locations) (U.S. FDA, 2013b). The FDA is also working with food manufacturers to design a uniform format for front-of-package labels that would include key nutrient information. They believe this addition will help to address obesity and diet-related diseases in this country by encouraging consumers to compare brands and make healthier food choices. Some manufacturers have already begun to adopt new front-of-package labeling despite the lack of regulatory guidelines.

Percent Daily Values (%DV) – *measures of the nutritional values of food; used in nutrition labeling.*
nutrition claims – *statements of reduced calories, fat, or salt on the food labels.*

FIGURE 12-3   A typical food label.

Nutrition Facts
Serving Size 3/4 cup (30g)
Servings Per Container about 15

Amount Per Serving	Cereal	Cereal with 1/2 cup Skim Milk
Calories	100	140
Calories from Fat	5	5

	% Daily Value**	
Total Fat 0.5g*	**1%**	**1%**
Saturated Fat 0g	**0%**	**0%**
Polyunsaturated Fat 0g		
Monounsaturated Fat 0g		
Cholesterol 0mg	**0%**	**0%**
Sodium 220mg	**9%**	**12%**
Potassium 190mg	**5%**	**11%**
Total Carbohydrate 24g	**8%**	**10%**
Dietary Fiber 5g	**21%**	**21%**
Soluble Fiber 1g		
Insoluble Fiber 4g		
Sugars 6g		
Other Carbohydrate 13g		
Protein 3g		
Vitamin A	15%	20%
Vitamin C	0%	2%
Calcium	0%	15%
Iron	45%	45%
Vitamin D	10%	25%
Thiamin	25%	30%
Riboflavin	25%	35%
Niacin	25%	25%
Vitamin B$_6$	25%	25%
Folate	25%	25%
Vitamin B$_{12}$	25%	35%
Phosphorus	15%	25%
Magnesium	15%	20%
Zinc	10%	15%
Copper	10%	10%

*Amount in Cereal. One half cup skim milk contributes an additional 40 calories, 65mg sodium, 200mg potassium, 6g total carbohydrate (6g sugars), and 4g protein.

**Percent Daily Values are based on a 2,000 calorie diet. Your daily values may be higher or lower depending on your calorie needs:

	Calories:	2,000	2,500
Total Fat	Less than	65g	80g
Saturated Fat	Less than	20g	25g
Cholesterol	Less than	300mg	300mg
Sodium	Less than	2,400mg	2,400mg
Potassium		3,500mg	3,500mg
Total Carbohydrate		300g	375g
Dietary Fiber		25g	30g

FIGURE 12-4   Commonly used labeling terms defined.

WHAT SOME CLAIMS MEAN

high-protein: at least 10 grams (g) high-quality protein per serving

good source of calcium: at least 100 milligrams (mg) calcium per serving

more iron: at least 1.8 mg more iron per serving than reference food. (Label will say 10 percent more of the Daily Value for iron.)

fat-free: less than 0.5 g fat per serving

low-fat: 3 g or less fat per serving. (If the serving size is 30 g or less or 2 tablespoons or less, 3 g or less fat per 50 g of the food.)

reduced or fewer calories: at least 25 percent fewer calories per serving than the reference food

sugar-free: less than 0.5 g sugar per serving

reduced sugar: reduced sugar: at least 25% less sugar per serving when compared with a similar food

sodium-free: less than 5 mg of sodium per serving

light or lite (two meanings):

■ one-third fewer calories or 50% less fat per serving than the reference food. (If more than half of the food's calories are from fat, the fat must be reduced by 50 percent)

■ a "low-calorie" or "low-fat" food whose sodium content has been reduced by 50 percent of the reference food

low cholesterol: 20 mg or less of cholesterol and 2 g or less of saturated fat per serving

12-4a Calories from Fat

Food labels must disclose the amount of fat, saturated fat, trans-fats, and number of calories derived from fat in a product. Consumers can use this information to determine the percentage of total calories that are derived from fat:

$$\text{Percent of calories from fat} = \frac{\text{Calories from fat/serving}}{\text{Calories/serving}} \times 100$$

If a food is not labeled or does not include the number of calories from fat, you can determine this figure by multiplying the total fat grams by 9 (number of calories in 1 fat gram):

$$\text{calories from fat} = \text{grams (g) of fat/serving} \times 9 \text{ (cal/g)}.$$

Knowing the percentage of calories from fat can help the consumer make an educated decision about a food's nutrient quality and avoid being misled by claims that a product is low-fat, fat-free, nutritious, or healthy. The following examples illustrate this point:

Cheddar cheese 1 ounce = 115 calories and 9 g of fat:

Calories from fat = 9 × 9 = 81
Percent calories from fat = 81/115 × 100 = 70%

Eggs one egg = 75 calories and 6 g of fat:

Calories from fat = 6 × 9 = 54
Percent calories from fat = 54/75 × 100 = 72%

90% fat-free ground beef 3 ounces = 185 calories and 10 g of fat:

Calories from fat = 10 × 9 = 90
Percent calories from fat = 90/185 × 100 = 49%

Low-fat cream cheese 1 tablespoon = 30 calories and 2.3 g of fat:

Calories from fat = 2.3 × 9 = 20.7
Percent calories from fat = 20.7/30 × 100 = 69%

In each example, the grams of fat (9, 6, 10, and 2.3) appear to be relatively low, yet they represent more than 50 percent of the total calories. This may surprise many consumers and illustrates why this information is important to know. Should these foods be eliminated from our diets? No, but they should be consumed in moderation (portion size) and perhaps less often. For example, if you order a lean hamburger with 49 percent fat-calories, it might be better to skip the French fries at 47 percent fat-calories and substitute an apple, banana, or lettuce salad, which contain less than 10 percent of their calories from fat.

PARTNERING with FAMILIES

Children's Sugar Consumption

Dear Families,

Several meal-planning tools are available to help you meet children's nutrient needs for growth and well-being and limit those that are not beneficial. The *Dietary Guidelines for Americans*, for example, encourage individuals to reduce added sugars in their diet for better health.

▶ Follow a diet that is moderate in sugar. Many foods, such as milk/dairy products and fruit, supply naturally occurring sugars as well as important vitamins and minerals. Foods that have sugars added during processing or preparation contribute extra calories and are often low in essential dietary nutrients. Although sugar is not harmful when consumed in limited amounts, it also has no particular benefits.

(continued)

Children's Sugar Consumption (*continued*)

▶ Know your food labels: A *reduced sugar* food item contains at least 25 percent less sugar than the reference food. *No added sugar* or *without added sugar* foods indicate that no sugars were added during processing or packaging. *Sugar-free* foods contain less than 0.5 grams sugar per serving.

▶ The following terms, if listed as the first or second ingredient on a food label, indicate the food is likely high in sugar: brown sugar, corn sweetener or corn syrup, fructose, fruit juice concentrate, glucose, dextrose, high-fructose corn syrup, honey, lactose, maltose, molasses, raw sugar, table sugar (sucrose), agave syrup.

▶ Major food sources of sugar in the United States include sodas, cakes, candy, cookies, pies, fruit drinks and punches, and dairy desserts such as ice cream. Healthier foods that contain added sugar should also be limited in children's diet: chocolate milk, presweetened cereals, prepared puddings, and fruits packed in syrup. If these foods are served, do so in moderation and choose smaller serving sizes. (A serving of soda in the 1950s was 6.5 ounces compared to a 20-ounce serving today!)

You can find many suggestions and recipes for healthy snacks and meals that are low in sugars (and economical) on the ChooseMyPlate website (http://www.choosemyplate.gov).

CLASSROOM CORNER

Teacher Activities

Tasting a Rainbow . . .

(PreK–2; NHES **National Health Education Standards 1.2.1 and 8.2.1)**

Concept: Fruits and vegetables are healthy foods to eat and we should eat a variety of them.

Learning Objectives

▶ Children will learn that fruits and vegetables are healthy foods to eat.

▶ Children will experience tasting a variety of fruits and vegetables.

Supplies

▶ one red fruit and vegetable (apple, strawberry, tomato, watermelon, red pepper)

▶ one orange fruit and vegetable (orange, acorn squash, orange pepper, cantaloupe, yam, carrot)

▶ one green fruit and vegetable (grape, lime, spinach, kale, honeydew, green pepper, apple, pear, broccoli, bean, pea, kiwi)

▶ one yellow fruit and vegetable (banana, mango, pineapple, lemon, yellow squash, corn)

▶ one purple fruit and vegetable (purple grape, purple cabbage, purple potato)

▶ one blue fruit (blueberry)

▶ hand wipes, plates, forks

(*continued*)

CLASSROOM CORNER

Teacher Activities *(continued)*

Learning Activities

▶ Read and discuss one of the following books:

- *Apples Grow on a Tree* (How fruits and vegetables grow) by Mari Schul
- *The ABCs of Fruits & Vegetables* by Steve Charney & David Goldbeck
- *The Vegetables We Eat* by Gail Gibbons

▶ Talk with the children about how bodies need nutritious foods, such as fruits and vegetables, to stay healthy and help us grow. Show children a picture of a rainbow; explain that fruits and vegetables come in many colors, like a rainbow.

▶ Have children wash their hands with wipes. Hand each child a plate with fruit, a plate with vegetables, and a fork. Make sure all the fruits and vegetables are cut into bite-sized pieces to prevent choking. Talk about how the colors of the food on their plates are the same as those in a rainbow.

▶ Give children an opportunity to sample each item and talk about how each tastes. Focus the activity on the importance of tasting a variety of fruits and vegetables instead of on children's likes and dislikes.

▶ Make a chart or flannel board with the following color labels across the top: red, yellow-orange, green, purple, white. One day, ask the children to name fruits that represent each of the colors. Another day, have the children identify vegetables that are these colors. Talk about why it is important to eat fruits and vegetables that are different colors.

▶ Older children can begin to identify and chart the primary nutrient strength of various fruits and vegetables. (For example, oranges, green peppers, strawberries, and watermelon are high in vitamin C. Carrots, sweet potatoes, and broccoli are rich in vitamin A.)

Evaluation

▶ Children will name several kinds of fruits and vegetables.

▶ Children will taste a variety of fruits and vegetables.

Additional lesson plans for grades 3–5 are available on CourseMate.

Summary

▶ The Dietary Reference Intakes (DRIs) are nutrient goals based on gender and age that are considered essential for maintaining health. They are used for policy development, dietary assessment, meal planning, and determining the nutrient contribution on food labels.

▶ The *Dietary Guidelines for Americans* are a set of recommendations that encourage consumers to: make healthy food choices to meet nutrient needs and reduce the overconsumption of nutrient groups known to have health risks, increase their physical activity, and implement food safety practices.

▶ MyPlate is the newest nutrition tool. It offers practical advice for making healthier food choices and engaging in physical activity every day. Information provided on the ChooseMyPlate website (http://www.choosemyplate.gov) is attractive, comprehensive, and easy for consumers to use and understand.

▶ Food labels must include a list of all ingredients in a product; nutrient values, fat, and calories present in the item based on serving size. Warnings must identify ingredients that are known allergens. The manufacturer's contact information must also be provided.

- Determining the percentage of calories from fat in a given food serving is useful for comparing and choosing nutrient-rich foods and limiting excessive dietary fat intake.

◖ Terms to Know

nutrients *p. 321*
essential nutrient *p. 321*
malnutrition *p. 321*
undernutrition *p. 321*
nutrition *p. 321*

Dietary Reference Intake
    (DRI) *p. 322*
Dietary Guidelines for
    Americans *p. 324*
protein *p. 329*

calcium *p. 329*
Percent Daily Values (%DV)
    p. 331
nutrition and health claims
    p. 331

◖ Chapter Review

A. By Yourself:

1. Match the foods in **Column I** to the appropriate food group in **Column II**. Some foods may include more than one food group.

Column I	Column II
1. Black beans	a. Dairy group
2. Rice	b. Protein foods
3. Spaghetti with tomato sauce	c. Grain group
4. Fish taco	d. Vegetable group
5. Macaroni and cheese	e. Fruit group
6. Peanut butter sandwich	f. Oils
7. French fries	g. Empty calories
8. Frozen yogurt	
9. Popcorn	
10. Bacon	
11. Carbonated beverages	
12. Watermelon	

2. Practice calculating the percentage of calories from fat by using the labels on ten different food products. What did you learn that was surprising? How will you use this information in your diet?

B. As a Group:

1. Describe the energy sources in food. What nutrients yield energy and how much does each provide?

2. Discuss how an individual might use the Dietary Guidelines for Americans to improve their personal well-being.

3. Explain what Dietary Reference Intakes (DRIs) are and how they can be used for planning a child's daily diet.

4. Explore the ChooseMyPlate website (http://www.choosemyplate.gov). Have each student identify and discuss the features that were most informative and useful. Are there any limitations to the site and, if so, what are they?

5. Explain how foods labeled *low-fat*, *fat-free*, and *reduced calories* differ.

◖ Case Study

Ruby runs a small child care program in her home. The preschool-age children begin arriving at 7 A.M. each morning and leave by 5:30 P.M. Ruby prepares and serves them breakfast, lunch, and two snacks throughout the day. This year, she has encountered several children who have challenging food allergies and food preferences. What suggestions would you offer to help Ruby in each of the following situations?

1. Layla, age 4, breaks out in hives whenever she has eaten too many strawberries or oranges. She will occasionally accept a small serving of applesauce or a few bites of banana but few other fruits. What two nutrients are probably deficient in Layla's diet? What other fruits or vegetables can Ruby serve to supply these essential vitamins?

2. Ailani, age 3, is lactose intolerant and unable to drink milk or to eat dairy products. What nutrient is most likely deficient in Ailani's diet? What other foods can Ruby serve to meet Ailani's nutrient needs?

3. Carlos, age 5, doesn't like milk and demands fruit juice or lemonade instead. What two nutrients are most likely deficient? What adjustments can Ruby make in his diet to meet these needs?

4. Mariko, age 2, prefers a daily diet of rice or noodles that have been drenched in soy sauce. She will take a few bites of tofu when her mother insists, but refuses meats, fish, and most vegetables. What nutrients is she missing? What health concerns would you have about Mariko's current dietary pattern? What can Ruby do to improve Mariko's dietary intake?

5. Sophia's favorite breakfast foods include bacon, sausages, doughnuts, and biscuits with gravy. What nutrients is she consuming in excess? What food groups and nutrients is she lacking? Should Ruby be concerned, and what can she do to encourage healthier eating habits?

◖ Application Activities

1. Record your personal food intake for the past 24 hours. Go to http://www.choosemyplate.gov; locate the SuperTracker and use the Food-A-Pedia feature to analyze your 24-hour food intake. Compare your results to the RDAs for your age and gender. How did you measure up? Explore the other features on this site (e.g., Food Tracker, Physical Activity Tracker) and create a plan to help identify and reach your goals.

2. Plan a day's menu for a 4-year-old girl who does an extra 45 minutes of vigorous activity each day. Include the recommended servings from each food group and total calories she should consume each day.

3. What fruit and vegetable choices would supply vitamin C to a child who has a citrus allergy?

4. A 50 pound child burns approximately 300 calories per hour (or 5 calories per minute) during moderately vigorous play (e.g., walking, running, climbing). How many minutes would this child have to play to burn off the calories in each of the following foods?

Cheese pizza (1 slice)	= 380 calories
Beef tacos (2)	= 340 calories
Seafood sushi	= 260 calories
Chicken vegetable soup (1 cup)	= 130 calories
Apple pie (1 piece)	= 335 calories

Fruit smoothie, no dairy (1 cup)   = 130 calories

French fries (medium order)   = 410 calories

Strawberries (1 cup fresh)   = 46 calories

Helpful Web Resources

Academy of Nutrition & Dietetics	http://www.eatright.org
Canada's Food Guide	http://www.hc-sc.gc.ca/fn-an/food-guide-aliment/index-eng.php
Food and Drug Administration (FDA) (Food labels)	http://www.fda.gov/Food/default.htm
ChooseMyPlate for Preschoolers	http://www.choosemyplate.gov/preschoolers.html
Nutrition Action Health Newsletter	http://www.cspinet.org/nah/index.htm

Visit the Education CourseMate for this textbook to access the eBook, Did You Get It? quizzes, Digital Downloads, TeachSource Video Cases, flashcards, and more. Go to CengageBrain.com to log in, register, or purchase access.

References

Akbaraly, T., Ferrie, J., Berr, C., Brunner, E., Head, J., Marmot, M., Singh-Manoux, A., Ritchie, K., Shipley, M., & Kivimaki, M. (2011). Alternative Healthy Eating Index and mortality over 18 years of follow-up: Results from the Whitehall II cohort, *American Journal of Clinical Nutrition*, 94(1), 247–253.

American Heart Association (AHA). (2012). Physical activity and children. Accessed on July 13, 2012 from http://www.heart.org/HEARTORG/GettingHealthy/Physical-Activity-and-Children_UCM_304053_Article.jsp.

Batada, A., Bruening, M., Marchlewicz, E., Story, M., & Wootan, M. (2012). Poor nutrition on the menu: Children's meals at America's top chain restaurants, *Childhood Obesity*, 8(3), 251–254.

Bucholz, E., Desai, M., & Rosenthal, M. (2011). Dietary intake in Head Start vs. non-Head Start preschool-aged children: Results from the 1999–2004 National Health and Nutrition Examination survey, *Journal of the American Dietetic Association*, 111(7), 1021–1030.

Colapinto, C., O'Connor, D., Dubois, L., & Tremblay, M. (2012). Folic acid supplement use is the most significant predictor of folate concentrations in Canadian women of childbearing age, *Applied Physiology, Nutrition, & Metabolism*, 37(2), 284–292.

Isoldi, K., Dalton, S., Rodriguez, D., & Nestle, M. (2012). Classroom "cupcake" celebrations: Observations of foods offered and consumed, *Journal of Nutrition Education & Behav*ior, 44(1), 71–75.

Miller, L., & Cassady, D. (2012). Making healthy choices using nutrition facts panels: The roles of knowledge, motivation, modification goals, and age, *Appetite*, 59(1), 129–139.

National Association for Sport & Physical Education (NASPE). (2012). National guidelines for physical activity. Accessed on July 13, 2012 from http://www.aahperd.org/naspe/standards/nationalGuidelines/PAguidelines.cfm.

Osborne, C., & Forestell, C. (2012). Increasing children's consumption of fruit and vegetables: Does the type of exposure matter?, *Physiology & Behavior*, 106(3), 362–368.

Pabayo, R., Spence, J., Casey, L., & Storey, K. (2012). Food consumption patterns in preschool children, *Canadian Journal of Dietetic Practice & Research*, 73(2), 66–71.

Parletta, N., Milte, C., & Meyer, B. (2013). Nutritional modulation of cognitive function and mental health, *The Journal of Nutritional Biochemistry*, 24(5), 725–743.

U.S. Department of Agriculture (USDA). (2010). *Dietary Guidelines for Americans.* Accessed on July 13, 2012 from http://www.cnpp.usda.gov/dietaryguidelines.htm.

U.S. Food & Drug Administration (U. S. FDA). (2013a). Food Allergen Labeling and Consumer Protection Act of 2004. Accessed on May 7, 2013 from http://www.fda.gov/Food/GuidanceRegulation/GuidanceDocumentsRegulatoryInformation/Allergens/ucm106187.htm.

U.S. FDA. (2013b). Overview of FDA proposed labeling requirements for restaurants, similar retail food establishments and vending machines. Accessed on May 7, 2013 from http://www.fda.gov/Food/IngredientsPackagingLabeling/LabelingNutrition/ucm248732.htm.

Feeding Infants

- **#1 a, b, and c:** Promoting child development and learning
- **#2 a, b, and c:** Building family and community relationships
- **#3 a, b and d:** Observing, documenting, and assessing to support young children and families
- **#4 a, b, and d:** Using developmentally effective approaches to connect with children and families
- **#5 a and c:** Using content knowledge to build a meaningful curriculum
- **#6 c:** Becoming a professional

Learning Objectives

After studying this chapter, you should be able to:

LO 15-1 Explain how the feeding relationship helps to satisfy the infant's needs in other developmental areas.

LO 15-2 Discuss the advantages and disadvantages of breast and formula feeding.

LO 15-3 Demonstrate how to feed an infant correctly (e.g., food preparation, positioning, burping).

LO 15-4 Describe how to determine when an infant is developmentally ready for semi-solid foods.

LO 15-5 Identify and discuss several health concerns associated with infant feeding.

15-1 Profile of an Infant

An infant's growth and development occurs at a rate that is significantly more rapid than at any other period in the life cycle (Marotz & Allen, 2013). Infants will double their birth weight during the first 5 to 6 months and nearly triple it by the end of the first year. Birth length typically increases by 50 percent as the child approaches his first birthday.

Food and the feeding relationship play important roles in meeting the infant's early biological, learning, and developmental needs. Feedings accompanied by close physical contact, emotional connections, verbal and non-verbal interchanges, and tender loving care (TLC) begin to foster a sense of self-awareness and trust. Failure to meet infants' physical and emotional needs can lead to serious delays in growth and development even though they are receiving all of the essential nutrients (Bigelow & Power, 2012). Infants also gradually begin to learn about the different flavors, colors, temperatures, textures, and variety of foods from adults who understand how to help them transition from a diet that consists solely of breast milk or formula to one that includes semi-solid foods and later involves them in family meals (Teacher Checklist 15-1).

Did You Know...

that an infant gains between 1 1/2 and 2 pounds per month during the first 6 to 7 months? Can you imagine what would happen if we continued to grow at this rate?

Did You Get It?

A baby born at 6 pounds should weigh approximately _____ pounds by his or her first birthday?

a. 12

b. 18

c. 24

d. 15

Take the full quiz on CourseMate.

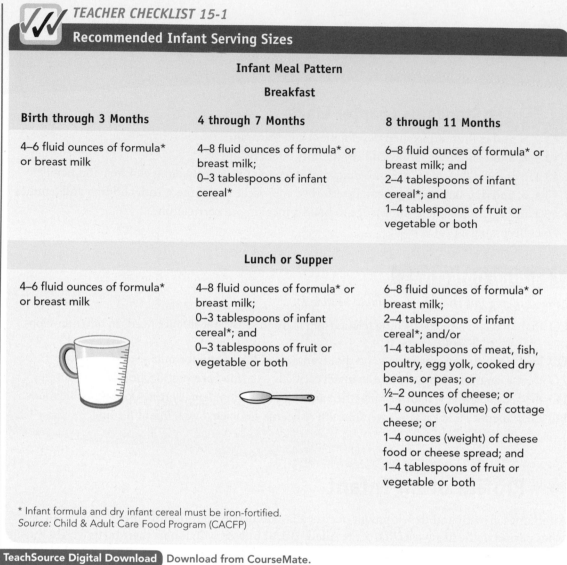

TEACHER CHECKLIST 15-1

Recommended Infant Serving Sizes

Infant Meal Pattern

Breakfast

Birth through 3 Months	4 through 7 Months	8 through 11 Months
4–6 fluid ounces of formula* or breast milk	4–8 fluid ounces of formula* or breast milk; 0–3 tablespoons of infant cereal*	6–8 fluid ounces of formula* or breast milk; and 2–4 tablespoons of infant cereal*; and 1–4 tablespoons of fruit or vegetable or both

Lunch or Supper

4–6 fluid ounces of formula* or breast milk	4–8 fluid ounces of formula* or breast milk; 0–3 tablespoons of infant cereal*; and 0–3 tablespoons of fruit or vegetable or both	6–8 fluid ounces of formula* or breast milk; 2–4 tablespoons of infant cereal*; and/or 1–4 tablespoons of meat, fish, poultry, egg yolk, cooked dry beans, or peas; or ½–2 ounces of cheese; or 1–4 ounces (volume) of cottage cheese; or 1–4 ounces (weight) of cheese food or cheese spread; and 1–4 tablespoons of fruit or vegetable or both

* Infant formula and dry infant cereal must be iron-fortified.
Source: Child & Adult Care Food Program (CACFP)

TeachSource Digital Download Download from CourseMate.

15-2 Meeting the Infant's Nutritional Needs for Growth and Brain Development

Infancy is characterized by a rapid rate of growth and development that must be supported by an adequate intake of protein, carbohydrates, and fat. Infants' nutrient and caloric needs remain high, relative to their body size, throughout the first year, but are greatest during the first 4 months when growth is most rapid. For example, a newborn requires approximately 50 calories per pound of body weight daily until 5 to 6 months of age. One-fourth to one-third of these calories is used for growth. As the infant progresses through the first year and becomes more mobile, fewer calories are needed for growth and more are required for physical activity. By 6 months of age, the infant requires only 40–45 calories per pound.

Meeting the infant's critical energy and nutrient needs presents a significant feeding challenge. Small stomach capacity limits the quantity of food they are able to consume at a given meal. As a result, infants need to be offered frequent, small feedings of nutrient-dense foods—sometimes as many as six to eight feedings in a 24-hour period during the first few months.

15-2a Prenatal Influence on Infants' Nutritional Needs and Brain Development

A well-balanced maternal diet that includes all essential nutrients supports healthy fetal development, including brain and central nervous system formation. A mother's nutritional status during pregnancy has immediate and long-term effects on the infant's early nutrient needs and well-being (Voss et al., 2012). Mothers who gain excessive weight during pregnancy give birth to infants who are more likely to become overweight as they mature (Poston, 2012). Mothers who do not obtain critical dietary nutrients (especially protein) and calories during pregnancy are more likely to have a **low-birthweight (LBW)** infant. These infants experience a high rate of serious illness and premature death during their first year. Low-birth weight infants are also at significant risk for additional problems such as:

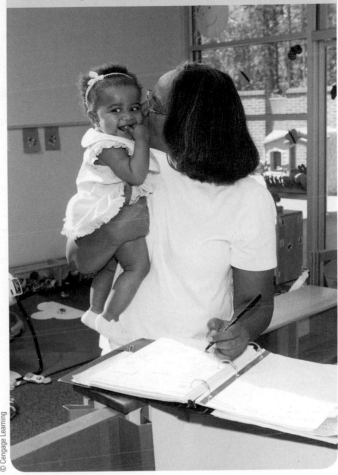

▼ A mother's nutrition during pregnancy influences her infant's early nutritional needs.

© Cengage Learning

▶ poor regulation of body temperature
▶ respiratory distress, including SIDS
▶ increased susceptibility to infection
▶ difficulty in metabolizing carbohydrates, fats, and proteins
▶ delayed development of kidneys and digestive organs
▶ poorly calcified bones—reduced bone density
▶ poor iron stores resulting in neonatal anemia
▶ vitamin deficiencies (especially vitamin E, folacin, and vitamin B_6) during neonatal period (birth to 28 days)
▶ attention disorders, cognitive delays, and behavior problems

Infants at highest risk for these problems are often born to teenage mothers, who must meet their own nutritional needs for growth in addition to providing nutrients for the developing fetus. Women who smoke, are pregnant with multiple babies, or who fail to consume adequate calories and nutrients during pregnancy are also more likely to give birth to LBW infants.

Common prenatal nutritional deficiencies that produce LBW infants include:

▶ protein
▶ energy
▶ folacin
▶ vitamin D
▶ vitamin B_6

Prenatal nutrient deficiencies may be partially corrected by supplementing the infant immediately after birth, but the effects of malnutrition are seldom completely reversed. The WIC (Special Supplemental Nutrition Program for Women, Infants, and Children) program, which provides supplemental food for income-eligible pregnant, breastfeeding and non-breastfeeding women and their infants and children up to the age of 5 who are at nutritional risk, has been effective in reducing the incidence of child malnutrition (Black et al., 2012). WIC currently provides nutrition, health care, and child care information in multiple languages for approximately 9 million clients in the United States, including 5 million children and 2 million infants (Figure 15–1) (USDA, 2012).

----

low-birthweight (LBW) – *weighing less than 5.5 pounds (2,500 grams) at birth.*

FIGURE 15-1   **Breastfeeding information is available in multiple languages from WIC.**

MiPirámide en Acción:
Consejos para Mamás en Período de Lactancia

¿Cómo Puedo Adelgazar Después de que Nazca Mi Bebé?

Amamantar es lo mejor para las mamás y para sus bebés por muchas razones. Una de las razones es que la lactancia facilita la pérdida del peso que ganó durante el embarazo, al quemar las calorías extras. Además, la leche materna ayuda a combatir infecciones y reduce las alergias, de modo que los bebés alimentados con leche materna se enferman con menor frecuencia.

Siga su **Plan MiPirámide para Mamás** (ver reverso) para elegir la cantidad adecuada de cada grupo de alimentos. Además, visite a su médico. Mientras está amamantando, su médico puede monitorear su peso y decirle si está perdiendo peso como debería. Si está perdiendo peso muy lentamente, disminuya la cantidad de calorías que está consumiendo. La mejor manera de ingerir menos calorías es reduciendo la cantidad de "calorías extras."

¿Qué son las "calorías extras"?

Las calorías extras son los azúcares agregados o grasas sólidas en los alimentos. Los siguientes son algunos ejemplos de alimentos con "calorías extras":

- Refrescos o gaseosas
- Golosinas
- Postres
- Galletas
- Cereales azucarados
- Alimentos fritos
- Queso
- Leche entera
- Yogur endulzado
- Salchichas
- Carnes grasas

Busque opciones que sean de bajo contenido graso, sin grasa, sin azúcar ni edulcorantes o sin azúcares agregados.

United States Department of Agriculture

15-2b The First 6 Months

The months following an infant's birth are marked by rapid growth and critical neurological developments. Access to high-quality nutrition is especially important during this time to support the numerous changes that are occurring. Infants who are malnourished or who do not receive proper nutrition tend to be smaller in size, grow at a slow rate, and have fewer brain cells and poorer intellectual capacity (Galler et al., 2012). Providing a malnourished infant with proper nutrition will not completely reverse the negative effects it has had on brain development and other body systems.

During the first 6 months, the infant's nutritional needs can be met solely with formula or breast milk (and vitamin D supplementation). Breast milk and formula are both rich in fat and provide approximately 650 calories per quart to meet the infant's high energy needs (Kim & Friel, 2012). The full-term infant is born with a temporary store of iron and vitamin A that lasts for approximately the first 5 to 6 months. However, premature infants may require additional supplementation with these nutrients during this period because they have had less time to acquire adequate reserves. No semi-solid foods are needed or advised until the infant is at least 5 months of age. Younger infants are not developmentally or physiologically ready to ingest or digest solid foods. (This is discussed later in the chapter.)

The benefits of breastfeeding continue to gain increased attention and support. The American Academy of Pediatrics (AAP) and the American Academy of Family Physicians (AAFP) urge mothers to breastfeed infants exclusively for at least the first 6 months and, if possible, to continue until the infant turns 1 year of age (AAP, 2012). Scientific evidence has shown a positive relationship between breastfeeding and a reduced risk of some childhood health conditions, including SIDS, ear infection (otitis media), allergies and asthma, diabetes, and bacterial meningitis (Salone, Vann, & Dee, 2013; Gale et al., 2012). In addition, researchers have found that some children show small advantages in developmental and intellectual function (Andres et al., 2012; Isaacs et al., 2011). The nutrient advantages of breast milk are summarized in Table 15–1.

TABLE 15–1   Advantages of Breast Milk

Breast Milk:

- has all of the nutrients needed by the infant for the first 6 months (with the exception of adequate vitamin D)
- contains proteins that are more digestible than cow's milk protein
- contains lactose, the main carbohydrate component, which aids in calcium absorption and in establishing beneficial intestinal flora
- provides **antibodies** (immunoglobulin) that protect the infant from some infectious illnesses
- has a higher content of the essential fatty acids (omega 3 and 6)
- provides taurine* and dietary nucleotides**
- is associated with lower obesity rates
- is less likely to cause food allergies
- reduces the risk of bacteria entering the infant's body from unsanitary formula preparation
- is inexpensive, convenient, and always available at the correct temperature
- contains less sodium (salt) than formulas
- fosters emotional bonding between mother and infant
- is a biologically active substance that adjusts its nutrient composition to meet the infant's changing needs

*Taurine is a free amino acid (not found in proteins) that is particularly important for the normal growth and development of the central nervous system. It is now added to many formulas, especially those for premature infants.
**Dietary nucleotides play a role in infant cell growth and improved antibody production. The AAP recommends these nutrients be added to all commercial formulas.

Breastfeeding requires that mothers increase their intake of certain nutrients in order to maintain their own health and the quality of breast milk (Table 15–2).

Some mothers may elect formula feeding as the best approach after giving careful consideration to their health and lifestyle factors. Conditions that might cause a mother to choose formula feeding are:

- maternal illness or surgery
- medications the mother may need to take
- demands that require the mother to be away from the child for long periods of time
- personal preference
- use of addictive drugs, including alcohol and tobacco

Regardless of the feeding method that is chosen, teachers must be accepting and willing to assist families in meeting their infants' nutritional needs. Mothers should never be made to feel guilty or that they have made the wrong decision.

15-2c The Teacher and the Breastfeeding Mother

Many mothers continue to breastfeed their infants while employed outside of the home. They may use a breast pump or hand express milk and refrigerate or freeze it so the infant can be fed breast milk while her mother is at work. Breast milk can be refrigerated (40°F) in a sterile container and used

TABLE 15–2   Breastfeeding and a Mother's Dietary Needs

Mothers who are breastfeeding need to increase their daily intake of calories and nutrients, including:

- approximately 500 additional calories
- 15–20 additional grams of protein
- vitamins A, C, and folacin
- calcium (equivalent of one extra serving)
- an additional 4 cups of fluids
- vitamin B_{12} and D supplementation (if no animal products are consumed)

antibodies – *special substances produced by the body that help protect against disease.*

TEACHER CHECKLIST 15-2

Supporting the Nursing Mother

Early childhood programs can provide an environment that will support mothers who wish to nurse their infants at the facility by:

- creating a private area that is quiet and comfortable
- having a place where mothers can wash their hands before and after nursing
- providing a comfortable chair (a rocking chair if possible) and a foot rest to relieve back strain
- making water or other fluids available for mothers to drink
- having the infant ready (e.g., awake, diapers changed, infant's hands cleaned) when mother arrives

TeachSource Digital Download   Download from CourseMate.

within 48 hours; it can also be frozen (0°F), preferably in hard plastic containers (to avoid breakage or tears) and used within 3 months from the time it was expressed. Frozen breast milk must never be refrozen once it has thawed. Containers should be clearly labeled with the date and infant's name.

Some nursing mothers have flexible work schedules that allow them to take time off to feed their infants. Teachers should accommodate and assist mothers whenever they are able to make these arrangements during the day (Teacher Checklist 15-2).

Safe Handling of Breast Milk Human milk varies in color, consistency, and odor, depending on the mother's diet and the container in which it is stored. Because breast milk is not homogenized, the cream may rise to the top of the container. Shaking it briefly before feeding helps blend the layers. For safe handling, the teacher should always follow these steps:

- Wash hands thoroughly before touching any milk containers. Avoid touching the inside of bottles or caps.
- Request that mothers label containers with the date when milk was collected; use the oldest milk first.
- If breast milk is to be stored for more than 48 hours, it should be frozen. (See Teacher Checklist 15-3 for safe thawing instructions.)
- Frozen breast milk may be safely stored in a freezer (0°F) for up to 3 months.

15-2d The Teacher and the Formula-Fed Infant

Although breastfeeding offers important health benefits, some infants in early childhood programs will be formula fed. The infant's family and health care provider will determine which formula is best for the infant. Commercial infant formulas are prepared to closely resemble breast milk in composition relative to the amount of protein, carbohydrate, and fat. Most infant formulas are made from

TEACHER CHECKLIST 15-3

Thawing Frozen Breast Milk Safely

1. Wash your hands with soap and water before touching the breast milk container.
2. Place the sealed container of breast milk in a bowl of warm water for about 30 minutes, or hold the container of 4 ounces of human milk under warm running water for approximately four minutes. **NEVER MICROWAVE BREAST MILK!** Microwaving can alter the nutritional composition of breast milk and also cause burns to the infant due to uneven heating.
3. Swirl the container to blend any fat that may have separated and risen during thawing.
4. Feed thawed milk immediately or store in the refrigerator for a maximum of 24 hours.

NEVER REFREEZE BREAST MILK.

TeachSource Digital Download   Download from CourseMate.

modified cow's milk or soy products and are available in powder, liquid concentrates, or as ready-to-feed solutions. Infants who have difficulty tolerating milk-based formulas may be switched to one that is soy-based. Although soy-based formulas are considered to be safe for infants, there has been some concern expressed about the plant-based estrogens they contain and their effect on infant growth. Soy can also cause allergic reactions in some infants (De Greef et al., 2012). Unmodified cow's milk should not be given to infants prior to 1 year of age because it often causes digestive disorders including intestinal bleeding. Goat's milk is also not recommended as it does not contain adequate nutrients.

15-2e Preparation of Formula

Two safety factors that are especially important to follow when preparing infant formula are:

1. *Sanitation*—Sanitary formula preparation using **aseptic procedures** prevents serious illness that can result when bacteria are introduced into the formula. Hands should be washed carefully and all utensils sanitized prior to mixing the formula. Sterilized (boiled) or bottled water should be used when preparing formula from a powdered concentrate. Honey should never be added to any formula for an infant younger than 1 year of age.

> ⚠ **CAUTION**
>
> *Honey contains* Clostridium botulinum *spores, which, in an infant's intestine, can produce a dangerous, life-threatening toxin.*

Each formula type (ready-to-feed, concentrated liquid, powdered) requires different preparation techniques that must be followed precisely according to the manufacturers' directions on the label.

2. *Accuracy*—Accurate measuring and mixing of formula (according to directions) ensures that the infant will receive needed calories and nutrients in the amounts required for optimal growth and development. Adding too much water dilutes the formula and nutrients the infant receives and can lead to malnutrition. Adding too little water results in an "over-rich" formula that may cause digestive problems, excessive caloric intake, and obesity over time. Skim or low-fat milks should not be used in formula preparation because their low fat content is inadequate to satisfy daily caloric needs in the amount (volume) that infants are able to consume. It is recommended that 40 to 50 percent of the infant's calories come from fat. Adequate fat intake also plays a critical role in normal brain and central nervous system development and is needed to form the myelin sheath, or the insulation, around new nerve fibers. Essential fatty acids (linolenic and linoleic) in breast milk and formulas are also required for healthy cell growth and visual system development. The equivalent of 1 tablespoon of a polyunsaturated fat, such as corn oil or safflower oil, will meet the infant's need for these essential fatty acids. Table 15–3 provides a summary of common infant formulas.

▶❙❙ TeachSource Video Connections

© 2015 Cengage Learning

Infants and Toddlers: Health and Nutrition

Successful feeding requires patience and an understanding of the infant's physical requirements and developmental abilities. With time, caregivers become sensitive to changes in the infant's behavior that signal different needs. As you watch the learning video, *Infants and Toddlers: Health and Nutrition,* consider the following questions:

1. Why did the teacher make a point of telling Ethan that she was putting him in the infant seat?
2. Why did the teacher wash the infant's hands as well as her own before the feeding?
3. Why is it important to feed an infant in an upright position?
4. Why did the caregiver gently stroke the infant's check before offering the bottle?

Watch on CourseMate.

aseptic procedure – *treatment to produce a product that is free of disease-producing bacteria.*

TABLE 15–3   Examples of Common Infant Formulas

Standard Formulas		
Enfamil®, Enfamil A+® Enfamil® Lower Iron; Similac® & Similac® with Iron; SMA & SMA Lo Iron; Gerber® Good Start®	20 cal./oz.	Modified cow's milk
Soy Formulas		
Similac® Soy Isomil®; Nursoy; Enfamil® ProSobee®; Gerber® Good Start® Soy Formula	20 cal./oz.	Hypoallergenic formula
Therapeutic Formulas		
Nutramigen®; Pregestimil®; Similac Expert Care® Alimentum	20 cal./oz.	Hypoallergenic formula
Phenyl-Free® 1	22 cal./oz.	For phenylketonurics (PKU)
Pedialyte®	3 cal./oz.	Electrolyte/fluid replacement
Pregestimil®; Similac Sensitive®	20–24 cal./oz.	Lactose-free milk
Enfamil® Premature; Enfamil® EnfaCare®; Similac® Special Care®; Similac Expert Care® NeoSure	20–24 cal./oz.	Premature infant formula

Did You Get It?

Which health risk or manifestation has not been directly linked to low-birth-weight infants?
   a. neonatal anemia
   b. high susceptibility to pathogens and infections
   c. ineffective regulation of body temperature
   d. increased hardening of the arteries

Take the full quiz on CourseMate.

15-3 Feeding Time for the Infant

How often an infant needs to be fed is determined by the family, infant, and health care provider. On-demand feeding is usually recommended for young infants. This approach allows caregivers to adjust the amount and frequency of feedings to meet the infant's unique needs. An infant will signal when he is hungry and is, therefore, the best source of information about when to feed or not to feed (Table 15–4). It is important that parents and teachers learn to read an infant's cues because not all crying indicates a desire for additional food (Thompson, 2012). Noting the infant's body language as well as the tone, intensity, and length of crying can be helpful in determining if she is indeed hungry, distressed about a wet diaper, or simply wants to be picked up and held. Although the frequency and amount of feeding varies from infant to infant, a typical pattern is:

0–1 months	6 feedings of 2–4 oz./feeding
1–2 months	6 feedings of 3–5 oz./feeding
2–3 months	5 feedings of 4–6 oz./feeding
4–5 months	5 feedings of 5–7 oz./feeding
6–7 months*	5 feedings of 6–8 oz./feeding
8–12 months*	3 feedings of 8 oz./feeding

*Also taking solid foods

TABLE 15–4   **Behavioral Signs of Hunger and Fullness (Satiety)**

Hunger Indicators
begins to suck on fingers or fist
makes lip smacking sounds
sticks tongue out
searches for breast or bottle (rooting)
squirms or appears restless
begins crying (a late sign)

Fullness Indicators
falls asleep
turns head away
releases nipple
clamps mouth/lips tightly
becomes distracted while feeding

An infant who is consuming adequate breast milk or formula will usually have at least six or more wet diapers and several bowel movements a day.

Feeding an infant involves much more than simply getting the nipple into the mouth. Cleanliness at feeding time is of prime importance. The caregiver's hands must be soap-washed prior to every feeding. Formula should be tested against the inside of the wrist to make sure it is the right temperature for the infant to drink.

 CAUTION

Infant formula in a bottle should not be heated in a microwave. The fluid formula may become dangerously hot while the outside of the bottle feels cool. This method of heating has severely burned some infants.

Feeding time should be relaxed and preceded by a few minutes of talking and playing with the infant. When adults cuddle, maintain eye contact, and verbally interact with the infant they are satisfying critical social, emotional, and communication needs. The feeding experience also meets the infant's need for close human contact (bonding).

The infant should be held in a sitting position with her head resting against the caregiver's upper arm. Tilting the bottle slightly upward will keep the nipple filled and prevent the infant from swallowing excess air, which can cause gas and **distention**. (See Figure 15–2 illustrates different nipples that can be used for bottle feeding.) Allow at least 20 minutes per feeding to avoid hurrying the infant. Infants will signal by turning their head away, releasing or playing with the nipple, or pushing away from the adult when they have had enough to eat. It is important to recognize these cues and not force the infant to continue feeding.

15-3a Burping

Because infants naturally swallow air when sucking, they should be burped two or three times during the feeding and again when they have finished eating. The infant can be placed

▼ **Feedings should be a relaxed time for social and emotional engagement with the infant.**

© Cengage Learning

---

distention – *the state of being stretched or enlarged.*

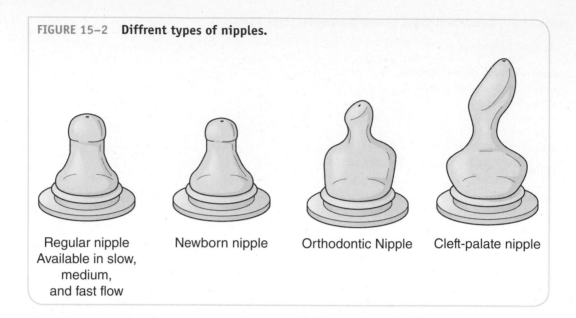

FIGURE 15–2   **Diffrent types of nipples.**

Regular nipple
Available in slow,
medium,
and fast flow

Newborn nipple

Orthodontic Nipple

Cleft-palate nipple

in either an upright position over the adult's shoulder or face-down across the adult's lap. In either position, the adult should gently pat or rub the infant's back. It is normal for infants, especially those who are formula-fed, to experience **regurgitation** and to spit up small amounts of their feeding. However, the frequency and amount spit up generally decreases with age.

> ⚠️ **CAUTION**
>
> *An infant's bottle should never be propped up, nor should the baby ever be left unattended while feeding. Infants do not have sufficient motor control to remove the bottle from their mouth and may aspirate the milk after they fall asleep. This practice (bottle propping) also increases the risk of baby bottle tooth decay (BBTD) and ear infections.*

15-3b Water

Breast milk or formula is usually sufficient to meet infants' water requirement until the time semi- or solid foods are added to their diet. However, there may be reasons, such as warm days, vomiting, or diarrhea, when an infant may need supplemental water to prevent dehydration. A thirsty infant often acts like a hungry baby. If the infant appears to be hungry shortly after feeding, a small amount of unflavored water can be offered. This amount should be limited to no more than 4 ounces daily to ensure that water does not replace the infant's milk consumption. *Water sweetened with sugar or flavored drinks should not be fed to infants.* Fluids with added **electrolytes** (salts and minerals) should be given only with a doctor's recommendation.

15-3c Supplements

Vitamin or mineral supplements are sometimes recommended for infants. In general, breast milk or formula is adequate to meet most of the infant's nutritional needs with the exception of vitamin D and the mineral fluoride. Breastfed infants are usually given a vitamin D supplement; however, the formula-fed infant receives adequate amounts of this vitamin and should

---

regurgitation – *the return of partially digested food from stomach to mouth.*
electrolytes – *substances that, when in solution, become capable of conducting electricity; examples include sodium and potassium.*

not be supplemented. Fluoride is present in breast milk in scant amounts and only added in low levels to concentrated and powdered formulas. However, the American Dental Association (ADA) and American Academy of Pediatric Dentistry (AAPD) do not recommend supplementation before 12 months of age because excess fluoride can have toxic effects and cause tooth discoloration (ADA, 2011). Infants who are breastfed longer than 6 months may require supplementation with iron because milk is a poor source of this mineral. Introducing iron-fortified foods around this time is also beneficial.

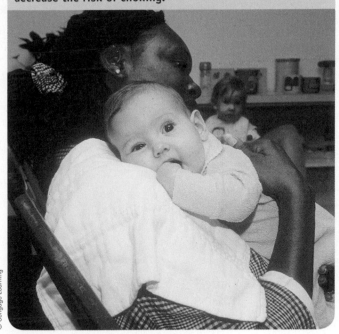
▼ **Infants should be burped during and after feedings to decrease the risk of choking.**

© Cengage Learning

CAUTION

Fluoride supplements combined with vitamin D are not safe to use with the formula-fed infant. Formulas are already fortified with vitamin D and excessive intake of this vitamin may have serious consequences for the infant.

Did You Get It?

If you sense that an infant with a moderate case of diarrhea is thirsty after finishing her formula on a warm, dry day, you should:

a. provide additional water that has been sweetened with sugar to replace lost calories

b. provide a large amount of additional water to compensate for the water lost from diarrhea

c. provide a small addition of unsweetened water

d. not provide additional water

Take the full quiz on CourseMate.

15-4 Introducing Semi-Solid (Pureed) Foods

The teacher, family, and health care professional must cooperate closely when infants are being introduced to semi-solid foods. Finely cut, pureed foods high in fluid content, such as cereals, fruits, and vegetables can be introduced when the infant is about 5 or 6 months of age. It is around this time that infants have the **physiological** and **developmental readiness** to eat and digest semi-solid foods.

15-4a Developmental Readiness

At approximately 5 months of age, infants are able to move food to the back of their mouth and to swallow without an initial sucking action. They have also developed the ability to open their mouth and chew, to hold their head erect, to sit for short periods, and to lean forward toward the spoon. At about 4 to 5 months, infants begin showing interest in touching, holding, and tasting objects—food and otherwise. It is important to note that at this age infants are able to signal when they have had enough to eat by turning their head away from food. This behavior should be respected and the offering of food discontinued. Ignoring these signals can gradually lead to overeating and obesity.

developmental or physiological readiness – *growth (both physical and cognitive) and chemical processes that lead to the ability to perform a function.*

TEACHER CHECKLIST 15-4

Age-Related Infant Eating Behaviors

Age	Common Infant Behaviors
1–3 months	• becomes fussy when hungry • turns face toward nipple • sucks vigorously but may choke on occasion
4–6 months	• assumes more symmetrical sitting position • grasps for objects • puts objects in mouth • closes hands around bottle • turns head away from food when no longer hungry • leans toward food-containing spoon
6–7 months	• teeth erupt • shows up-and-down chewing motions • grasps finger foods by using entire hand (**palmar grasp**) and gets them to mouth • drinks small amounts of liquid from a cup • holds bottle with both hands
7–8 months	• sits alone with little support • uses finger and thumb (**pincer grip**) to pick up small food pieces • is better able to manipulate food in the mouth • is more successful when drinking from a cup • begins self-feeding with help
9–12 months	• grasps and releases objects with greater precision • reaches for the spoon • feeds self with some help • drinks successfully from a cup • is more aware of surrounding environment • mimics motions and activities that are observed

TeachSource Digital Download) Download from CourseMate.

15-4b Physiological Readiness

By 5 to 6 months of age, the infant's digestive system has matured and is now able to metabolize complex carbohydrates and proteins other than milk protein. This is also about the time that the iron stores present at birth are nearly depleted. Semi-solid foods such as iron-enriched cereals and pureed vegetables and fruits can gradually be introduced into the infant's diet to supplement dwindling iron reserves. High protein meat products should not be added until infants are approximately 6 to 8 months of age because the nitrogen-containing wastes from their digestion are difficult for immature kidneys to handle.

Teacher Checklist 15-4 presents age-related, developmental factors that influence infant feeding behavior. However, it is important to remember that infants are unique individuals and their rate of development can vary (Marotz & Allen, 2013). Infants who have developmental delays or special needs may require additional time to acquire some of these skills. Differences in cultural practices also influence when children are encouraged to attempt self-feeding (Holub & Dolan, 2012; Kuo et al., 2011). Foods should be introduced according to the individual infant's abilities, interests, and nutritional needs.

New foods should be introduced slowly with only a few baby spoonsful offered one or two times daily. (See Teacher Checklist 15-1 for appropriate serving sizes.) Iron-fortified infant cereals such as rice or barley are usually the first addition because they are less likely to cause allergic reactions.

palmar grasp – *using the entire hand to pick up objects.*
pincer grip – *using the thumb and finger to pick up an object.*

Cereals can be thinned with formula, breast milk, or water to make them more acceptable to the infant. Semi-solid foods should always be fed with a spoon and not from a bottle.

A suggested sequence for introducing semi-solid and solid foods is:

5–6 months	iron-enriched cereals
6–8 months	vegetables, followed by fruits
8–9 months	meat and meat substitutes

Initially, it is better to offer individual foods rather than mixtures. If an infant does experience an allergic or sensitivity reaction, the offending food can more easily be identified. Sugar, salt, and butter should not be added to an infant's food. Parents may choose to prepare pureed foods at home or to purchase commercially prepared food. Either is acceptable as long as the foods are nutritionally adequate. Table foods (removed before they have been seasoned) can be pureed in a blender. For example, if a family's meal consists of baked chicken, peas, and rice, an appropriate infant serving would be 2 tablespoons chicken, 2 tablespoons peas, and ¼ cup rice (all pureed). Preparing food in this manner begins to expose infants to a variety of flavors and allows families to control the ingredients. Initially, it may be wise to limit too many high-fiber foods. Home-prepared pureed food can also be frozen in ice cube trays, removed after frozen, stored in a tightly sealed container, and thawed for use as needed.

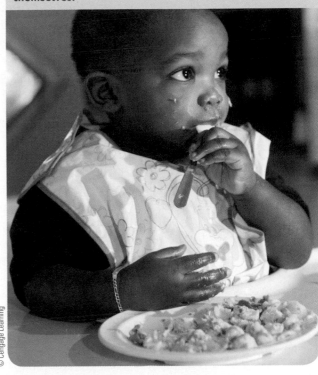

▼ **Older infants begin to show interest in feeding themselves.**

© Cengage Learning

If commercially prepared infant foods are used, plain fruits, vegetables, and meats should be chosen rather than "dinners" or "desserts," which are typically extended with starches and other additives. Information on the labels of commercially prepared infant and toddler foods should be read carefully in order to make nutritious selections (Figure 15–3). Remember that ingredients on food labels are listed in descending order according to the amount present. The first ingredient in an acceptable infant food should always be fruit, vegetable, or meat—not water, cereal,

FIGURE 15–3 Special labeling rules.

Nutrition Facts
Serving Size 1 jar (140g)

Amount Per Serving	
Calories 110	

Total Fat	0g
Sodium	10mg
Total Carbohydrate	27g
Dietary Fiber	4g
Sugars	18g
Protein	0g

%Daily Value	
Protein 0% •	Vitamin A 6%
Vitamin C 45% •	Calcium 2%
Iron 2%	

Nutrition Label for Foods for Children Under Four Years Old.

Nutrition Facts
Serving Size 1 jar (140g)

Amount Per Serving	
Calories 110	Calories from Fat 0

Total Fat	0g
Saturated Fat	0g
Cholesterol	0mg
Sodium	10mg
Total Carbohydrate	27g
Dietary Fiber	4g
Sugars	18g
Protein	0g

%Daily Value	
Protein 0% •	Vitamin A 6%
Vitamin C 45% •	Calcium 2%
Iron 2%	

Nutrition Label for Foods for Children Two to Four Years Old.

or other starch. When feeding a child prepared infant foods, a small portion should be removed from the jar, placed in a bowl, and the contents returned to the refrigerator. If infants are fed directly from the jar, bacteria and enzymes in saliva can cause the remaining contents to break down and become watery.

Infants may begin to drink small amounts of liquid from a cup at about 6 to 7 months of age. They like to help hold the cup and bring it to their mouth, although many spills should be expected. By 6 to 7 months, infants are also able to pick up and chew on finger foods. An infant's teeth are beginning to erupt at this age, and the provision of "chew foods" such as dry toast, dry cereal, or baby biscuits can aid the teething process. (Refer to Teacher Checklist 15-1.)

15-4c Infants with Special Needs

Although eating appears to be a natural process, infants who are born prematurely or who have a range of health problems, including genetic disorders and congenital malformations, may present special feeding challenges and nutritional needs. For example, infants born with Down syndrome typically have weak facial muscles, which make sucking difficult and less efficient. Later, these children have a tendency to overeat and to gain excessive weight. Some infants may have conditions that require surgery, which can increase their need for certain nutrients at a time when they may not be receptive to food. It is especially important that infants with special needs obtain all of the nutrients necessary for healthy growth and brain development during the months following birth.

An infant's eating behaviors may be further challenged by infection, medication side effects, unpleasant medical treatments, swallowing difficulties, dental problems, inactivity, special diets, and fatigue. These factors may make it difficult for the infant with special needs to eat and to maintain an interest in food. Families may be referred to a feeding clinic where the infant's physical and nutritional needs can be evaluated and where they can receive assistance. Nutritional services are also available through Early Head Start, IDEA (Individuals with Disabilities Education Act, Part C), WIC (Special Supplemental Nutrition Program for Women, Infants, and Children), hospital clinics, and other community-based programs.

CONNECTING TO EVERYDAY PRACTICE

Salty Beginnings

Adults worldwide are being encouraged to lower their salt intake. The *Dietary Guidelines for Healthy Americans* urge adults to limit their sodium intake to 2,300 mg (the equivalent of 1 teaspoon) daily. Recognized organizations, such as the World Health Organization (WHO), the American Medical Association (AMA), and the American Heart Association (AHA) continue to issue public warnings about the links between sodium intake, hypertension (high blood pressure), and heart disease (Frisoli et al., 2012). Certain populations, especially minorities, older adults, and the obese, are known to be at greater risk for these conditions. However, we are also learning that excessive salt intake can contribute to the early development of these same diseases in children. Although infants appear to initially dislike the taste of salt, they quickly learn to like it and even to acquire a preference for it as they transition to finger foods (Stein, Cowart, & Beauchamp, 2012). Adults who are aware of this connection can play an influential role in shaping children's early eating habits.

Think About This:

▶ What high-salt (sodium) finger foods are frequently offered to infants?

▶ How much salt (sodium) do the infants in your program receive in a typical day?

▶ What healthy, low-salt finger food options can you suggest for snacks?

▶ What can you do to encourage families to lower their salt intake and to substitute low-salt food items for infants?

Increasing numbers of infants with special needs are being enrolled in early childhood programs. Teachers must work closely with their families to learn as much about the child's condition, medical treatments, nutritional needs, and ways they can collaborate to ensure the infant's healthy development.

Did You Get It?

Should you introduce protein-rich meat products to a 4½-month-old infant who has progressed, slightly early, from formula to semisolid foods?

a. Yes, the iron present in the body at birth is nearly depleted.

b. Yes, the child needs this type of protein now more than ever.

c. Yes, the child needs both iron and protein from meat.

d. No, the child is still too young to digest and metabolize meat products.

Take the full quiz on CourseMate.

15-5 Common Feeding Concerns

15-5a Food Allergies

Allergic responses to food are common and may cause a variety of symptoms, including runny nose, wheezing, diarrhea, constipation, bloating, vomiting, hives, and eczema (Lack, 2012). An infant who experiences these symptoms should be seen by the child's health care provider. If there is a family history of allergies, introduction of semi-solid foods may be delayed until the infant reaches at least 6 months of age (Przyrembel, 2012). Allergic reactions are more commonly associated with certain foods such as citrus juice(s), eggs, cereal products (other than rice), chocolate, nuts and nut butters, and fish/shellfish. Parents may delay including these particular foods in the infant's diet and then introducing them only one at a time later on.

If an infant experiences an allergic reaction to a specific food, that food should be eliminated from the diet and reintroduced at a later time. If a milk-based formula seems to be the offending food, it may be necessary to replace it with one formulated from modified proteins or soybeans.

15-5b Colic

Some seemingly healthy infants develop colic-like symptoms between 3 and 16 weeks of age. They experience considerable distress, including abdominal discomfort, cramping, and prolonged periods of intense crying that often occur in late afternoon or evening and at approximately the same time each day (Kvitvaer, Miller, & Newell, 2012; Salisbury et al., 2012). Consoling an infant who has colic is difficult and typically ineffective. Although the exact cause of this condition is unknown there is some evidence to suggest that reflux may be a contributing factor and that changing the type of formula being fed will sometimes relieve the symptoms (Hasan & Ng, 2012). Mothers who are breastfeeding should continue to do so, but may want to monitor their diet closely for highly spiced or strongly flavored foods that may trigger or contribute to the infant's discomfort. Fortunately, most infants outgrow colic at about 3 to 4 months of age.

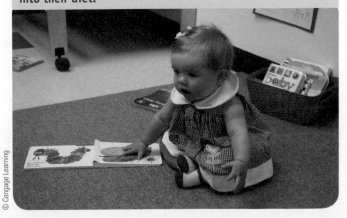

▼ **Children should be observed carefully for potential allergic reactions when new foods are being introduced into their diet.**

© Cengage Learning

15-5c **Vomiting and Diarrhea**

Common causes of vomiting and diarrhea in infants include:

- food allergies or food sensitivities
- overfeeding
- infections: systemic or food-borne
- introducing solid foods before an infant is able to digest them
- incorrect formula preparation
- use of fruit juice
- swallowed air
- reflux

It is normal for young infants to spit up or to vomit. The muscle (sphincter), positioned at the stomach opening, is responsible for keeping stomach contents in place. This sphincter requires time to fully develop before it is able to function properly; this process may take longer in some young infants and, until then, may cause them to spit up after almost every feeding. However, when vomiting is accompanied by back arching, difficulty feeding, and pulling away from the nipple, this condition is known as gastroesophageal reflux (GER). It is often resolved by feeding the infant in an upright position (and remaining upright for a short time afterward), changing formula type, and maturation (the condition usually disappears around 18 months-of-age). When the condition consistently interferes with feeding and growth or causes the infant to wheeze, cough, or have difficulty breathing, it is recognized as a disease (GERD) (Sullivan & Sundaram, 2012). Medication may be prescribed if the condition persists despite changes in feeding practices.

Fluid and electrolyte replacement are primary considerations when an infant has been ill and experienced repeated vomiting and diarrhea. These infants require approximately 3 ounces of replacement fluids per pound of body weight. There are also numerous commercial ready-to-feed (RTF) rehydrating formulas available (Pedialyte®, Equalyte®, Infalyte®, and Rehydralyte®); however, parents should check with their health care provider before giving any of these solutions to an infant. Fruit juices, carbonated beverages, tea, or adult electrolyte formulas are not recommended because of their high sugar and low electrolyte content. The ultimate goal is a gradual progression and eventual return to the infant's normal diet.

Acute diarrhea due to an infection, and characterized by accompanying fever, must be attended to immediately. The infant's physician should be contacted for advice and appropriate treatment.

15-5d **Anemia**

Inadequate iron intake can result in low-hemoglobin-type anemia that may delay the growth process and cause the infant to be lethargic (Gibbs et al., 2012). Iron stores present at birth are usually exhausted by 6 months of age unless the infant is receiving an iron-fortified formula. Adding iron-enriched cereals to an infant's diet at about 5 to 6 months of age is usually sufficient to prevent anemia from developing. Some infants may initially experience constipation or diarrhea when placed on an iron-fortified formula but this usually corrects itself with time.

15-5e **Baby Bottle Tooth Decay**

Infants who are allowed to recline or to sleep with a bottle or breast in their mouth may develop baby bottle tooth decay (BBTD). This condition, also referred to as early childhood caries, is caused by the prolonged presence of sugars in formula, breast milk, or juices in the child's mouth. Tooth decay can also develop when cavity-causing bacteria are transferred from an adult to the infant via saliva through practices such as cleaning the infant's pacifier in person's mouth or tasting food from the infant's spoon. Bacteria in saliva feed on the sugars in milk and juices and create acids that cause decay. When infants have finished a feeding, their gums should be wiped with a damp cloth. Weaning infants to a cup at about 8 months of age also reduces the risk of BBTD. Pacifiers should never be dipped in sugar or other sugary substances.

15-5f Ear Infection

Feeding an infant in a reclining position or propping the bottle while an infant is lying down (and not being held) increases the risk of ear infection (Abrahams & Labbok, 2011). An infant should always be held in a semi-upright position during feedings, and for a short while after a feeding is completed, to prevent milk from traveling back into the eustachian tubes and ear canals.

15-5g Obesity

Obesity results when energy intake exceeds an infant's needs for growth, maintenance, and activity. Infant feeding practices thought to play a role in obesity include overeating during bottle feedings, prolonged breastfeedings, early introduction of semi-solid foods, and feeding cereal (or other foods) from a bottle (Li et al., 2012).

It is important that caregivers be alert to signs that an infant is satisfied and has consumed enough during feedings. Stopping periodically gives the infant a chance to assess her own hunger and to respond appropriately when the bottle is again offered. It is important to respect the infant's judgment about the amount of food desired at a given time. Urging an infant to finish milk remaining in a bottle or to continue breastfeeding may ignore his or her signs of fullness (satiety), which include:

- closing the mouth or turning away from the bottle
- falling asleep
- crying or fussing at repeated attempts to continue feeding
- biting or playing with the nipple
- pushing the bottle or breast away

Some authorities believe that continuously ignoring these signs may cause the infant to stop recognizing and communicating signs of fullness and, thus, end an important means of regulating food intake. This can have serious, long-term consequences for children and adults who no longer know when to stop eating. To establish the point at which the infant is satisfied, the teacher should stop after a few minutes of solid-food feeding and play with the child before offering more food. This practice aids in determining whether the infant is eating because of hunger or simply to gain the caregiver's attention.

Introducing semi-solid foods before infants are old enough or serving foods high in sugar or fat may contribute to a calorie intake that is greater than needed and can lead to obesity (Schell & Gallo, 2012; Thompson, 2012). Continuing to offer solid food after the infant seems satisfied also contributes to obesity and may set the stage for overeating later in life.

Physical activity is also important for encouraging a healthy appetite and balanced weight. Infants should have multiple opportunities throughout the day to move about and should not remain in one position for longer than an hour at any time (unless sleeping). Repositioning an infant every 30 to 40 minutes also promotes the use of different muscle groups. For example, an infant might first be placed on his tummy to play, then rolled onto his back under an activity gym, and later moved to an infant seat. Older infants can be enticed to move about by placing toys out of their reach or by engaging them in rolling a ball back and forth. These are also important steps for helping children to continue developing an active lifestyle.

15-5h Choking

Occasional episodes of choking are not uncommon in young infants. The frequency of these events tends to diminish as the muscles used for swallowing continue to mature. The danger of choking is increased when infants are allowed to eat too quickly or to drink from a propped bottle while lying down. Choking can be minimized during breast or bottle feedings by holding the child in a semi-reclining position with the head elevated. Stopping for brief periods and burping the infant periodically are also effective strategies to prevent choking.

When 6- to 7-month-old infants begin to eat finger foods such as dry bread, crackers, or dry cereal, they must be monitored closely because these items may increase the risk of choking. Again, this danger can be minimized by placing the infant in a sitting position and breaking or cutting foods into small pieces that are easy to chew and swallow. Semi-solid foods can be ground or mashed with a small amount of liquid to prevent choking. Because the majority of choking episodes occur in infants, it is essential that parents and teachers be prepared by completing CPR training.

15-5i Teething

An infant's teeth begin to erupt at around 6 months of age. This can be a stressful period for some infants and may temporarily disrupt their feeding pattern. As a result, some infants may begin to wean themselves from breast or bottle feedings and prefer foods that can be chewed such as dry cereal pieces, toast, or teething biscuits. Cold or frozen teethers also help to relieve gum discomfort. Appropriate chewing toys and food items should be made available to discourage infants from picking up and chewing on inappropriate or unsafe objects. Diarrhea accompanying teething is usually due to infectious organisms and is not caused by the teething process. In an early childhood program, it is important to ensure that toys are frequently sanitized to reduce the risk of spreading illness from one infant to another.

15-5j Constipation

Breast-fed infants are generally not troubled by constipation. Because breast milk is so easily digested, only a small amount of waste product remains to be excreted. Infants who are formula-fed, especially with soy-based or iron-enriched products, are more likely to experience constipation. Giving them additional water is often sufficient to address the problem. However, if the formula-fed infant fails to have a bowel movement for more than three or four days, the family should contact their health care provider for advice.

Did You Get It?

You should administer approximately _____ oz of fluid per pound of bodyweight to an infant experiencing repeated diarrhea whose pediatrician recommended giving the infant an electrolyte replacement solution.

a. 3
b. 5
c. 8
d. 0 (You should never give this solution to a baby with diarrhea; it is for vomiting only.)

Take the full quiz on CourseMate.

PARTNERING with FAMILIES

Feeding Your Infant

Dear Families,

Birth (and even before) is an ideal time to begin addressing your child's nutritional well-being. What you eat during pregnancy influences your infant's health and food preferences. Following your infant's birth, you can encourage his or her development of healthy eating habits by serving nutritious foods and creating positive mealtime experiences.

▶ Breast milk and/or infant formula is recommended as the infant's primary source of nutrition for the first year. Cow's milk does not meet the infant's nutritional requirements for rapid growth rate and should not be offered until after the infant's first birthday.

▶ Always hold, cuddle, and talk with your infant during feedings. This practice fosters important emotional connections between you and your infant. It also reduces the potential for choking, ear infections, and baby bottle tooth decay.

▶ Wait until your infant is about 5 to 6 months old before introducing solid foods. Choose a single-grain (usually rice) iron-fortified cereal as the first food to feed to your infant. Only introduce one food at a time and serve it for several days to determine if your infant has any allergies or intolerances.

(continued)

PARTNERING with FAMILIES

Feeding Your Infant   *(continued)*

▶ Be wary of food additives, especially in commercially produced infant foods. "Desserts" and "dinners" often contain additives and offer less nutritional value than plain cereal, vegetables, fruits, and meats. Experiment with making your own pureed infant foods.

▶ Introduce 100 percent fruit juices when your infant is about 6 to 7 months of age.

▶ Don't serve infants fruit drinks, sodas, or other beverages that are high in sugar and offer few nutrients.

▶ Always cut food in small pieces and avoid foods that cause choking (especially grapes, peanuts, hotdogs, popcorn, raw vegetables).

▶ Learn CPR!

CLASSROOM CORNER

Teacher Activities

Planning Healthy Snacks

(PreK–2; NHES grades 3–5; National Health Education Standards 1.2.1, 2.2.3, 6.2.1; 1.5.1, 2.5.5, 6.5.1)

Concept: Healthy food choices provide important energy.

Learning Objectives

▶ Children will learn to plan healthy snacks.

▶ Children will identify foods that help bodies stay healthy.

Supplies

▶ Paper

▶ Crayons or markers

▶ Computer and Internet access (for older children)

▶ MyPlate placemats (can be printed from http://www.choosemyplate.gov)

▶ Magazine pictures of healthy snack items

▶ Glue sticks

Learning Activities

▶ Discuss the importance of choosing healthy snacks (e.g., growth, energy, staying healthy/ not sick). Use the MyPlate food guide to talk about and to illustrate foods that are considered healthy and why it is important to select a variety of foods (and colors) from each group, including some that are new.

▶ Draw a grid on a large sheet of paper (for each day of the week). Have younger children plan a week's worth of afternoon snacks by selecting items from two different food groups; teachers can fill in the grid with foods that children name or children can glue food pictures from magazines onto the grid. Older children can explore the ChooseMyPlate.gov website online and learn about healthy food options before developing their menu. Arrange to have the cook prepare snacks from the children's menu; older children may be able to prepare their own snacks each day.

Evaluation

▶ Children will make healthy food choices and state why this is important.

▶ Children will use the menu to create a healthy snack plan.

Summary

▸ The first year of an infant's life is one of very rapid growth and developmental change.

- By 12 months of age, most infants will triple their birth weight and increase their length by 50 percent.
- Satisfying an infant's needs for all essential nutrients supports healthy growth and development.

▸ All nutrients that an infant requires for growth and development during the first 6 months can be supplied by either breast milk or formula. Formula is similar in nutrient composition but does not provide the infant with disease-protecting antibodies.

▸ It is important for caregivers to recognize and acknowledge an infant's behavioral signals that indicate hunger or satiety.

▸ Infants are developmentally and physiologically ready to eat semi-solid foods at around 5 to 6 months of age.

- Single-grain, iron-fortified cereals (usually rice) are the first semi-solid foods introduced at around 5 to 6 months of age.
- Vegetables, fruits, and meats are added over the next three months.

▸ Caregivers must anticipate common food-related problems such as allergies, colic, vomiting and diarrhea, anemia, ear infection, obesity, and choking.

Terms to Know

low-birthweight (LBW)
   infant *p. 383*
antibodies *p. 385*
aseptic procedure *p. 387*
distention *p. 389*

regurgitation *p. 390*
electrolyte(s) *p. 390*
developmental or physiological
   readiness *p. 391*

palmar grasp *p. 392*
pincer grip *p. 392*

Chapter Review

A. By Yourself:

1. Provide a rationale for why an infant's bottle should not be propped up during feedings.

2. In what order should the following foods be introduced?

    pureed peas   pureed meat products

    crisp toast   pureed peaches

    iron-fortified barley cereal

3. At approximately what age should an infant be introduced to each of these foods?

4. Describe three social factors that make feeding time more enjoyable for an infant.

5. Explain why unmodified cow's or goat's milk should not be given to an infant before 1 year of age.

6. What steps can teachers take to support a mother who wants to continue breastfeeding her infant?

B. As a Group:

1. Discuss why it is important not to feed infants semi-solid foods before 5 to 6 months of age.

2. Debate the advantages and disadvantages of breastfeeding versus formula feeding.

3. Describe several feeding practices that are thought to contribute to infant obesity.

4. Discuss baby bottle tooth decay (BBTD) and feeding practices that will prevent this condition.

5. Evaluate the nutrient contributions of several commercial infant foods by using the http://ndb.nal .usda.gov website. Make recommendations for healthy choices based on your findings.

6. Observe several mothers while they are feeding their infant. In what ways did the mothers and infants communicate verbally and nonverbally with each other? Discuss how you could use this information to help first-time mothers.

◖ Case Study

Donica M's first child, Leandra recently celebrated her 2-month birthday. Although she is thoroughly in love with her infant, Donica finds that being a new mother can be a demanding and frustrating experience at times. Since giving birth, she has been exceptionally tired because Leandra awakens several times during the night and seems to be hungry. Donica's mother lives nearby and occasionally helps out with Leandra's care. She has suggested that putting cereal in Leandra's nighttime bottle might help to "fill her up so she will sleep through the night." She has also advised Donica to cut larger holes in the nipple "so Leandra will get more food during each feeding and won't have to work as hard."

◗ Should Donica follow her mother's advice?

◗ What are the dangers, if any, of feeding an 8-week-old infant cereal from the bottle?

◗ How might feeding practices have changed since Donica was an infant?

◗ What are the potential short- and long-term consequences of feeding semi-solid food from a bottle?

◗ How would you respond if you were the teacher and Donica asked you to feed Leandra in this manner?

◖ Application Activities

1. Mrs. Jones, mother of 2-month-old Kelly, has been on maternity leave from her job. She is preparing to return to work and has made arrangements for Kelly to stay in a nearby family child care home. Mrs. Jones wants to continue breastfeeding, but is concerned that she will have to switch Kelly over to formula. In what ways can the care provider support Mrs. Jones' interests in continuing to breastfeed?

2. Visit the infant food section of your local grocery store and read the ingredient list on several food items. Select ten foods that you consider to be nutritious choices for a young infant based on the label ingredients. Discuss the criteria you used to make this determination.

3. Plan an instructional manual for new employees in an infant care facility. What social aspects of infant feeding would be important to address? What information should also be included regarding nutrition and sanitation?

4. If applicable, review state regulations relating to infant feeding guidelines in early childhood programs. Comment on the adequacy of information provided.

5. Identify and discuss the health and feeding problems that low-birthweight infants are more likely to experience. What prenatal nutrient deficiencies are more common among infants with low-birthweight?

◖ Helpful Web Resources

Administration for Children & Families   http://www.acf.hhs.gov

Healthy Children.org (AAP)   http://www.healthychildren.org

Keep Kids Healthy   http://www.keepkidshealthy.com

La Leche League	http://www.lalecheleague.org
National Network for Child Care	http://www.nncc.org
Office on Women's Health	http://www.womenshealth.gov
Public Health Agency of Canada	http://www.phac-aspc.gc.ca

 Visit the Education CourseMate for this textbook to access the eBook, Did You Get It? quizzes, Digital Downloads, TeachSource Video Cases, flashcards, and more. Go to CengageBrain.com to log in, register, or purchase access.

References

American Academy of Pediatrics (AAP). (2012). Breastfeeding and the use of human milk, *Pediatrics,* 129(3), e827–e841.

American Dental Association. (ADA). (2011). Fluoride and infant formula: Frequently asked questions. Accessed on July 26, 2012 from http://www.ada.org/4052.aspx.

Andres, A., Cleves, M., Bellando, J., Pivik, R., Casey, P., & Badger, T. (2012). Developmental status of 1-year-old infants fed breast milk, cow's milk formula, or soy formula, *Pediatrics,* 129(6), 1134–1140.

Bigelow, A., & Power, M. (2012). The effect of mother–infant skin-to-skin contact on infants' response to the Still Face Task from newborn to three months of age, *Infant Behavior & Development,* 35(2), 240–251.

Black, M., Quigg, A., Cook, J., Casey, P., Cutts, D., Chilton, M., Meyers, A., Ettinger de Cuba, S., Heeren, T., Coleman, S., Rose-Jacobs, R., & Frank, D. (2012). WIC participation and attenuation of stress-related child health risks of household food insecurity and caregiver depressive symptoms, *Archives of Pediatrics & Adolescent Medicine,* 166(5), 444–451.

De Greef, E., Hauser, B., Devreker, T., Veereman-Wauters, G., & Vandenplas, Y. (2012). Diagnosis and management of cow's milk protein allergy in infants, *World Journal of Pediatrics,* 8(1), 19–24.

Frisoli, T., Schmieder, R., Grodzicki, T., & Messerli, F. (2012). Salt and hypertension: Is salt dietary reduction worth the effort?, *The American Journal of Medicine,* 125(5), 433–439.

Gale, C., Logan, K., Santhakumaran, S., Parkinson, J., Hyde, M., & Modi, N. (2012). Effect of breastfeeding compared with formula feeding on infant body composition: A systematic review and meta-analysis, *American Journal of Clinical Nutrition,* 95(3), 656–669.

Galler, J., Bryce, C., Waber, D., Hock, R., Harrison, R., Eaglesfield, G., & Fitzmaurice, G. (2012). Infant malnutrition predicts conduct problems in adolescents, *Nutritional Neuro-science,* 15(4), 186–192(7).

Gibbs, C., Wendt, A., Peters, S., & Hogue, C. (2012). The impact of early age at first childbirth on maternal and infant health, *Paediatric & Perinatal Epidemiology,* 26(Suppl. 1), 259–284.

Hasan, N., & Ng, P. (2012). The management of reflux in infants, *InnovAiT,* 5(2), 69–75.

Holub, S., & Dolan, E. (2012). Mothers' beliefs about infant size: Associations with attitudes and infant feeding practices, *Journal of Applied Developmental Psychology,* 33(3), 158–164.

Isaacs, E., Ross, S., Kennedy, K., Weaver, L., Lucas, A., & Fewtrell, M. (2011). 10-year cognition in preterms after random assignment to fatty acid supplementation in infancy, *Pediatrics,* 128(4), e890–898.

Kim, J., & Friel, J. (2012). Lipids and human milk, *Lipid Technology,* 24(5), 103–105.

Kuo, A., Inkelas, M., Slusser, W., Maidenberg, M., & Halfon, N. (2011). Introduction of solid food to young infants, *Maternal & Child Health Journal,* 15(8), 1185–1194.

Kvitvaer, B., Miller, J., & Newell, D. (2012). Improving our understanding of the colicky infant: A prospective observational study, *Journal of Clinical Nursing,* 21(1-2), 63–69.

Lack, G. (2012). Update on risk factors for food allergy, *Journal of Allergy & Clinical Immunology,* 129(5), 1187–1197.

Li, R., Magadia, J., Fein, S., & Grummer-Strawn, L. (2012). Risk of bottle-feeding for rapid weight gain during the first year of life, *Archives of Pediatrics & Adolescent Medicine,* 166(5), 431–436.

Marotz, L., & Allen, K. (2013). *Developmental profiles: Pre-birth through adolescence* (7th ed.). Belmont, CA: Wadsworth Cengage.

Poston, L. (2012). Gestational weight gain: Influences on the long-term health of the child, *Current Opinion in Clinical Nutrition & Metabolic Care,* 15(4), 252–257.

Przyrembel, H. (2012). Timing of introduction of complementary food: Short- and long-term consequences, *Annals of Nutrition & Metabolism,* 60(2), 8–20.

Salisbury, A., High, P., Twomey, J., Dickstein, S., Chapman, H., Liu, J., & Lester, B. (2012). A randomized control trial of integrated care for families managing infant colic, *Infant Mental Health Journal,* 33(2), 110–122.

Salone, L., Vann, W., & Dee, D. (2013). Breastfeeding: An overview of oral and general health benefits, *The Journal of the American Dental Association,* 144(2), 143–151.

Schell, L., & Gallo, M. (2012). Overweight and obesity among North American Indian infants, children, and youth, *American Journal of Human Biology*, 24(3), 302–313.

Stein, L., Cowart, B., & Beauchamp, G. (2012). The development of salty taste acceptance is related to dietary experience in human infants: A prospective study, *American Journal of Clinical Nutrition*, 95(1), 123–129.

Sullivan, J., & Sundaram, S. (2012). Gastroesophageal reflux, *Pediatrics in Review*, 33(6), 243–254.

Thompson, A. (2012). Developmental origins of obesity: Early feeding environments, infant growth, and the intestinal microbiome, *American Journal of Human Biology*, 24(3), 350–360.

U.S. Department of Agriculture (USDA). (2012). "WIC Program data: National level annual summary." Accessed on July 26, 2012 from http://www.fns.usda.gov/pd/37WIC_Monthly.htm.

Voss, W., Jungmann, T., Wachtendorf, M., & Neubauer, A. (2012). Long-term cognitive outcomes of extremely low-birth-weight infants: The influence of the maternal educational background, *Acta Paediatrica*, 101(6), 569–573.

Feeding Toddlers and Young Children

- **#1 a, b, and c:** Promoting child development and learning
- **#2 a, b, and c:** Building family and community relationships
- **#3 a, b, and d:** Observing, documenting, and assessing to support young children and families
- **#4 a, b, and d:** Using developmentally effective approaches to connect with children and families
- **#5 a, and c:** Using content knowledge to build meaningful curriculum
- **#6 c:** Becoming a professional.

Learning Objectives

After studying this chapter, you should be able to:

LO 16-1 Discuss the developmental characteristics typical of toddlers, preschoolers, and school-age children.

LO 16-2 Explain the challenges involved in getting toddlers to eat and how these challenges can be addressed.

LO 16-3 Describe the unique nutrient requirements of preschoolers and school-age children and ways to meet their needs.

LO 16-4 Discuss how adults can foster children's healthy eating behaviors.

LO 16-5 Identify and discuss the common health problems associated with children's poor eating patterns.

16-1 Developmental Profiles: Toddlers, Preschoolers, and School-Aged Children

Toddlers (1- to 2½-year-olds) are delightful individuals, but they can be challenging at times. They are beginning to assert their independence, yet need and want limits. They have an insatiable curiosity, yet prefer most things to be predictable and always conducted in the same way. They are becoming increasingly mobile and active, but still need to be monitored closely and protected from unsafe conditions in their environment.

Many toddlers spend considerable time each day in early education programs while their parents work or attend school. These opportunities expose children to social and eating experiences that often differ from those they are accustomed to at home. Children begin to learn that other people may do things differently, but this doesn't necessarily translate into a willingness to join in.

Although toddlers are growing at a much slower rate than they did as infants, they continue to need adequate calories and essential nutrients to maintain growth and activity levels. However, the amount of food they are willing and able to eat often seems insufficient to adults. Children's small stomach capacity and short attention span limit what they are able to consume at any one time. One way to address mealtime challenges is to serve small amounts of food more often and on a consistent schedule. Yet toddlers may resist eating on a schedule and reject foods they are served as they struggle to become independent. They have learned the power of the word "no" and use it repeatedly. They quickly learn to shape adults' behavior by refusing to eat or, at other times, by eating to gain adult favor.

▼ **Preschool-age children prefer to do things by themselves, but may still need adult assistance.**

© Cengage Learning

The toddler is often described as being **neophobic**, especially when it comes to eating—that is, they become distressed and are often reluctant to try new or unfamiliar foods (Tan & Holub, 2012). This behavior may limit the toddler's willingness to eat an increasing variety of foods. When adults understand that this behavior is characteristic of most toddlers, they can begin to exercise more patience and ingenuity as they introduce new foods into children's diet (Musher-Eizenman et al., 2011).

Many toddlers also become avid television watchers. What they observe is likely to affect their behavior and food preferences. Researchers have noted that foods advertised on popular children's television programs are often of poor nutrient quality. They have also found that commercials create a desire for foods high in calories, refined sugars, and fat (Harris et al., 2012). Furthermore, hours spent sitting in front of the television reduce valuable time that toddlers should be spending in active play. Inactivity limits the calories that are burned and can ultimately contribute to childhood obesity.

Preschool-aged children (2½- to 6-year-olds) are generally more easygoing and cooperative than toddlers. They are willing to listen and to follow adult directions in an effort to please, but are not always compliant. Although they prefer to do things for themselves, they may still need some adult assistance to be successful. Structure continues to be important for preschoolers, who are also more likely to respect it than toddlers do. They are learning more appropriate ways of expressing themselves, yet may still be somewhat hesitant at times to accept change. Families and teachers can anticipate that many of these developmental characteristics will be reflected in the preschooler's eating behaviors and responses to food.

School-aged children are becoming increasingly aware of a much bigger world. They are energetic, curious, eager to learn, and able to understand increasingly complex situations. Friends and friendships gradually replace time spent with family, although school-aged children still need and find comfort in knowing they can rely on their parents. Watching television, playing electronic games, and participating in organized activities now consume more of their time.

Family meal practices, including cultural eating habits and food preferences, remain an important factor in determining the school-aged child's mealtime behaviors (Anderson et al., 2012). However, the favorite foods of friends and peers also begin to influence their food choices. School-aged children enjoy helping with meal planning, grocery shopping, and food preparation. Their appetite is generally good, but it also tends to fluctuate with growth spurts and activity levels.

Did You Get It?

Toddlers displaying _____ behavior frequently refuse new food options and experiences with which they are not familiar.

  a. ombrophobic

  b. nouveauphobic

  c. neophobic

  d. ailurophobic

Take the full quiz on CourseMate.

neophobic – *fear of things that are new and unfamiliar.*

16-2 The Challenges of Feeding Toddlers

Toddlers are driven to assert their independence and to let their preferences be known. This includes their firm announcement of the foods they will or will not eat. Fortunately, their "will" and "will not" foods change almost daily. However, great care must be taken so that families and teachers do not become involved in a battle of wills over what the toddler will eat and when it will be eaten. Mealtime friction can be minimized by respecting adult and child responsibilities in the feeding relationship (Satter, 2000). Adults are responsible for:

- serving a variety of nutritious foods
- deciding when food is offered
- setting a positive example by eating a variety of foods

The child is responsible for:

- choosing what foods will be eaten from those that have been offered
- deciding how much of the offered food to eat

16-2a What Foods Should Be Served and How Much

Families and teachers have a responsibility to provide children with a variety of nutritious foods each day. As discussed in Chapter 12, the MyPlate guidelines are easy to follow and ensure that children's daily nutrient needs will be met (Figure 16–1, or visit www.ChooseMyPlate.gov). Teacher Checklist 16-1 presents a summary of the basic food groups and recommended amounts that children should consume each day.

When feeding toddlers, it is preferable to serve slightly less than they are expected to eat. In this way toddlers are not overwhelmed by the amount of food on their plates and are able to assert their independence by requesting more. An appropriate serving size for a toddler is

FIGURE 16–1 ChooseMyPlate.

Source: US Department of Agriculture, Food and Nutrition Service.

United States Department of Agriculture

✓✓ TEACHER CHECKLIST 16-1

Recommended Daily Food Group Intakes

Food Group	Toddlers	Preschoolers	School-Aged
Grains	3 ounces	4-ounces	5–6 ounces
Vegetables	1 cup	1½ cups	2–2½ cups
Fruits	1 cup	1–1½ cups	1½ cups
Dairy	2 cups	2 cups	3 cups
Meat & meat alternates	2 ounces	3–4 ounces	5 ounces
Oils	Use sparingly		

TeachSource Digital Download Download from CourseMate.

approximately one-fourth of an adult serving for each food group with the exception of the dairy group (see Figure 16–2):

Milk - 1/2 cup
Meat/meat alternate - 1 ounce
Fruits and Vegetables - 2 tablespoons
Breads and Cereals - 2 tablespoons rice, cereal, or pasta; 1/2 slice bread

The toddler's acceptance of foods is highly influenced by their sensory qualities, especially taste, texture, and temperature. Young children's mouths are sensitive to temperature extremes; foods that are too cold or too hot will often be refused. Hot foods that are comfortable for adults may burn the toddler's mouth. Toddlers also have an abundance of taste buds that intensify the flavors of some foods. This may explain, in part, why toddlers often refuse vegetables such as broccoli, spinach, brussels sprouts, and beets. Food textures may also be challenging, especially as toddlers are transitioning from soft, pureed foods to table foods. They still have an active gag reflex and are also prone to choking. For this reason, foods must be cut into small pieces (1/4 inch or less) so they are easy to pick up and chew. Toddlers also prefer foods that are served individually

FIGURE 16–2   Sample menu with serving sizes for toddlers.

BREAKFAST	LUNCH	DINNER
Whole milk (1/2 cup)	Whole milk (1/2 cup)	Whole milk (1/2 cup)
Pancake (small)	Beef patty (1 oz)	Finely diced chicken (1 oz)
or	Broccoli (2 tbsp)	Cooked carrots (2 tbsp)
Whole wheat toast (1/2 slice)	Diced watermelon (2 tbsp)	Diced plums (2 tbsp)
Fruit preserves (1 tsp)	Whole wheat bread (1/2 slice)	Brown rice (1/4 cup)
Diced peaches (1/4 cup)	Margarine (1 tsp)	Margarine (1 tsp)
MIDMORNING SNACK	**MIDAFTERNOON SNACK**	**EVENING SNACK**
Vanilla wafers (3)	Cheese cube (1/2 oz)	Applesauce (1/2 cup)
Orange juice (1/2 cup)	Whole wheat crackers (2)	Graham crackers (2)
	Water	Water

(and not touching) rather than combined in mixtures. For example, instead of serving spaghetti and meatballs, green beans, and a mixed fruit salad, the same basic foods could be presented as:

- Ground beef patty
- Green beans
- Whole grain bread or pasta
- Diced peaches
- Milk

Remember that toddlers' appetite typically decrease as their growth rate slows. Adults should not become overly concerned if children are suddenly eating less. It is also important to avoid pressuring, nagging, or forcing children to eat more food than they may want or need. Doing so can cause food to take on an emotional association and potentially lead to eating disorders.

Table 16–1 presents an overview of age-related eating behaviors that may be helpful in understanding children's changing responses to food. Adults can use this knowledge to establish realistic expectations and to create positive feeding experiences for children of all ages.

TABLE 16–1   Age-Related Eating Behaviors

Age	Behavior
12–24 months	Has a decreased appetite Is sometimes described as a finicky or fussy eater; may go on food jags Uses spoon with some degree of skill Helps feed self
2-year-old	Has fair appetite Expresses strong likes and dislikes; may go on food jags Prefers simple food, dislikes mixtures, wants food served in familiar ways Learns table manners by imitating adults and older children
3-year-old	Has fairly good appetite; prefers small servings; likes only a few cooked vegetables Feeds self independently, if hungry Uses spoon in semi-adult fashion; may spear with fork and spread with a blunt knife Dawdles over food when not hungry
4- to 5-year-old	Eats well, but not at every meal May develop dislikes of certain foods and refuse them to the point of tears if pushed; often adapts to preferences of family and teachers Enjoys helping with meal preparation Uses all eating utensils; becomes skilled at spreading jelly or peanut butter, pouring milk on cereal, or cutting soft foods such as bread
6- to 7-year-old	Has good appetite; eats most foods Is willing to try new foods, but is unpredictable Able to use eating utensils, but not always correctly Easily distracted; has difficulty sitting through a meal
8- to 9-year-old	Usually has a good appetite; boys eat more than girls Prefers to eat when hungry rather than at specified times Is open to trying new foods, but prefers certain "favorites" Enjoys cooking Eats quickly so they can resume previous activity
10- to 12-year-old	Always hungry; seems to eat non-stop and large amounts at one time Needs a big snack after school Dislikes few foods; interested in trying foods from other cultures and those seen on television Seems to forget manners that were previously learned

Source: Adapted from Marotz, L. R., & Allen, K. E. (2013). *Developmental profiles: Pre-birth through adolescence.* (7th ed.). Belmont, CA: Wadsworth Cengage.

16-2b When to Serve Food

The timing of meals and snacks is an important consideration when feeding toddlers. Too much time between feedings will result in an overly hungry, cranky child who may lose interest in food when it is finally presented. Meals and snacks spaced too closely together will not allow ample time for a child to become hungry again, resulting in a poor eating response. Most young children also eat better at meals if they are not tired and if they have been given an advanced warning so they can "wrap up" their play activities. Allowing time for a quiet story before mealtime can set the stage for a pleasant, relaxed, and more satisfying mealtime experience for everyone.

Because toddlers have a critical need for nutrients and a small stomach capacity, they must eat more often than the three-meal family pattern. An ideal eating pattern includes:

- breakfast
- midmorning snack
- lunch
- midafternoon snack
- dinner
- bedtime snack, if needed

Snacks chosen from each of the food groups can be planned to meet a portion of the child's daily nutrient needs. Foods commonly promoted on television as "snacks," such as chips, snack cakes, frosted cookies, candy bars, fruit "drinks," and sodas have no place in the toddler's daily meal pattern. These foods consist primarily of empty calories and provide little if any nutritional value. Healthy snack choices include:

- cheese cubes and pita wedges
- crackers with peanut butter or hummus
- 100 percent fruit juices – orange or other juices fortified with vitamin C
- diced, raw vegetables – cucumber slices, cherry tomatoes, mushrooms, zucchini, red and orange peppers, jicama
- lightly cooked (steamed) vegetables– broccoli florets, green beans, carrots, edamame, sweet potato strips
- fruits – apple and orange wedges, bananas, applesauce, diced peaches, pears, plums, nectarines, kiwi, pineapple
- whole grain crackers and breads
- dry, nonsweetened cereals
- yogurt with fresh fruit or granola

16-2c Making Mealtime Comfortable, Pleasant, and Safe

Children are more likely to eat in comfortable surroundings. Furniture should be of an appropriate size; table height should be comfortable for children to reach and chairs should permit their feet to rest flat on the floor. If a highchair or youth chair is used, it must have a stable base, washable eating tray, crotch safety strap, and support for the child's feet. Eating utensils should be child-sized and nonbreakable. Children's forks should have short, blunt tines and broad, short, easy-to-grasp handles. Spoons should also have short, blunt handles and shallow bowls for easy use. An upturned rim around plates provides a means for "trapping" elusive bits of food. Plates divided into two or three compartments can also reduce frustration for toddlers as they develop self-feeding skills. Small (4 to 6 ounces) plastic cups with a broad base are easy for children to hold and also reduce potential spills.

Toddlers are developing hand/eye coordination and improved fine motor skills that enable them to better handle utensils and to feed themselves. They should be encouraged to practice these skills but should not be given too many difficult-to-manage foods. Peas that roll off of a spoon or soups that spill before they reach the child's mouth can quickly discourage even the most determined toddler. Finger foods served along with foods that require a fork or spoon encourage self-feeding and reduce mealtime frustration. Meats and cheeses cut into small cubes and vegetables and fruits sliced into small pieces are easier (and safer) for toddlers to pick up and chew. Although adults may not think that peas, mashed potatoes, and rice are finger foods, toddlers often do. A little flexibility in the choice of feeding methods can pay off in terms of the toddler's increased willingness to eat.

Sanitation is also an important consideration in feeding the toddler. The aseptic environment required when they were infants is no longer necessary or possible to maintain. However, cleanliness is of prime importance when preparing, serving, and eating food. Hand washing before and after meals is mandatory for toddlers as they often eat with their hands. Teachers must also wash their hands carefully before handling or eating food and again after cleaning up from a meal.

Did You Know...

that french fries account for 25 percent of the vegetables consumed by children? Fewer than 20 percent of children eat five or more daily servings of fruits and vegetables.

Did You Get It?

To present toddlers with a variety of foods at each meal and minimize mealtime friction, adults should:

  a. insist that the toddler eat a little bit of everything
  b. tell the toddler to choose one or two options
  c. take a bite from each option, model the behavior, and present the toddler with a small serving
  d. allow the toddler to choose from the options according to his or her desire

Take the full quiz on CourseMate.

16-3 The Challenges of Feeding Preschoolers and School-Age Children

As children mature, they also become more willing to eat. However, some preschoolers will have even firmer ideas of the foods they do or do not like. During active growth periods, the child's appetite and food acceptance are usually quite good. However, as growth slows, so does the child's appetite. It is during this latter stage that parents and teachers may become unduly concerned. (This concern may have the consequence of establishing a food-emotion link that can lead to feeding problems and eating disorders.) In most cases, there is no real cause for concern; growing, energetic children will usually eat when they are hungry. Remember that during this age, food should be offered frequently. If the child does not finish lunch, a nutrient dense midafternoon snack can make up for nutrients that may be lacking.

Children's attitudes about food and eating patterns are formed during the preschool years and often carried over into adulthood. For this reason, it is important that teachers and families work together to help children develop healthful eating practices and positive feelings about food. Rules regarding acceptable eating behaviors should provide constructive guidance and be enforced consistently. However, they should also allow some flexibility for both the adult and child in order to avoid a power struggle during mealtimes.

▼ Creating a comfortable eating environment encourages children's independence and ability to feed themselves.

© Cengage Learning

16-3a Guidelines for Feeding the Preschooler

As with toddlers, the MyPlate model provides a simple guide for feeding preschoolers. Foods are needed from all of the food groups, but the amounts required are somewhat larger (Figure 16–3). Appropriate serving sizes for preschoolers are:

> 1/2 to 3/4 cup milk
> 1/2 to 1 slice of bread
> 1 tablespoon for each year of age for:
> > fruits (approximately 1/4 cup)
> > vegetables (approximately 1/4 cup)
> > meat or meat alternative (approximately 1 1/2 ounces)

The appearance and other sensory qualities of foods still influence the 3- to 5-year-olds' willingness to eat. Foods presented in colorful combinations, shapes, and textures are attractive and inviting. Preschool-age children also prefer their foods served lukewarm, and are likely to reject or play with items that are too hot or too cold until they reach an acceptable temperature. Serving slightly smaller food portions prevents children from feeling visually overwhelmed and provides them with an opportunity to ask for more. Involving children in meal preparation is also an effective strategy for improving their interest in trying a new food or meal they have helped to make.

Creating a comfortable mealtime environment continues to be important for preschool-age children. Appropriately sized furniture, dishes, and silverware encourage independence. Although many 3- to 5-year-olds still have difficulty managing eating utensils skillfully, they are becoming increasingly adept with continued practice. For example, younger children may find it easier to handle a plastic knife when initially learning how to spread and cut their bread. Including a few finger foods in meals and ignoring unintentional messes also promotes a positive eating experience.

16-3b Nutrient Needs of School-Aged Children

Although energy expenditures and growth rates are highly variable from child to child, the need for a well-balanced diet continues to be critical for school-aged children. For the most part, they

---

FIGURE 16–3   **Sample menu with serving sizes for preschool-age children.**

BREAKFAST	LUNCH	DINNER
Low-fat milk (3/4 cup)	Low-fat milk (3/4 cup)	Low-fat milk (3/4 cup)
Pancake (1)	Beef patty (1 1/2 oz)	Diced chicken (1 1/2 oz)
or	Broccoli (1/4 cup)	Cooked carrots (1/4 cup)
Whole wheat toast (1/2 slice)	Diced watermelon (1/4 cup)	Diced plums (1/4 cup)
Fruit preserves (1 tsp)	Whole-wheat bread (1/2 slice)	Brown rice (1/4 cup)
Diced peaches (1/2 cup)	Margarine (1 tsp)	Margarine (1 tsp)

MIDMORNING SNACK	MIDAFTERNOON SNACK	EVENING SNACK
Vanilla wafers (3)	Cheese cube (1 1/2 oz)	Applesauce (1/2 cup)
Orange juice (1/2 cup)	Whole wheat crackers (2)	Graham crackers (2)
	Water	Water

are eager eaters and open to trying new foods. Peers and social groups outside of the child's family, including school and television, begin to compete with long-standing family eating patterns and food preferences. However, families still play an important role in terms of their expectations, the foods they provide at home, and the importance they place on eating meals together.

School-aged children are able to consume considerably more food at a sitting and, thus, require fewer in-between-meal snacks than when they were younger. Although many children receive a portion of their daily nutrients from meals eaten at school, they are usually eager for, and need, a substantial after-school snack. Having access to a supply of healthy fruits, vegetables, low-fat dairy products, and whole grain foods allows children to independently select and prepare nutritious snacks that also reinforce healthy eating habits. Appropriate serving sizes for school-aged children are:

1 cup milk (2 percent)
1 slice bread or 3/4 cup dry cereal
1/2 to 3/4 cup fruits/vegetables
1 ounce meat or meat alternative (snack); 2 ounces (meals)

The MyPlate guide serves as an effective tool for ensuring that children's meals and snacks include all essential nutrients.

16-3c Feeding Children with Special Needs

Children who have developmental disabilities or special health conditions may present a range of unique nutritional needs and feeding challenges. Impaired motor abilities may make self-feeding and/or swallowing difficult. Medications, such as antibiotics and those taken for seizure disorders can increase a child's need for certain nutrients or interfere with a child's appetite. Some genetic conditions, such as **Down syndrome** and **Prader-Willi syndrome**, increase the tendency for obesity and, thus, make it necessary to carefully monitor children's food intake. Other children may have difficulty recognizing and communicating when they are hungry or have had enough to eat. Children who experience autism spectrum disorders often restrict their food intake to a select few items and may require considerable coaxing before they will even take a few bites (Rogers, Magill-Evans, & Rempel, 2012). Food intolerances and allergies to foods containing wheat, dairy, or gluten, for example, can make it challenging to meet children's essential nutrient requirements.

Because nutrition is essential to healthy development and well-being, teachers must pay careful attention to identifying and addressing each child's unique nutrient needs. Maintaining close communication ties with families can help teachers learn more specifically about a child's condition and how it may affect eating ability and nutrient requirements. Families should also be encouraged to keep teachers informed of changes in children's medical condition and treatments that might affect eating behavior. Teachers can be instrumental in monitoring children's growth and overall health by checking their height and weight periodically. They can also consult with hospital dietitians and public health nurses for advice or assistance with children's feeding problems.

▼ **Children must always wash their hands before and after eating.**

© Cergage Learning

Down syndrome – *a genetic disorder that is characterized by unique facial features, intellectual disabilities, and motor delays.*
Prader-Willi syndrome – *a chromosomal disorder that causes learning and behavior problems, poor muscle tone, short height, and overeating that can lead to obesity.*

Did You Get It?

Because the temperature of food is an important factor in enticing young children to eat, you should consider serving food _____, as most children appear to prefer food at that temperature.
  a. extremely hot
  b. lukewarm
  c. hot
  d. cold

Take the full quiz on CourseMate.

16-4 Healthy Eating Habits

Children between the ages of 1 and 5 years are in the process of establishing lifelong eating patterns. This makes the feeding of toddlers and young children an especially important responsibility. Steps that families and teachers can take to promote children's healthy eating habits include:

  ❯ serving a variety of nutritious foods
  ❯ eating with the children and modeling an enjoyment of a variety of nutritious foods

One of the most important goals in helping children develop healthy eating habits is to expose them to an increasing number and variety of foods from each food group. It is especially important to cultivate their interest in the fruit and vegetable groups because these foods are the primary source of many vitamins and minerals. Children should also experience familiar foods prepared in a variety of different ways in order to broaden their eating experiences.

Toddlers and preschoolers have a strong preference for sweet foods and a dislike for most vegetables. Knowing this, parents and teachers can downplay sweets in children's diets while increasing their exposure to fruits and vegetables. One way to approach this challenge might be to involve children in planting vegetables in containers or a small classroom garden, harvesting the mature produce, and then helping to prepare the vegetables for a meal. Teachers can also set an example by eating a variety of vegetables in front of the children, commenting on how delicious they are, and indicating pleasure (such as smiling). This power of suggestion can have a contagious effect on children's willingness to at least try a few bites. Teacher Checklist 16-2 provides additional suggestions for introducing children to new or unfamiliar foods.

✔✔ TEACHER CHECKLIST 16-2
Introducing New or Unfamiliar Foods

1. Introduce only one new food at a time.
2. Serve the new food along with other familiar foods.
3. Serve only small portions of the new food—begin with one bite or teaspoonful.
4. Introduce new foods when the child is hungry.
5. Allow the child time to examine an unfamiliar food in her own curious way.
6. Talk about the new food: its taste, color, texture, where it comes from.
7. Involve the child in grocery shopping and preparing the new food item.
8. Encourage the child to taste the new food. If rejected, accept the refusal and try again on another occasion. As foods become more familiar, they are also more readily accepted.
9. Determine what is not liked about a rejected food. Perhaps preparing it in a different manner will improve its appeal.
10. Let the child observe you eating and enjoying the new food!

Children in group settings often begin to imitate the eating behaviors of their teachers and peers. For this reason, it is particularly important that adults sit and eat with the children at mealtime, engage in pleasant social conversation, taste a variety of foods, and avoid displaying a dislike for any food. Children are quick to pick up and copy negative reactions to foods.

Older children enjoy being involved in meal planning and preparation. For example, children in an after-school program might develop the weekly snack menu from a teacher-provided list of healthy foods rich in vitamins, minerals, and fiber. School-age children can also be assigned specific food preparation roles and trusted to perform them with skill and confidence. Not only does this acknowledgement appeal to the child's sense of responsibility, but it also fosters positive self-esteem. Involving school-aged children in food-related activities provides multiple opportunities to learn about foods and to reinforce healthy eating and physical activity habits. This is important because school-aged children are especially vulnerable to conflicting messages about body image and weight control. Their involvement with food contributes to a better understanding of the important connections between eating behaviors and well-being.

Rewards should not be offered to children for trying a new food, nor should food be used to reinforce any other form of desired behavior. Adults are often tempted to use food (especially dessert or popular sweet snacks) as an incentive to get children to eat the nutritious portion of a meal. This practice causes desserts to assume undue importance for the child and is unlikely to result in any long-term acceptance of unfamiliar or disliked foods. Appropriate desserts, such as fresh fruits or fruit-based dishes, should be nutritious (nutrient dense) and planned as a basic part of the meal. For example, a zucchini or carrot bar or slice of pumpkin bread may disguise vegetables that a child might otherwise refuse. Also, a child should never be asked to present a "clean plate" before receiving their dessert. This is one sure way to start the child on a road to obesity or eating disorders (Zhang & McIntosh, 2011).

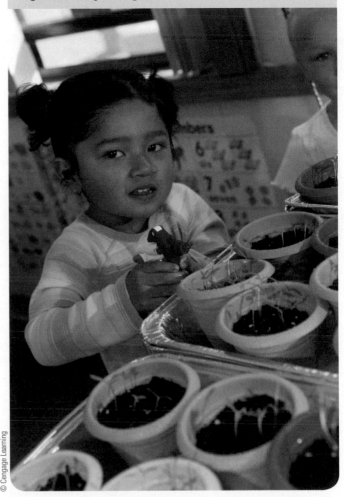

▼ **Gardening helps children to learn about where food originates and improves their interest in trying vegetables they have grown.**

© Cengage Learning

Did You Get It?

What is not one of the recommended practices to encourage children to try and even begin to like healthy fruits and vegetables?

- **a.** modeling the eating and enjoyment of these foods
- **b.** planting and cultivating a garden with these foods
- **c.** explaining why fruits and vegetables are so vitally important
- **d.** involving children in the preparation and cooking of these foods

Take the full quiz on CourseMate.

16-5 Health Problems Related to Eating Patterns

Teaching children healthful eating practices can have lifelong positive outcomes. A number of health conditions are now thought to be directly or indirectly related to dietary patterns, including:

- **dental caries** (tooth decay)
- obesity (excess body fat)
- **hypertension** (high blood pressure)
- cardiovascular disease (CVD)
- diabetes mellitus

16-5a Dental Caries

Dietary sugars are known to increase the occurrence of dental caries. However, several factors determine sugar's decay-causing potential, including the form (solid, in solution, sticky), frequency of consumption, and when it is eaten (meals versus snacks) more than does total sugar intake. Sugar obtained from fresh fruits and vegetables may actually offer some protection from tooth decay while also supplying essential nutrients for the actively growing child (Hess et al., 2012).

16-5b Obesity

The prevention of obesity begins with infant feeding. The infant's signals of **satiety** should be noted and feeding stopped when they occur. (See Table 15–4.) Toddlers and preschoolers will usually signal or stop eating when they have had enough food, unless eating or not eating is their best way to gain attention. Forcing children to continue eating interferes with their ability to recognize when they are full and can contribute to excessive weight gain and obesity. However, many children are also consuming more calories than are needed. Increased portion sizes have made it difficult for them to recognize what is actually an appropriate serving (Friedman et al., 2012) (Figure 16–4).

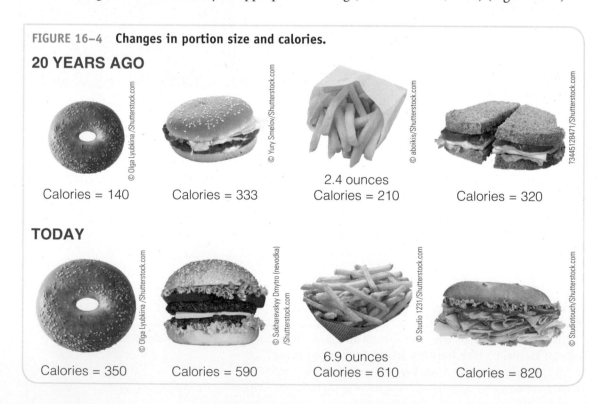

FIGURE 16–4   Changes in portion size and calories.

20 YEARS AGO

Calories = 140   Calories = 333

2.4 ounces
Calories = 210   Calories = 320

TODAY

Calories = 350   Calories = 590

6.9 ounces
Calories = 610   Calories = 820

---

dental caries – *tooth decay.*
hypertension – *elevation of blood pressure above the normally accepted values.*
satiety – *a feeling of satisfaction or fullness*

Approximately 33 percent of U.S. children are overweight or obese, an incidence that has nearly tripled over the past 20 years (AHA, 2012). Although a slight genetic potential for obesity exists in some families, this does not mean that all family members will become obese. Thus, serving children nutritious foods, teaching them to make wise choices, involving them in physical activity, and limiting their sedentary activities, such as television viewing and computer or video games, is critical for maintaining normal body weight and reducing the risk of childhood obesity (Lent et al., 2012; Skouteris et al., 2012) (Figure 16–5).

16-5c Hypertension

For many years hypertension (high blood pressure) has been correlated with a high intake of dietary sodium (salt). Children who have a family history of hypertension are at greater risk for developing the condition and may benefit from reducing their salt intake (Frisoli et al., 2012). Although sodium is an essential nutrient for infants and young children, their needs can easily be met without the use of a salt shaker. Many convenience, processed, and fast foods are high in sodium and should be avoided by individuals who may be genetically predisposed to hypertension. The amount of salt added to foods prepared at home or school can easily be controlled and often reduced without affecting the flavor outcome.

Did You Know...

the average child consumes the equivalent of 3,387 mg of salt per day? This is approximately 1,300 mg more than recommended.

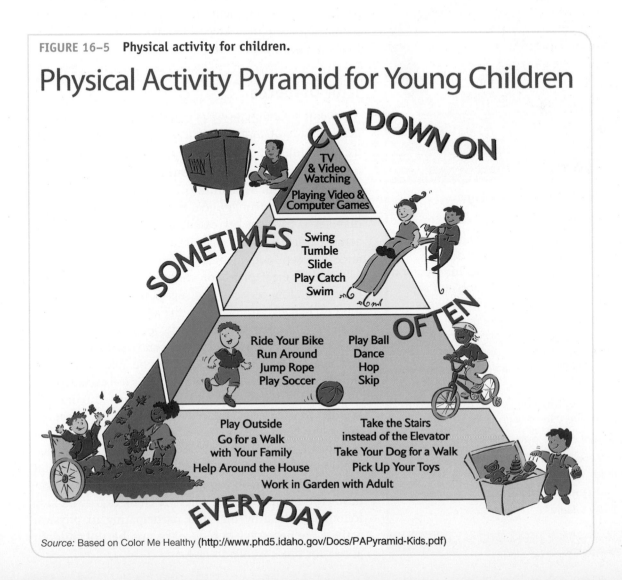

FIGURE 16–5 **Physical activity for children.**

Physical Activity Pyramid for Young Children

CUT DOWN ON

TV & Video Watching

Playing Video & Computer Games

SOMETIMES

Swing
Tumble
Slide
Play Catch
Swim

OFTEN

Ride Your Bike
Run Around
Jump Rope
Play Soccer

Play Ball
Dance
Hop
Skip

Play Outside
Go for a Walk
with Your Family
Help Around the House
Work in Garden with Adult

Take the Stairs
instead of the Elevator
Take Your Dog for a Walk
Pick Up Your Toys

EVERY DAY

Source: Based on Color Me Healthy (http://www.phd5.idaho.gov/Docs/PAPyramid-Kids.pdf)

16-5d Cardiovascular Disease

Cardiovascular disease (CVD) is most often associated with high levels of certain fatty substances in the blood. Although cholesterol is frequently cited as the culprit, the true causative agents of CVD are high intakes of dietary fat and saturated fatty acids. Over 60 percent of overweight children ages 5 to 10 already have at least one risk factor for heart disease that can be attributed to a high fat diet (Halfon, Verhoef, & Kuo, 2012).

The testing and monitoring of young children's blood cholesterol levels remain controversial. The American Academy of Pediatrics has endorsed new recommendations issued by the National Heart, Lung, & Blood Institutes that all children be tested between 9 and 11 years of age and again when they reach 17 to 21 years (AAP, 2011). Some health professionals argue that this results in over-testing and contributes to increased health care costs. What all experts do agree upon is to lower dietary fat (e.g., cholesterol, saturated, trans-fats) and sodium intakes while increasing children's physical activity.

A child who has high blood cholesterol levels should have his diet monitored closely to include no more than 30 percent of calories from fat and 10 percent or less calories from saturated fat. However, dietary fats, including cholesterol, should not be restricted before the age of 2 (unless medically prescribed) because they provide essential fatty acids necessary for normal neurological development. Any adjustments made in a child's diet must ensure that all nutrient requirements for normal growth and development are being met. In many cases, increasing the child's physical activity level is sufficient to lower blood cholesterol.

16-5e Diabetes

Although type 1 diabetes is most commonly diagnosed in children and adolescents, it is not caused by the quality of a child's diet. However, the disease does have a profound effect on a child's eating pattern and growth (Hockenberry & Wilson, 2012). There is no one "diabetic diet." The primary goal in feeding a child who has diabetes is to meet her essential nutrient needs and to achieve normal blood sugar levels by maintaining a balance between food, medication (insulin), and activity.

Typical meal plans for children who have diabetes include limiting concentrated sugars, planning meals with food exchanges, and matching the amount of medication (insulin) administered with activity levels and the amount of carbohydrates consumed in meals and snacks. It is important that children who have diabetes be able to eat foods similar to their peers so they don't always feel excluded.

Type 2 diabetes typically develops during the middle- to later years and in overweight adults. However, there has been a dramatic increase in the number of young children with type 2 diabetes in recent years due to the epidemic of childhood obesity. Approximately half of all children newly diagnosed with diabetes each year have type 2 (CDC, 2012). Lifestyle changes that include following a healthy diet and participating in physical activity are necessary to reduce the numbers of children at risk for this chronic disease.

Video supplied by the BBC Motion Gallery

▶❚❚ **TeachSource Video Connections**

Technology and Media Use by Children and Adolescents

Today's children are growing up surrounded by an array of advanced electronic and media devices. These items provide children with opportunities for socialization, entertainment, and learning and are considered commonplace and essential. However, experts are concerned that excessive use of these devices is having negative effects on children's health. As you watch the learning video, *Technology and Media Use by Children and Adolescents,* consider the following questions:

1. What negative outcomes are often attributed to children's extensive use of technology?

2. Why do you think these outcomes occur?

3. What types of foods are children most likely to consume while watching television or a video?

4. How can parents help children use their time and technology wisely?

Watch on CourseMate.

16-5f Common Feeding Behaviors and Concerns

Consuming Excessive Milk Children who drink milk to the exclusion of other foods may be at risk for iron-deficiency anemia and vitamin C (ascorbic acid) deficiency because it is a poor source of both nutrients. Children who consume more than 16 to 24 ounces of milk daily may have difficulty eating enough food from other food groups to adequately meet their nutrient needs. Water offered between meals and when additional milk is requested can help to satisfy children's thirst and discourage excess dairy consumption. Special attention should also be paid to including iron-rich foods in daily meals to protect children from developing iron-deficiency anemia. Examples of foods high in iron are presented in Chapter 17 (Table 17–1).

Refusal to Eat and Selective Eating Toddlers and preschoolers occasionally refuse food either because they are overly tired, asserting their newly found independence, or simply not hungry. If health problems do not explain a child's short-term disinterest in food, it may be best to ignore the behavior. Remember that most active, growing children will soon become hungry and decide to eat. If nutritious food is provided for meals and snacks and if adults do not give in to children's requests for unhealthy food substitutions, hunger will eventually win over the challenge of refusal. However, it is also important that adults do not "try too hard" or attempt to coax or pressure children to eat because this can lead to unpleasant power struggles. In most cases, children will gradually grow out of this stage when adults refrain from nagging or pressuring them to eat.

Children who have autism spectrum disorders often exhibit a significant aversion to foods and are especially sensitive to their textures. Prolonged food refusal or selectivity may require professional behavioral intervention, close monitoring of children's nutrient intake, and nutrient supplementation (Sira & Fryling, 2012).

Dawdling and Messiness These are the trademarks of young children and cannot be avoided, although they can be controlled. Children dawdle for various reasons—they have eaten enough, they'd rather eat something else, or they have learned that it gets attention. Establishing and consistently enforcing mealtime rules will usually end dawdling behaviors. The teacher should decide upon an appropriate length of time for eating (approximately 20–25 minutes), warn the child when there is not much time remaining, and then remove the child from the table when time is up. This may result in some temporary unhappiness, but children quickly learn to eat when given the opportunity. However, it is important to avoid hurrying them at mealtimes and to allow children sufficient time to finish their food.

Although children need to learn to feed themselves and to manage eating utensils, they may find some foods especially challenging. This learning process can result in understandable and forgivable messiness that should be overlooked. However, some children intentionally create messes to gain adult attention. In these cases, the child's behavior should be ignored to avoid reinforcing or encouraging it from being repeated. Removing the child from the table can also be an effective way to extinguish undesirable behavior.

Food Jags Food jags are temporary phases during which children are willing to eat only a limited number of their favorite foods. These periods are not an uncommon occurrence among preschool-aged children and may simply reflect transitions in their tastes and interest in food. However, prolonged refusal of foods from all food groups can eventually result in nutrient deficiencies and the development of unhealthy eating habits. In most instances, adult patience and a few preventive measures offer the best approach.

Meals and snacks served to young children should always include a variety of choices from all food groups. Serving the same few favorite foods over and over strengthens children's preference for these items and narrows the range of foods they are willing to eat. Involving children in food preparation can also be an effective strategy for helping children to overcome food jags. Fortunately, most children soon tire of a limited food selection and will resume their normal eating pattern.

Inconsistent Adult Approaches to Feeding Problems This concern relates to several behavioral challenges that have previously been discussed. It is important that families and teachers

CONNECTING TO EVERYDAY PRACTICE

"Surfing the Web" for Information

The Internet has become a primary source of health and nutrition information for many consumers. Many of us have "surfed the Web" at one time or another to learn more about a particular condition, dietary recommendation, or research finding that was recently reported in the news. Public awareness and interest in wellness topics has significantly increased as a result of having online access to health and nutrition websites. However, limited regulation and oversight of information posted on many websites has concerned health care professionals (Boyer, 2013; Mager, 2012).

Think About This:

▶ How can you determine if the information provided is accurate and trustworthy?

▶ What are your thoughts about allowing commercial advertising on these websites?

▶ What nutrition and medical information websites would you recommend to friends, children's families, or visit for your own personal use?

communicate and agree on a consistent approach to handling children's food-related problems. It doesn't matter if the problem is weaning from excessive milk intake, decreasing dawdling behaviors, confronting eating refusals, or dealing with food jags. What is essential is that any interventions designed to address the child's problematic behaviors must be enforced consistently by teachers and the family. Children cannot be expected to learn acceptable behavior if the rules vary from setting to setting.

Did You Know...

that fast food restaurants serve more than 50 million Americans every day? Children who consume fast food meals several times a week drink less milk, eat fewer fruits and vegetables, take in more calories, and have a higher BMI.

Food Additives and Hyperactivity The Feingold diet, initially published in 1973, proclaimed a link between sugar, food additives, and children's hyperactivity (ADHD). However, several subsequent double-blind studies have failed to demonstrate any relationship. Recent studies have suggested that a small number of children may experience allergic-type responses to some additives, which could explain their behavior (Turner & Kemp, 2012). For these children, eliminating the offending agent from their diet did result in improvement. Sugar has also been thought to cause hyperactivity, but this association remains unfounded. Restricting a child's sugar intake has not been shown to improve behavior or learning. Actually, a biochemical case can be made for sugar as a calming and sleep-inducing agent. There is no harm in eliminating sugar and food additives, including artificial dyes, from children's diet as long as nutritious foods from all food groups are provided.

Fast-Food Consumption The current cultural pattern of two-working-parents and single-parent families has led to significant changes in eating practices. More meals are eaten outside of the home today, especially in fast-food restaurants, than in previous decades. Families have also become more reliant on convenience and processed foods from local grocery stores for meals. These collective changes have raised serious public health concerns about children's food intake, especially of fast foods, and their long-term effects on health (Saelens et al., 2012). Most fast foods are high in calories, cholesterol, fat, and salt, which over time can contribute to serious health problems such as cardiovascular disease, hypertension, diabetes, and obesity. Fast foods also tend to be low in fiber, vitamins A and C, and calcium (unless milk is the selected beverage). A too-frequent scenario is a mother and young child at a fast-food restaurant. The mother shares a few bites of her hamburger with the child, whose meal is rounded out with French fries and a small cola. An occasional fast-food meal for children is not problematic if care is taken to make up for any nutrient deficiencies by selecting healthy options and serving nutritious foods at other times in the day.

Commercial Advertising Television commercials and other media advertising formats exert a strong influence on children's ideas about food. It is estimated that a child is exposed to approximately 3 hours of commercial advertising per week and 20,000 to 30,000 commercials each year (Harrison & Liechty, 2012). More than half of these involve food, particularly sweetened cereals, cookies, candy, sugary beverages, and fast-food offerings (Andreyeva, Kelly, & Harris, 2011). Most advertised foods are high in sugar and/or fat and are too calorie-dense to be healthful choices for young children. An additional concern is the extent to which children's food preferences are being shaped by television food commercials and, in turn, influence adult food purchases.

Young children consider television to be reality and do not understand the persuasive nature of commercial advertising (Graff, Kunkel, & Mermin, 2012). For these reasons, it is important that adults talk with children about the purpose of commercial messaging, limit their television viewing time, and encourage more active play to address childhood obesity.

Did You Get It?

The genetic potential for obesity in families is:

a. about equal to that of environmental factors

b. great

c. the single biggest cause of obesity

d. slight

Take the full quiz on CourseMate.

PARTNERING with FAMILIES

Feeding Toddlers and Young Children

Dear Families,

Mealtimes should be pleasant, social opportunities when family members can spend time together and build positive connections. Having a child who is a "picky" or selective eater can be disruptive and cause considerable turmoil during an otherwise enjoyable mealtime experience. It is important never to force or bribe children to eat. This will only cause them to be even more resistant. Instead, show patience, encourage children to participate in food preparations, and mealtimes will gradually become pleasant eating experiences again.

▶ Let children help with menu planning. Take them along to the grocery store and give them a list with several items to find or have them help you pick out fresh fruits and vegetables. Challenge them to find a new (nutritious) food item for the family to try.

▶ Get children involved in preparing foods. Have them assist with mixing, washing and peeling vegetables, and setting the table.

▶ Serve foods that a child dislikes along with a favorite or familiar food.

▶ Prepare foods in different ways to add fun and interest to meals. For example, try freezing fresh fruits and serving them frozen, incorporate a new vegetable into muffins or cookie bars, or make a tropical fruit salsa to top off grilled fish or a veggie burger.

▶ Do not give up on a food item if your child does not accept it the first time. It may take ten to fifteen exposures to an unfamiliar food before the child is willing to eat it.

▶ Serve meals and snacks at scheduled times. Children are more likely to eat if there is adequate time planned between their meals and snacks.

▶ Avoid sharing and passing your own food dislikes on to your children.

▶ Engage children in family conversations during mealtimes. You are letting children know they are valued family members when you listen and show interest in what they have to say.

▶ Finally, most children will get the nutrients they need, even if only small amounts of food are consumed. Continue to offer a wide variety of colorful foods and make mealtime a positive, pleasant family experience.

CLASSROOM CORNER

Teacher Activities

Tasting Pears . . .

(PreK–2; **NHES** National Health Education Standards, 1.2.1, 1.2.2)

Concept: The same food can have different tastes and textures.

Learning Objectives

▶ Children will learn that pears come in a variety of tastes.

▶ Children will experience tasting three kinds of pears.

Supplies

▶ Two Anjou pears, two Bosc pears, two Bartlett pears, hand wipes, small plates, napkins

Learning Activities

▶ Read and discuss the following book:
  • *Too Many Pears!* by Jackie French
  • *Orange Pear Apple Bear* by Emily Gravett

▶ Tell children there are different varieties of pears. Talk about the importance of eating fruit each day (fiber, vitamins).

▶ Have children wash their hands with wipes and then pass around each pear for children to feel and look at the differences and similarities. Have children describe each pear's color, texture, and shape and talk about differences.

▶ Next, hand a napkin and a plate to each child. Place a small bite of each pear on a plate for children to taste; this can be done one at a time or the plate can have a sample of each pear on it.

▶ Give children an opportunity to taste each pear and talk about how each one tastes. Talk about the different tastes and textures.

▶ Repeat the activity using variations of other foods, such as vegetables, eggs, or grains.

Evaluation

▶ Children will state why pears are a healthy food choice.

▶ Children will taste a sample of each type of pear.

Additional lesson plans for grades 3–5 are available on CourseMate.

Summary

▶ Children's growth rate begins to slow soon after their first birthday and contributes to a decreased interest in food. Children also begin to experience many behavioral changes as they transition from toddlers to preschoolers and on to the school-age years that directly influence their nutrient needs and eating patterns.

▶ Mealtimes with toddlers can be challenging. To minimize potential friction, adults are responsible for: (a) serving a variety of nutritious foods, (b) deciding when to offer food, and (c) setting a positive example by eating a variety of nutritious foods.

▶ Children are responsible for deciding: (a) what to eat and (b) how much to eat.

▶ It is important that children's meals include a range of nutritious foods from all food groups because lifetime food patterns are being formed during the toddler, preschool, and school-age years.

▶ Adults play an important role in shaping children's eating behaviors by planning and providing meals that include a variety of foods and serving as positive role models.

▶ Consuming a nutritious diet can minimize children's risk of developing food-related health problems, including dental caries, obesity, hypertension, heart disease, and diabetes.

Terms to Know

neophobic *p. 406*   Prader-Willi syndrome *p. 413*   hypertension *p. 416*
Down syndrome *p. 413*   dental caries *p. 416*   satiety *p. 416*

Chapter Review

A. By Yourself:

1. Name three ways to make mealtimes comfortable and pleasant for children.

2. Explain the teacher's major responsibilities in toddler feeding situations.

3. Suggest approximate serving sizes for a 2-year-old and a 4-year-old for each of the following foods: bread, peas, applesauce, orange juice, banana, cooked chicken, noodles, baked beans.

B. As a Group:

1. Watch 1 hour of Saturday morning cartoons on television and discuss the following:

   a. What foods were presented in the majority of commercials?

   b. What adjectives did the announcer use to describe the foods being advertised?

   c. What other media effects were used to capture and maintain children's interest?

   d. Imagine that you are a 4-year-old. On your next trip to the grocery store with your mother, what products would you want her to buy? Why?

2. Visit a fast-food restaurant that features hamburgers and observe the following:

   a. How many toddlers and preschoolers are present?

   b. What foods are the children eating and drinking?

   c. What foods might have been ordered from the menu to provide a more nutritious or healthier meal?

   d. Ask the restaurant for nutritional information or visit its website. Are you surprised by any of the calorie and nutrient values?

3. Visit a local supermarket and observe the advertising techniques used to draw children's attention to certain foods and products.

   a. What cereals are shelved at a child's eye level? Describe features on the boxes that are used to capture children's attention.

   b. What types of foods are displayed at the end of aisles?

   c. What food items are typically displayed at the checkout counter?

   d. What types of free food samples are being offered that would appeal to young children? What is the intended purpose of these promotions?

Case Study

Maria, age 7 years, is new to the community and has recently enrolled in your after-school program. She and her parents speak Portuguese, but very little English. The other children are intrigued with Maria and her "different" language. They eagerly attempt to teach her some English words by pointing to and repeating the names of foods and objects with exaggerated clarity. Although Maria seems to enjoy their attention and is responding to their efforts, you (teacher) are concerned that she still eats very little during snack time.

1. Why should you be concerned that Maria is not eating?

2. What steps can you take to learn more about her family's food preferences?

3. Where might you access information about foods and food preferences native to Maria's culture?

4. Where might you access materials to aid in Maria's care and your ability to communicate with her family?

5. Where might you locate an interpreter for assistance?

Application Activities

1. Jason, 18 months old, has recently been enrolled in an all-day early childhood program. His health assessment reveals that he is anemic. Observations of his eating habits suggest that he dislikes meat and vegetables but eats large quantities of fruits and drinks at least two cups of milk at every meal and snack. What changes in eating habits should the teacher try to foster to improve Jason's iron status?

2. Formulate plans for the dining area of an early childhood program that will promote children's self-feeding skills. Include a discussion of appropriate furniture and eating utensils. Plan a 1-day menu (one meal and two snacks) that will further enhance children's self-feeding efforts.

3. Flore, 4 years old, arrives at her family child-care provider's home every morning with a bag of doughnuts. Her mother informs the provider that it is okay for Flore to eat the doughnuts because she doesn't like what is being served for breakfast. The other children have also begun to ask for doughnuts. How should the provider handle this situation? What factors must be considered?

4. Prepare a 5-day snack menu for toddlers, preschoolers, and school-age children that features nutrient-dense foods.

Helpful Web Resources

American Diabetes Association	http://www.diabetes.org
American Heart Association (childhood obesity)	http://www.americanheart.org
Council for Exceptional Children	http://www.cec.sped.org
Food Allergy & Anaphylaxis Network	http://www.foodallergy.org

Visit the Education CourseMate for this textbook to access the eBook, Did You Get It? quizzes, Digital Downloads, TeachSource Video Cases, flashcards, and more. Go to CengageBrain.com to log in, register, or purchase access.

References

American Academy of Pediatrics (AAP). (2011). Physicians recommend all children, ages 9–11, be screened for cholesterol. Accessed on August 27, 2012 from http://www.aap.org/en-us/about-the-aap/aap-press-room/pages /Physicians-Recommend-all-Children,-Ages-9-11,-Be-Screened-for-Cholesterol.aspx.

American Heart Association (AHA). (2013). Overweight in children. Accessed on May 8, 2013 from http://www.heart .org/HEARTORG/GettingHealthy/Overweight-in-Children_UCM_304054_Article.jsp.

Anderson, S., Must, A., Curtin, C., & Bandini, L. (2012). Meals in our household: Reliability and initial validation of a questionnaire to assess child mealtime behaviors and family mealtime environments, *Journal of the Academy of Nutrition & Dietetics*, 112(2), 276–284.

Andreyeva, T., Kelly, I., & Harris, J. (2011). Exposure to food advertising on television: Associations with children's fast food and soft drink consumption and obesity, *Economics & Human Biology*, 9(3), 221–233.

Boyer, C. (2013). The Internet and health: International approaches to evaluating the quality of web-based health information. In, G. Carlisle, P. Duquenoy, & D. Whitehouse (Eds.), eHealth: Legal, Ethical and Governance Challenges, Part 3, 245–274.

CDC. (2012). Children and diabetes. Accessed on August 26, 2012 from http://www.cdc.gov/diabetes/projects/cda2. htm.

Friedman, A., Bennett, T., Barbarich, B., Keaschuk, R., & Ball, G. (2012). Food portion estimation by children with obesity: The effects of estimation method and food type, *Journal of the Academy of Nutrition & Dietetics*, 112(2), 302–307.

Frisoli, T., Schmieder, R., Grodzicki, T., & Messerli, F. (2012). Salt and hypertension: Is salt dietary reduction worth the effort?, *Acta Pharmacologica Sinica*, 33, 189–193.

Graff, S., Kunkel, D., & Mermin, S. (2012). Government can regulate food advertising to children because cognitive research shows that it is inherently misleading, *Health Affairs*, 31(2), 392–398.

Halfon, N., Verhoef, P., & Kuo, A. (2012). Childhood antecedents to adult cardiovascular disease, *Pediatrics in Review*, 33(2), 51–51.

Harris, J., Speers, S., Schwartz, M., & Brownell, K. (2012). US food company branded advergames on the Internet: Children's exposure and effects on snack consumption, *Journal of Children & Media*, 6(1), 51–68.

Harrison, K., & Liechty, J. (2012). US preschoolers' media exposure and dietary habits: The primacy of television and the limits of parental mediation, *Journal of Children & Media*, 6(1), 18–36.

Hess, J., Latulippe, M., Ayoob, K., & Slavin, J. (2012). The confusing world of dietary sugars: Definitions, intakes, food sources and international dietary recommendations, *Food & Function*, 3, 477–486.

Hockenberry, M., & Wilson, D. (2012). *Wong's essentials of pediatric nursing*. (9th ed.). St Louis: Mosby.

Lent, M., Hill, T., Dollahite, J., Wolfe, W., & Dickin, K. (2012). Healthy children, healthy families: Parents making a difference! A curriculum integrating key nutrition, physical activity, and parenting practices to help prevent childhood obesity, *Journal of Nutrition Education & Behavior*, 44(1), 90–92.

Marotz, L. R., & Allen, K. E. (2013). *Developmental profiles: Pre-birth through adolescence*. (7th ed.). Belmont, CA: Wadsworth Cengage.

Mager, A. (2012). Search engines matter: From educating users towards engaging with online health information practices, *Policy & Internet*, 4(2), 1–21.

Musher-Eizenman, D., Oehlhof, M., Hauser, J., Galliger, C., & Sommer, A. (2011). Emerald dragon bites vs. veggie beans: Fun food names increase children's consumption of novel healthy foods, *Journal of Early Childhood Research*, 9(3), 191–195.

Rogers, L., Magill-Evans, & Rempel, G. (2012). Mother's challenges in feeding their children with autism spectrum disorder—Managing more than just picky eating, *Journal of Developmental & Physical Disabilities*, 24(1), 19–33.

Saelens, B., Sallis, J., Frank, L., Couch, S., Zhou, C., Colburn, T., Cain, K., Chapman, J., & Glanz, K. (2012). Obesogenic neighborhood environments, child and parent obesity: The Neighborhood Impact on Kids study, *American Journal of Preventive Medicine*, 42(5), e57–e64.

Satter, E. (2000). *How to get your child to eat . . . But not too much*. Palo Alto, CA: Bull Publishing Co.

Sira, B., & Fryling, M. (2012). Using peer modeling and differential reinforcement in the treatment of food selectivity, *Education & Treatment of Children*, 35(1), 91–100.

Skouteris, H., McCabe, M., Ricciardelli, L., Milgrom, J., Baur, L., Aksan, N., & Aquila, D. (2012). Parent–child interactions and obesity prevention: A systematic review of the literature, *Early Child Development & Care*, 182(2), 153–174.

Tan, C., & Holub, S. (2012). Maternal feeding practices associated with food neophobia, *Appetite*, 59(2), 483–487.

Turner, P., & Kemp, A. (2012). Intolerance to food additives—Does it exist?, *Journal of Paediatrics & Child Health*, 48(2), E10–E14.

Zhang, L., & McIntosh, W. (2011). Children's weight status and maternal and paternal feeding practices, *Journal of Child Health Care*, 15(4), 389–400.

Epilogue

Looking Ahead . . . Making a Difference

As promised, this book has taken you on a journey. You have had an opportunity to learn about many topics that are important to children's health, safety, and nutrition. The new skills you have developed will improve your abilities to observe children and to detect the early signs of acute and chronic health conditions and impending illness. You have become more knowledgeable about children's health problems, including childhood obesity, communicable illness, chronic medical conditions, and sensory impairments and their impact on development. You have learned about the critical importance of helping children acquire health-promoting behaviors and modifying environments to protect children from unintentional injury and unnecessary exposure to illness. Your knowledge of children's critical nutrient needs and ways to address them through thoughtful lessons and menu planning has also undoubtedly improved.

Most importantly, you have gained a better understanding of the preventive health concept, not only as it applies to the care and education of young children, but also how to implement it in your own personal life. Undoubtedly, you have also become more aware of the valuable role you play as a positive role model for children who look up to adults and often imitate their behaviors. As stated throughout the book, teachers are in an ideal position to promote children's health, safety, and nutrition and to make this a priority. Their dedicated efforts to achieving this goal through the development of meaningful learning experiences and their commitment to partnering with families can truly make a difference in children's lives.

The ultimate goal and true mark of learning is change . . . change in the way one thinks, change in one's behavior. Undoubtedly, your journey through this book has changed you in some way and caused you to question, think, or act differently. However, the journey does not end here. New discoveries continue to enhance our understanding of health promotion, chronic diseases, nutrition, and safety every day. In turn, this information shapes our ideas and best practices for promoting children's lifelong wellness. Attention is increasingly being focused on several significant aspects of children's well-being, including:

- Improving the quality of schools and early childhood programs.
- Planning and serving meals/snacks that provide essential nutrients, reduce unnecessary fat and calories, and are respectful of cultural differences.
- Raising awareness about childhood obesity and the importance of physical activity and outdoor play.
- Maintaining the safety of food and food environments.
- Addressing and responding to the needs of children who have chronic medical conditions and developmental challenges.
- Building children's resiliency to stress, bullying, and everyday environmental pressures.
- Improving communication with families and engaging them in children's education.
- Increasing awareness and sensitivity to child and family differences.
- Recognizing environmental contaminants and their effect on children's health.
- Addressing the need for more parenting education.
- Encouraging physical activity as a lifestyle practice.

- Addressing the issues of child maltreatment and domestic violence.
- Advocating on behalf of children's interests.
- Improving children's access to medical and dental care.
- Reducing poverty and food insecurity.

This list is not inclusive. Some issues may be of greater concern and interest to particular communities or populations. Other issues may have a more universal appeal and affect the welfare of children everywhere. In either case, the future of children's well-being offers unique opportunities for innovative solutions and teacher commitment.

Continue this journey. Keep learning about new developments as they unfold, explore topics that pique your curiosity, and become an advocate for children's health, safety, and nutrition. Accept the challenge—look ahead and make a difference for children!

APPENDICES

APPENDIX A   National Health Education Standards

NHES Standard 1: Students will comprehend concepts related to health promotion and disease prevention to enhance health.

Rationale: The acquisition of basic health concepts and functional health knowledge provides a foundation for promoting health-enhancing behaviors among youth. This standard includes essential concepts that are based on established health behavior theories and models. Concepts that focus on both health promotion and risk reduction are included in the performance indicators.

PreK–Grade 2 Performance Indicators, Standard 1
1.2.1   Identify that healthy behaviors impact personal health.
1.2.2   Recognize that there are multiple dimensions of health.
1.2.3   Describe ways to prevent communicable diseases.
1.2.4   List ways to prevent common childhood injuries.
1.2.5   Describe why it is important to seek health care.

Grades 3–5 Performance Indicators, Standard 1
1.5.1   Describe the relationship between healthy behaviors and personal health.
1.5.2   Identify examples of emotional, intellectual, physical, and social health.
1.5.3   Describe ways in which safe and healthy school and community environments can promote personal health.
1.5.4   Describe ways to prevent common childhood injuries and health problems.
1.5.5   Describe when it is important to seek health care.

NHES Standard 2: Students will analyze the influence of family, peers, culture, media, technology, and other factors on health behaviors.

Rationale: Health is affected by a variety of positive and negative influences within society. This standard focuses on identifying and understanding the diverse internal and external factors that influence health practices and behaviors among youth, including personal values, beliefs, and perceived norms.

PreK–Grade 2 Performance Indicators, Standard 2
2.2.1   Identify how the family influences personal health practices and behaviors.
2.2.2   Identify what the school can do to support personal health practices and behaviors.
2.2.3   Describe how the media can influence health behaviors.

Grades 3–5 Performance Indicators, Standard 2
2.5.1   Describe how family influences personal health practices and behaviors.
2.5.2   Identify the influence of culture on health practices and behaviors.
2.5.3   Identify how peers can influence healthy and unhealthy behaviors.
2.5.4   Describe how the school and community can support personal health practices and behaviors.
2.5.5   Explain how media influences thoughts, feelings, and health behaviors.
2.5.6   Describe ways that technology can influence personal health.

NHES Standard 3: Students will demonstrate the ability to access valid information, products, and services to enhance health.

Rationale: Access to valid health information and health-promoting products and services is critical in the prevention, early detection, and treatment of health problems. This standard focuses on how to identify and access valid health resources and to reject unproven sources. Application of the skills of analysis, comparison, and evaluation of health resources empowers students to achieve health literacy.

PreK–Grade 2 Performance Indicators, Standard 3
3.2.1   Identify trusted adults and professionals who can help promote health.
3.2.1   Identify ways to locate school and community health helpers.

Grades 3–5 Performance Indicators Standard 3
3.5.1   Identify characteristics of valid health information, products, and services.
3.5.2   Locate resources from home, school, and community that provide valid health information.

NHES Standard 4: Students will demonstrate the ability to use interpersonal communication skills to enhance health and avoid or reduce health risks.

Rationale: Effective communication enhances personal, family, and community health. This standard focuses on how responsible individuals use verbal and non-verbal skills to develop and maintain healthy personal relationships. The ability to organize and to convey information and feelings is the basis for strengthening interpersonal interactions and reducing or avoiding conflict.

PreK–Grade 2 Performance Indicators, Standard 4
4.2.1   Demonstrate healthy ways to express needs, wants, and feelings.
4.2.2   Demonstrate listening skills to enhance health.
4.2.3   Demonstrate ways to respond in an unwanted, threatening, or dangerous situation.
4.2.4   Demonstrate ways to tell a trusted adult if threatened or harmed.

Grades 3–5 Performance Indicators, Standard 4
4.5.1   Demonstrate effective verbal and nonverbal communication skills to enhance health.
4.5.2   Demonstrate refusal skills that avoid or reduce health risks.
4.5.3   Demonstrate nonviolent strategies to manage or resolve conflict.
4.5.4   Demonstrate how to ask for assistance to enhance personal health.

NHES Standard 5: Students will demonstrate the ability to use decision-making skills to enhance health.

Rationale: Decision-making skills are needed to identify, implement, and sustain health-enhancing behaviors. This standard includes the essential steps that are needed to make healthy decisions as prescribed in the performance indicators. When applied to health issues, the decision-making process enables individuals to collaborate with others to improve their quality of life.

PreK–Grade 2 Performance Indicators, Standard 5
5.2.1   Identify situations when a health-related decision is needed.
5.2.2   Differentiate between situations when a health-related decision can be made individually or when assistance is needed.

Grades 3–5 Performance Indicators, Standard 5
5.5.1   Identify health-related situations that might require a thoughtful decision.
5.5.2   Analyze when assistance is needed in making a health-related decision.
5.5.3   List healthy options to health-related issues or problems.
5.5.4   Predict the potential outcomes of each option when making a health-related decision.
5.5.5   Choose a healthy option when making a decision.
5.5.6   Describe the outcomes of a health-related decision.

NHES Standard 6: Students will demonstrate the ability to use goal-setting skills to enhance health.

Rationale: Goal-setting skills are essential to help students identify, adopt, and maintain healthy behaviors. This standard includes the critical steps that are needed to achieve both short-term and long-term health goals. These skills make it possible for individuals to have aspirations and plans for the future.

PreK–Grade 2 Performance Indicators, Standard 6
6.2.1   Identify a short-term personal health goal and take action toward achieving the goal.
6.2.2   Identify who can help when assistance is needed to achieve a personal health goal.

Grades 3–5 Performance Indicators, Standard 6

6.5.1   Set a personal health goal and track progress toward its achievement.

6.5.2   Identify resources to assist in achieving a personal health goal.

NHES Standard 7: Students will demonstrate the ability to practice health-enhancing behaviors and avoid or reduce health risks.

Rationale: Research confirms that practicing health-enhancing behaviors can contribute to a positive quality of life. In addition, many diseases and injuries can be prevented by reducing harmful and risk-taking behaviors. This standard promotes the acceptance of personal responsibility for health and encourages the practice of healthy behaviors.

PreK–Grade 2 Performance Indicators, Standard 7

7.2.1   Demonstrate healthy practices and behaviors to maintain or improve personal health.

7.2.2   Demonstrate behaviors that avoid or reduce health risks.

Grades 3–5 Performance Indicators, Standard 7

7.5.1   Identify responsible personal health behaviors.

7.5.2   Demonstrate a variety of healthy practices and behaviors to maintain or improve personal health.

7.5.3   Demonstrate a variety of behaviors to avoid or reduce health risks.

NHES Standard 8: Students will demonstrate the ability to advocate for personal, family, and community health.

Rationale: Advocacy skills help students promote healthy norms and healthy behaviors. This standard helps students develop important skills to target their health-enhancing messages and to encourage others to adopt healthy behaviors.

PreK–Grade 2 Performance Indicators, Standard 8

8.2.1   Make requests to promote personal health.

8.2.2   Encourage peers to make positive health choices.

Grades 3–5 Performance Indicators, Standard 8

8.5.1   Express opinions and give accurate information about health issues.

8.5.2   Encourage others to make positive health choices.

The revised standards and performance indicators represent the collaborative work of the Joint Committee on National Health Education Standards and are presented in the *National Health Education Standards: Achieving Excellence*. This information can also be accessed from the CDC's website (http://www.cdc.gov /healthyyouth/sher/standards).

<table>
<tr><td>**APPENDIX B**</td><td>**Monthly Calendar: Health, Safety, and Nutrition Observances**</td></tr>
</table>

Teachers may find the following list helpful for developing educational lessons and activities that focus on national observances of children's health, safety, and nutrition concerns. Additional resources and information can be accessed on many websites, including those that follow.

January

Healthy Weight Week	Healthy Weight Network http://www.healthyweightnetwork.com
Poverty Awareness Month	Children's Defense Fund http://www.childrensdefense.org

February

American Heart Month	American Heart Association http://www.heart.org
Burn Awareness	Burn Prevention Foundation http://www.burnprevention.org
Children's Dental Health Month	American Dental Association http://www.ada.org
Girls and Women in Sports Day	National Association for Girls and Women in Sports http://www.aahperd.org/nagws/programs/ngwsd National Council of Youth Sports http://www.ncys.org
National Cancer Prevention	American Cancer Society http://www.cancer.org
National Eating Disorders Awareness	National Eating Disorders Association http://www.nationaleatingdisorders.org
Random Acts of Kindness	Random Acts of Kindness Foundation http://www.actsofkindness.org

March

Brain Injury Awareness Month	Brain Injury Association of America http://www.biausa.org
Diabetes Awareness	American Diabetes Association http://www.diabetes.org
National Developmental Disabilities Awareness Month	The ARC of the U.S. http://www.thearc.org
National Nutrition Month	Academy of Nutrition & Dietetics http://www.eatright.org
Poison Prevention Month	Poison Prevention Council http://www.poisonprevention.org
Save Your Vision Month	American Optometric Association http://www.aoa.org
Sleep Awareness Week	National Sleep Awareness Foundation http://www.sleepfoundation.org
Youth Violence Prevention	National Association of SAVE http://www.nationalsave.org

April

Child Abuse Prevention Month	Prevent Child Abuse America http://www.preventchildabuse.org
National Playground Safety Week	National Program for Playground Safety http://www.playgroundsafety.org

National Safe Kids Week   Safe Kids Worldwide
                                           http://www.safekids.org
Stress Awareness Month   American Counseling Association
                                           http://www.counseling.org

May

Allergy and Asthma Awareness   Allergy & Asthma Foundation of America
Month   http://www.aafa.org or http://www.aanma.org
Better Hearing and Speech Month   American Speech-Language-Hearing Association
(ASHA)   http://www.asha.org
Bike Safety Month   League of American Bicyclists
                                          http://www.bikeleague.org
                                          Safe Kids Worldwide
                                          http://www.usa.safekids.org
Buckle Up America Week   National Highway Traffic Safety Administration
                                          http://www.nhtsa.gov
Clean Air Month   American Lung Association
                                          http://www.lungusa.org
Healthy Vision Month   National Eye Institute
                                          http://www.nei.nih.gov/hrm
Lyme Disease Awareness Month   Lyme Disease Association
                                          http://www.lymediseaseassociation.org
Mental Health Month (Children)   Mental Health America
                                          http://www.nmha.org
National Hurricane Preparedness   National Weather Service
                                          http://www.weather.gov
National Melanoma/Skin Cancer   American Academy of Dermatology
Awareness   http://www.aad.org
Physical Fitness and Sports   President's Council on Fitness, Sports, & Nutrition
                                          http://www.fitness.gov

June

Home Safety Month   Home Safety Council
                                          http://www.homesafetycouncil.org
Lightning Safety Week   National Weather Service
                                          http://www.lightningsafety.noaa.gov
National Safety Month   National Safety Council
                                          http://www.nsc.org
Sun Safety Week   Sun Safety Alliance
                                          http://www.sunsafetyalliance.org

July

Fireworks Eye Safety Month   Prevent Blindness America
                                          http://www.preventblindness.org
UV (Ultra Violet) Eye Safety Month   American Academy of Ophthalmology
                                          http://www.aao.org

August

Children's Eye Health and Safety   Prevent Blindness America
Month   http://www.preventblindness.org
Immunization Awareness Month   Centers for Disease Control and Prevention
                                          http://www.cdc.gov/vaccines

September

America on the Move   America On the Move Foundation
                                          http://www.americaonthemove.org

Baby Safety Month	U.S. Consumer Product Safety Commission
	http://www.cpsc.gov
Fruit and Vegetable Month	Fruit and Vegetable Program Office Centers for
	Disease Control and Prevention/Produce for Better
	Health Foundation
	http://www.fruitsandveggiesmatter.gov
National Childhood Obesity	President's Council on Fitness, Sports, & Nutrition
Awareness Month	http://www.fitness.gov
National Preparedness Month	American Red Cross
	http://www.redcross.org
	Federal Emergency Management Agency (FEMA)
	http://www.ready.gov
National Yoga Month	Yoga Health Foundation
	http://www.yogamonth.org
Sickle Cell Awareness Month	Sickle Cell Disease Association of America, Inc.
	http://www.sicklecelldisease.org
Sports and Home Eye Safety	Prevent Blindness America
	http://www.preventblindness.org
Whole Grains Month	Whole Grains Council
	http://www.wholegrainscouncil.org

October

Eye Injury Prevention Month	American Academy of Ophthalmology
	http://www.aao.org
Fire Prevention Week	National Fire Protection Association
	http://www.nfpa.org
Health Literacy Month	National Institutes of Health (NIH)
	http://www.nih.gov
National Health Education Week	Society for Public Health Education
	http://www.sophe.org
National School Lunch Week	School Nutrition Association
	http://www.schoolnutrition.org/nslw
School Bus Safety Week	National Association for Pupil Transportation
	http://www.naptonline.org
SIDS Awareness Month	SIDS Alliance
	http://www.sidsalliance.org

November

American Diabetes Awareness Month	American Diabetes Association
	http://www.diabetes.org
Epilepsy Awareness Month	Epilepsy Foundation
	http://www.epilepsyfoundation.org
National Healthy Skin Month	American Academy of Dermatology
	http://www.aad.org

December

National Handwashing	Henry the Hand Foundation
Awareness Week	http://www.henrythehand.com
National Safe Toys Month	Consumer Product Safety Commission
	http://www.cpsc.gov
	Kids Health
	http://www.kidshealth.org

APPENDIX C   Federal Food and Nutrition Programs

Federal food programs are funded and regulated by the U.S. Department of Agriculture (USDA) and administered at the state level by the Department of Education or the Public Health Department. These programs are intended to improve the health and wellness of the recipients. Information about the availability of food and nutrition programs in a particular community can be obtained from city or county health departments, state office of public health, or the state department of education.

Child Nutrition Programs

Child nutrition programs provide cash assistance and/or food commodities for children enrolled in public schools, nonprofit private schools, early education centers, home-based child care programs, summer day camps, and after-school programs.

National School Lunch Program (www.fns.usda.gov/cnd/Lunch)

The National School Lunch Program (NSLP) is the oldest and largest federal child food program in existence, both in terms of the number of children it reaches (more than 30 million) and dollars spent. The NSLP is administered at the national level by the USDA and at the state level by the U.S. Department of Education. Participating public and nonprofit schools are reimbursed for serving children lunches that meet specific nutrient guidelines. After-school and enrichment programs are also eligible to apply for reimbursement for the snacks they provide to children (through age 18 years). The amount of money schools receive per meal depends upon whether the student qualifies for free, reduced price, or full price meals. The families of students eligible to receive free or reduced price meals must submit financial statements and meet family size and income guidelines. These categories are adjusted periodically to reflect changes in national poverty guidelines. Families caring for foster children are exempt from proving income eligibility.

Meals served to children participating in the school lunch program must comply with the Dietary Guidelines for Americans in addition to new nutrition standards established by the Healthy, Hunger-Free Kids Act 2010. Schools are required to serve more fruits and vegetables (especially fresh), whole grains, and fat-free or 1-percent milk each day. Meals must also be planned not to exceed new levels for sodium content and calories in an effort to address childhood obesity and improve children's long-term health.

School Breakfast Program (http://www.fns.usda.gov/cnd/Breakfast)

The School Breakfast Program, authorized by the Child Nutrition Act of 1975, has also undergone changes and must comply with the nutrition mandates outlined in the Healthy, Hunger-Free Kids Act 2010. This program makes provision for free, reduced price, or full price meals based on a family's income eligibility. The School Breakfast Program is available to public and nonprofit schools (Pre-K through high school) and to licensed nonprofit residential child care institutions.

Summer Food Service Program (http://www.summerfood.usda.gov)

The purpose of the Summer Food Service Program is to address the nutrition needs of children during months when school is not in session. Schools, parks and recreation centers, playgrounds, churches, day camps, housing projects, residential summer camps, and migrant centers located in communities or on Indian reservations where at least 50 percent of children qualify for free or reduced price meals can apply to become a sponsor site. Most sites also provide supervised play and educational activities. Funding for meals is provided by the USDA's Food and Nutrition Service and administered through state education departments. Meals must meet federal nutrition guidelines and are provided free-of-charge to any child on a first-come basis.

Child and Adult Care Food Program (http://www.fns.usda.gov/cnd/care)

The Child and Adult Care Food Program (CACFP) provides cash reimbursement for meals served to children in licensed early childhood centers, home-based child care programs, children in emergency shelters, at-risk after school programs, and adults living in group homes. The program benefits children 12 years old and under, disabled persons in an institution serving a majority of persons 18 years old and under, migrant children 15 years old and younger, children 18 years or younger staying in emergency shelters, and adults with disabilities. The USDA's Food and Nutrition Service provides funding for the CACFP program, which is administered through the Department of Education in most states. The program is designed to improve the quality of children's nutrient intake.

Programs are reimbursed for a maximum of two meals and one snack or one meal and two snacks. Reimbursement rates are based on a family's income eligibility. The meal pattern follows the same guidelines required for the National School Lunch Program that are adjusted by age categories: infants, children 1–2 years, children 3–5 years, children 6–12 years, and adults.

Family Nutrition Programs

Two governmental programs that provide food assistance to eligible families are the Special Supplemental Nutrition Program for Women, Infants, and Children, better known as WIC, and the Supplemental Nutrition Assistance Program (SNAP).

Women, Infants, and Children (http://www.fns.usda.gov/wic)

WIC is administered at the federal level by the USDA Food and Nutrition Service, which provides local public health and/or nonprofit health agencies with funding to operate this program. WIC offers nutrition education, health care referrals, and checks, vouchers, or electronic cards (EBT) that recipients can use to purchase foods rich in protein, iron, and vitamin C. Women who are pregnant and/or breastfeeding, infants, and children up to 5 years of age who are identified to be at nutritional risk and income-eligible are considered for this program. Participants receive specified amounts of the following foods:

- iron-fortified infant formula and baby foods
- iron-fortified adult cereals
- fresh fruits, vegetables, and juices rich in vitamin C
- whole grain bread
- fortified milk
- proteins, including cheese, eggs, peanut butter, tofu, and canned fish
- dried beans, peas, and legumes

Supplemental Nutrition Assistance Program (http://www.fns.usda.gov/snap)

SNAP is a food-assistance program designed to improve nutrient intake in low-income families; nearly half of the recipients are children under 18 years. Eligibility is based on a combination of financial and nonfinancial factors. The program is typically administered by either state or local welfare agencies. Monthly benefits are deposited electronically into a credit account that recipients are able to use for food purchases. The purpose of the electronic benefits transfer (EBT) is to reduce the potential for fraud. Funds may be used to purchase *allowed foods*, such as breads and cereals, fruits and vegetables, meats, fish or poultry, and dairy or seeds that can be used to grow food for consumption. Items not allowed include soap, cigarettes, paper goods, alcoholic beverages, pet foods, vitamins, or deli foods that may be eaten on the premises.

APPENDIX D   Children's Book List

Dental Health

Civardi, A. (2010). *Going to the Dentist*. Usborne Books.

Cousins, L. (2009). *Maisy, Charley, and the Wobbly Tooth: A Maisy First Experience Book*. Candlewick.

Katz, B. (2002). *Hello Reader: Make Your Way for Tooth Decay*. Cartwheel.

Keller, L. (2000). *Open Wide: Tooth School Inside*. Henry Holt & Company.

Lewison, W. (2002). *Clifford's Loose Tooth*. Scholastic.

Mayer, M. (2001). *Just Going to the Dentist*. Golden Books.

Miller, E. (2009). *The Tooth Book: A Guide to Healthy Teeth and Gums*. Holiday House.

Minarik, E. (2002). *Little Bear's Loose Tooth*. HarperFestival.

Munsch, R. (2002). *Andrew's Loose Tooth*. Scholastic.

Murkoff, H. (2002). *What to Expect When You Go to the Dentist*. HarperFestival.

Schuh, M. (2008). *At the Dentist (Healthy Teeth series)*. Capstone Press. (Also available in Spanish).

Ziefert, H. (2012). *ABC Dentist: Healthy Teeth from A to Z*. Blue Apple Books.

Illness/Germs

Berger, M. (1995). *Germs Make Me Sick!* HarperCollins.

Berger, M. (2002). *Why I Sneeze, Shiver, Hiccup, & Yawn*. HarperCollins.

Capeci, A. (2001). *The Giant Germ*. Scholastic Paperbacks.

Cote, P. (2002). *How Do I Feel?* Houghton Mifflin. (Spanish and English).

Dealey, E. (2002). *Goldie Locks Has Chicken Pox*. Scholastic.

Harvey, R. (2005). *Caillou: Is Sick*. Chouette Publishing.

Newman, A. (2012). *How to Catch a Cold*. MiLo Ink Books.

O'Brien-Palmer, M. (1999). *Healthy Me: Fun Ways to Develop Good Health and Safety Habits: Activities for Children 5–8*. Chicago Review Press.

Oetting, J. (2006). *Germs*. Children's Press.

Rice, J. (2002). *Those Mean, Nasty, Dirty, Downright Disgusting but Invisible Germs*. Redleaf Press.

Romanek, T. (2003). *Achoo: The Most Interesting Book You'll Ever Read About Germs*. Kids Can Press.

Ross, T. (2006). *Wash Your Hands!* Kane/Miller.

Rylant, C. (2003). *Mr. Putter & Tabby Catch the Cold*. Sandpiper.

Verdick, E. (2006). *Germs Are Not for Sharing*. Free Spirit Publishing. (Also available in Spanish)

Mental Health (Feelings)

Aboff, E. (2010). *Everyone Feels Scared Sometimes*. Picture Window Books.

Agassi, M. (2000). *Hands Are Not for Hitting*. Free Spirit Publishing.

Anholt, C. (1998). *What Makes Me Happy?* Candlewick Press.

Annunziata, J., & Nemiroff, M. (2009). *Sometimes I'm Scared*. Magination Press.

Baker, L. (2001). *I Love You Because You're You*. Cartwheel Books.

Bang, M. (1999). *When Sophie Gets Angry—Really, Really Angry*. Scholastic.

Beaumont, K. (2004). *I Like Myself!* Harcourt Children's Books.

Blumenthal, D. (1999). *The Chocolate-Covered-Cookie Tantrum*. Clarion Books.

Cain, J. (2000). *The Way I Feel*. Parenting Press.

Carle, E. (1999). *The Very Lonely Firefly*. Philomel Books.

Carle, E. (2000). *The Grouchy Ladybug*. Scholastic.

Child, L. (2007). *You Can Be My Friend*. Grosset & Dunlap.

Cole, J. (2010). *I'm a Big Brother*. HarperFestival.

Cole, J. (2010). *I'm a Big Sister*. HarperFestival.

Cook, J. (2005). *A Bad Case of Tattle Tongue*. National Center for Youth Issues.

Cruz, R. (2009). *Alexander and the Terrible, Horrible, No Good, Very Bad Day*. Antheneum.

Cutis, J. L. (1998). *Today I Feel Silly: And Other Moods That Make My Day*. HarperCollins.

Cutis, J. L. (2002). *I'm Gonna Like Me: Letting off a Little Self-Esteem*. Joanna Cotler.

Hallinan, P. K. (2005). *A Rainbow of Friends*. Ideals Children's Books.

Hankinson, S. (2008). *Carrot-Walnut Pie*. AuthorHouse. (Bullying)

Henkes, K. (2007). *Chrysanthemum*. Greenwillow Books.

Hudson, C., & Ford, B. (1990). *Bright Eyes, Brown Skin*. Just Us Books.

Karst, P. (2000). *The Invisible String*. DeVorss & Co. (Death)

Ketteman, H. (2000). *Armadillo Tattletale*. Scholastic Books.

Krasny, L., & Brown, M. (2001). *How to Be a Friend: A Guide to Making Friends and Keeping Them*. Little Brown & Co.

Lalli, J. (2007). *I Like Being Me: Poems for Children, About Feeling Special, Appreciating Others, and Getting Along*. Free Spirit Publishing.

Lewis, P. (2002). *I'll Always Love You*. Tiger Tales.

Lite, L. (2007). *A Boy and a Turtle: A Children's Relaxation Story to Improve Sleep, Manage Stress, Anxiety, Anger*. Stress Free Kids.

Lite, L. (2008). *The Angry Octopus*. Stress Free Kids.

Lovell, P. (2001). *Stand Tall, Molly Lou Melon*. Scholastic.

Masurel, C. (2003). *Two Homes*. Candlewick. (Divorce)

Meiners, C. (2003). *Share and Take Turns*. Free Spirit.

O'Neill, A. (2002). *The Recess Queen*. Scholastic.

Parr, T. (2011). *The I'M NOT SCARED Book*. Little, Brown.

Parr, T. (2009). *It's Okay to be Different*. Little, Brown.

Parr, T. (2005). *The Feelings Book*. Little, Brown Books for Young Readers.

Sáenz, B. (2009). *The Dog Who Loved Tortillas/La perrita que le encantaban las tortillas*. Cinco Puntos Press.

Silver, G. (2009). *Anh's Anger*. Plum Blossom Books.

Spelman, C. (2000). *When I Feel Angry*. Albert Whitman & Co.

Tarpley, N. (2001). *I Love My Hair*. Little Brown.

Tetik, B. (2009). *If You Are Mad Say It with Words*. BookSurge Publishing.

Thomas, P. (2000). *Stop Picking on Me*. Barrons.

Vail, R. (2002). *Sometimes I'm Bombaloo*. Scholastic.

Weninger, B., & Marks, A. (1995). *Good-bye Daddy*. North-South Books.

Willems, M. (2007). *My Friend Is Sad*. Hyperion Book CH.

Personal Health & Self-Care

Baker, K. (2001). *Brave Little Monster*. HarperCollins.

Berry, J. (2010). *I Love Getting Dressed (Teach Me About)*. Joy Berry Books.

Brown, M. (2005). *Good Night Moon*. HarperFestival.

Cason, S. (2008). *The Night-Night Dance*. Tate Publishing.

Chodos-Irvine, M. (2003). *Ella Sarah Gets Dressed*. Harcourt Children's Books.

Civardi, A. (2005). Usborne First Experiences Collection: "*Going to School*," "*Going to the Doctor*," "*Moving House*," "*The New Baby*." Usborne Publishing Ltd.

Fox, L. (2010) *Ella Kazoo Will Not Brush Her Hair*. Walker Books for Young Readers.

Giles, S. (2011). *The Children's Book of Healthy Habits*. Award Publications Ltd.

Katz, A. (2001). *Take Me Out of the Bathtub*. Scholastic.

Keats, E. J. (2000). *Dreams*. Puffin.

Murkoff, H. (2000). *What to Expect at Bedtime*. HarperFestival.

Murkoff, H. (2000). *What to Expect When You Go to the Doctor*. HarperFestival.

Reidy, J. (2010). *Too Purpley!* Bloomsbury USA Children's Books.

Ricci, C. (2007). *Show Me Your Smile! A Visit to the Dentist*. Simon Spotlight Nickelodeon.

Timberlake, A. (2003). The *Dirty Cowboy*. Farrar, Straus, & Giroux.

Wood, A. (2009). *The Napping House*. Harcourt Children's Books.

Yolen, J. (2000). *How Do Dinosaurs Say Goodnight?* Blue Sky Press.

Safety

Boxall, E. (2002). *Francis the Scaredy Cat*. Candlewick Press.

Caviezel, G. (2007). *Policeman's Safety Hints*. Barron's Educational Series.

Committee, C. B. (2000). *Buckles Buckles Everywhere*. Palmetto Bookworks.

Cook, J. (2007). *SCOOP (Children's Life Skills)*. National Center for Youth Issues.

Cuyler, M. (2001). *Stop, Drop, Roll*. Simon & Schuster.

Federico, J. (2009). *Some Parts Are Not for Sharing*. Tate Publishing.

Feigh, A. (2008). *On Those Runaway Days*. Free Spirit Publishing.

Hayward, L. (2001). *A Day in the Life of a Firefighter*. Dorling Kindersley Publisher.

Kelman, M. (2009). *Safety First!* Disney Press.

Kurtz, J. (2005). *Do Kangaroos Wear Seatbelts?* Dutton Juvenile.

MacLean, C. K. (2002). *Even Firefighters Hug Their Moms*. Dutton.

Mattern, J. (2007). *Staying Safe in the Car*. Weekly Reader Early Learning Library.

Meiners, C. (2006). *Be Careful and Stay Safe*. Free Spirit Publishing

Mitton, T. (2001). *Down by the Cool of the Pool*. Orchard Books.

Palatini, M. (2002). *Earthquack!* Simon & Schuster.

Pendziwol, J. (2006). *Once Upon a Dragon: Stranger Safety for Kids (and Dragons)*. Kids Can Press.

Prigger, M. (2002). *Aunt Minnie and the Twister*. Clarion.

Reasoner, C. (2003). *Bee Safe (The Bee Attitudes)*. Price Stern Sloan Publishers.

Spelman, C., & Weidner, T. (2000). *Your Body Belongs to You*. Albert Whitman.

Tekavec, H. (2002). *Storm Is Coming!* Dial.

Thomas, P. (2003). *I Can Be Safe*! Barrand's Educational Series.

Wahman, W. (2009). *Don't Lick the Dog: Making Friends with Dogs*. Henry Holt & Co.

Weeks, S. (2002). *My Somebody Special*. Harcourt, Inc.

Special Needs

Bunnett, R. (2006). *Friends at School*. Star Bright Books.

Chirstenson, D. (2012). *Elephant on My Chest*. Peebles Publishing Co. (Asthma)

Gaynor, K., Carswell, C., & Quirke, K. (2009). *A Birthday for Ben – Children with Hearing Difficulty*. Moonbeam Children's Books.

Gosselin, K. (2004). *Taking Diabetes to School*. JayJo Books.

Heelan, J. (2000). *Rolling Along: The Story of Taylor and His Wheelchair*. Peachtree Publishers LTD.

Lang, R. (2004). *Lara Takes Charge*. MLPI Books. (Chronic illness)

Lears, L. (2005). *Nathan's Wish: A Story about Cerebral Palsy*. Albert Whitman & Co.

Lewis, B. (2007). *In Jesse's Shoes*. Bethany House Publishers.

London, J. (1997). *The Lion Who Had Asthma*. Albert Whitman & Co.

Maguire, A. (2000). *Special People, Special Ways*. Future Horizons.

Millman, I. (2000). *Moses Goes to School*. Frances Foster Books/Farrar, Straus & Giroux.

Nausau, E. (2001). *The Peanut Butter Jam*. Health Press.

Peete, H. (2010). *My Brother Charlie*. Scholastic. (Autism)

Recob, A. (2009). *The Bugabees: Friends with Food Allergies*. Beaver Pond Press.

Shriver, M. (2001). *What's Wrong with Timmy?* Little Brown & Co.

Skinner, J. (2010). *Food Allergies and Me*. Create Space.

Smith, N. (2006). *Allie the Allergic Elephant: A Children's Story of Peanut Allergies*. Allergic Child Publishing Group.

Thomas, P. (2005). *Don't Call Me Special*. Barron's Educational Series. (Disabilities)

Willis, J. (2000). *Susan Laughs*. Henry Holt & Co. (Wheelchair)

Nutrition

Appleton, J. (2001). *Do Carrots Make You See Better?* Red Leaf Press.

Brennan, G., & Brennan, E. (2004). *The Children's Kitchen Garden: A Book of Gardening, Cooking and Learning*. Ten Speed Press.

Brown, M. (1997). *D.W. The Picky Eater*. Little, Brown Books for Young Readers.

Brown, P. (2009). *The Curious Garden*. Little, Brown Books for Young Readers.

Caplan, J. (2009). *Gobey Gets Full: Good Nutrition in a Nutshell*. BookSurge Publishing.

Carle, E. (2008). *The Very Hungry Caterpillar*. Philomel.

Chamberlin, M. (2006). *Mama Panya's Pancakes*. Barefoot Books.

Charney, S., Goldbeck, D., & Larson, M. (2007). *The ABCs of Fruits and Vegetables and Beyond*. Ceres Press.

Child, L. (2003). *I Will Never Eat a Tomato*. Candelwick

Compestine, Y. (2001). *The Runaway Rice Cake*. Simon & Schuster.

Cooper, H. (2005). *Pumpkin Soup*. Farrar, Straus & Giroux (BYR).

D'Aluisio, F. (2008). *What the World Eats*. Tricycle Press.

Ehlert, L. (2006). *Eating the Alphabet: Fruits and Vegetables from A to Z*. HMH Books.

Geeslin, C. (1999). *How Nanita Learned to Make Flan*. Atheneum.

Gibbons, G. (2000). *The Honey Makers*. HarperCollins.

Gibbons, G. (2008). *The Vegetables We Eat*. Holiday House.

Hutchins, P. (2007). *Ten Red Apples*. Greenwillow Books.

Katzen, M. (1994). *Pretend Soup and Other Real Recipes: A Cookbook for Preschoolers and Up*. Tricycle Press.

Kye, J. (2011). *Jojo Eats Dim Sum*. Wonderscopic.

Krauss, R. (2004). *The Carrot Seed*. HarperCollins.

Levenson, G. (2002). *Pumpkin Circle: The Story of a Garden*. Tricycle Press.

Lin, G. (2003). *Dim Sum for Everyone*. Dragonfly Books.

Lin, G. (2009). *The Ugly Vegetables*. Charlesbridge Publishing.

Leedy, L. (2007). *The Edible Pyramid: Good Eating Every Day*. Holiday House.

Montes, G. (2012). *My Grandmother's Tortillas*. Infinity Publishing.

Rabe, T. (2001). *Oh the Things You Can Do That Are Good for You!* Random House.

Reiser, L. (1998). *Tortillas and Lullabies*. Greenwillow Books.

Richards, J. (2006). *A Fruit Is a Suitcase for Seeds*. First Avenue Editions.

Rockwell, L. (2009). *Good Enough to Eat: A Kid's Guide to Food and Nutrition*. HarperCollins.

Rubin, A. (2012). *Dragons Love Tacos*. Dial.

Russ-Ayon, A., & June, C. (2009). *We Eat Food That's Fresh*. OurRainbow Press.

Sanger, A. (2001). *First Book of Sushi*. Tricycle Press.

Sayer, A. (2012). *Go! Go! Grapes: A Fruit Chant*. Beach Lane Books.

Sayer, A. (2011). *Rah! Rah! Radishes: A Vegetable Chant*. Beach Lane Books.

Schuh, M. (2006). *Being Active (Healthy Eating With My Pyramid)*. Capstone Press.

Sears, W., Sears, M., & Kelly, C. (2002). *Eat Healthy, Feel Great*. Little, Brown Young Readers.

Schneider, J. (2011). *Tales for Very Picky Eaters*. Clarion Books.

Sharmat, M. (2009). *Gregory, the Terrible Eater*. Scholastic.

Wells, P. (2003). *Busy Bears: Breakfast with the Bears*. Sterling Publications.

Wallace, N. (2004). *Apples, Apples, Apples*. Amazon Children's Publishing.

Woods, D., & Woods, A. (2000). *The Big Hungry Bear*. Child's Play Publishers.

Woomer, L. (2009). *Cookie*. Outskirts Press.

Physical Activity

Ackerman, K., & Gammell, S. (2003). *Song and Dance Man*. Knopf Books.

Blackstone, S. (2001). *Bear About Town*. Barefoot Books.

Blackstone, S., & Harter, D. (2007). *Bear on a Bike*. Barefoot Books.

Brown, M. (1991). *D.W. Flips*. Little, Brown Books for Young Readers.

Brown, M. (1996). *D.W. Rides Again*. Little, Brown Books for Young Readers.

Cole, J., Calmenson, S., & Tiegreen, A. (1990). *Miss Mary Mack and Other Children's Street Rhymes*. HarperCollins.

Cole, J., & Tiegreen, A. (1989). *Anna Banana: 101 Jump Rope Rhymes*. HarperCollins.

Craig, L. (2010). *Dancing Feet*. Knopf.

Davis, K. (2001). *Who Hops?* Voyager Books.

Doering-Tourville, A. (2008). *Get Up and Go: Being Active (How to Be Healthy)*. Picture Window Books.

Esbensen, B., & Leffler, M. (2000). *Jumping Day*. Boyds Mills Press.

Fallon, J., & Stower, A. (2007). *Snowball Fight!* Scholastic Inc.

Flemming, D. (1995). *In the Tall, Tall Grass*. Henry Holt & Co.

Hutchins, P. (2007). *Barn Dance!* Greenwillow Books.

Isadora, R. (2000). *Isadora Dances*. Puffin.

Kann, V. (2012). *Pinkalicious Soccer Star*. HarperCollins.

London, J., & Remkiewicz, F. (2001). *Froggy Plays Soccer*. Puffin.

London, J., & Remkiewicz, F. (2008). *Froggy Rides a Bike*. Puffin.

Miller, E. (2008). *The Monster Health Book: A Guide to Eating Healthy, Being Active & Feeling Great for Monsters & Kids*. Holiday House.

Rosen, M. (2009). *We're Going on a Bear Hunt*. Helen Oxenbury.

Schuh, M. (2006). *Being Active*. Capstone Press.

Shannon, G., & Trynan, A. (2000). *Frog Legs*. Greenwillow Books.

Shields, D. (2008). *Saturday Night at the Dinosaur Stomp*. Candlewick.

Stickland, P. (2000). *Ten Terrible Dinosaurs*. Puffin.

Thomas, P., & Facklam, P. (2008). *Snow Dance*. Pelican Publishing.

Torrey, R. (2003). *Beans Baker Bounces Back*. Random House Books.

Tourville, A. (2008). *Get Up and Go: Being Active*. Picture Window Books.

Walton, R., & Gorton, J. (2000). *My Two Hands, My Two Feet*. Puffin.

Winch, J. (2000). *Keeping Up With Grandma*. Holiday House.

APPENDIX E   Nutrient Information: Fast-Food Vendor Websites

Arby's	http://www.arbys.com
A&W	http://www.awrestaurants.com
Back Yard Burgers	http://www.backyardburgers.com
Baja Fresh	http://www.bajafresh.com
Blimpie	http://www.blimpie.com
Burger King	http://www.bk.com
Carl's Jr.	http://www.carlsjr.com
Chick-fil-A	http://www.chick-fil-a.com
Chipotle Mexican Grill	http://www.chipotle.com
Church's Chicken	http://www.churchs.com
Dairy Queen (DQ)	http://www.dairyqueen.com
Domino's Pizza	http://www.dominos.com
El Pollo Loco	http://www.elpolloloco.com
Einstein Bros. Bagels	http://www.einsteinbros.com
Hardee's	http://www.hardees.com
In-and-Out Burger	http://www.in-n-out.com
KFC	http://www.kfc.com
Krystal	http://www.krystal.com
Little Caesars	http://www.littlecaesars.com
Long John Silver's	http://www.ljsilvers.com
McDonald's	http://www.mcdonalds.com
On the Border	http://www.ontheborder.com
Pizza Hut	http://www.pizzahut.com
Quiznos	http://www.quiznos.com
Sonic Drive-In	http://www.sonicdrivein.com
Steak 'n Shake	http://www.steaknshake.com
Subway	http://www.subway.com
Taco Bell	http://www.tacobell.com
Wendy's	http://www.wendys.com
White Castle	http://www.whitecastle.com

*For additional information on the nutritional value of most foods, visit the USDA National Agricultural Library, Nutrient Data Laboratory database (http://ndb.nal.usda.gov).

Glossary

A

abdomen – the portion of the body located between the diaphragm (located at the base of the lungs) and the pelvic or hip bones.

absorption – the process by which the products of digestion are transferred from the intestinal tract into the blood or lymph or by which substances are taken up by the cells.

abuse – to mistreat, attack, or cause harm to another individual.

accreditation – the process of certifying an individual or program as having met certain specified requirements.

acute – the stage of an illness or disease during which an individual is definitely sick and exhibits symptoms characteristic of a specific illness or disease.

airborne transmission – the process by which germs are expelled into the air through coughs and sneezes, and transmitted to another individual via tiny moisture drops.

alkalis – group of bases or caustic substances that are capable of neutralizing acids to form salts.

amblyopia – a condition of the eye commonly referred to as "lazy eye"; vision gradually becomes blurred or distorted due to unequal balance of the eye muscles. There are no observable abnormalities of the eyes when a child has amblyopia.

amino acids – the organic building blocks from which proteins are made.

anaphylaxis – a severe allergic reaction that may cause difficulty breathing, itching, unconsciousness, and possible death.

anecdotal – brief notes describing a person's observations.

antibodies – special substances produced by the body that help protect against disease.

apnea – momentary absence of breathing.

aseptic procedure – treatment to produce a product that is free of disease-producing bacteria.

aspiration – accidental inhalation of food, fluid, or an object into the respiratory tract.

asymptomatic – having no symptoms.

attachment – an emotional connection established between infants and their parents and/or primary caregivers.

attitudes – beliefs or feelings one has toward certain facts or situations.

atypical – unusual; different from what might commonly be expected.

audiologist – a specially prepared clinician who uses nonmedical techniques to diagnose hearing impairments.

B

basal metabolic rate (BMR) – minimum amount of energy needed to carry on the body processes vital to life.

behavioral objectives – a clear and measurable description of a specific behavior that an individual is expected to learn.

C

calcium – mineral nutrient; a major component of bones and teeth.

calories – units used to measure the energy value of foods.

coenzymes – a vitamin-containing substance required by certain enzymes before they can perform their prescribed function.

cognitive – the aspect of learning that refers to the development of skills and abilities based on knowledge and thought processes.

collagen – a protein that forms the major constituent of connective tissue, cartilage, bone, and skin.

communicable – capable of being spread or transmitted from one individual to another.

complementary proteins – proteins with offsetting missing amino acids; complementary proteins can be combined to provide complete protein.

complete protein – protein that contains all essential amino acids in amounts relative to the amounts needed to support growth.

compliance – the act of obeying or cooperating with specific requests or requirements.

concepts – combinations of basic and related factual information that represent a broader statement or idea.

conductive loss – affects the volume of word tones heard, so that loud sounds are more likely to be heard than soft sounds.

contagious – capable of being transmitted or passed from one person to another.

convalescent – the stage of recovery from an illness or disease.

cost control – reduction of expenses through portion control inventory and reduction of waste.

critical control point (CCP) – a point or procedure in a specific food system where loss of control may result in an unacceptable health risk.

cryptosporidiosis – an infectious illness caused by an intestinal parasite. May be present in water (e.g., swimming pools, hot tubs, streams) contaminated with feces or from unwashed hands. Often causes severe diarrhea in children.

cyber-bullying – sending embarrassing or threatening messages to an individual via the Internet, electronic media, or cell phone.

cycle menus – menus that are written to repeat after a set interval, such as every three to four weeks.

D

deciduous teeth – a child's initial set of teeth; these teeth are temporary and gradually begin to fall out at around 5 years of age.

dehydration – a state in which there is an excessive loss of body fluids or extremely limited fluid intake. Symptoms may include loss of skin tone, sunken eyes, and mental confusion.

dental caries – tooth decay.

development – commonly refers to the process of intellectual growth and change.

developmental or physiological readiness – growth (both physical and cognitive) and chemical processes that lead to the ability to perform a function.

developmentally appropriate practices (DAP) – learning experiences and environments that take into account children's individual abilities, interests, and diverse needs. DAP also reflects differences among families and values them as essential partners in children's education.

diagnosis – the process of identifying a disease, illness, or injury from its symptoms.

Dietary Guidelines for Americans – a report that provides recommendations for daily food choices, to be balanced with physical activity, to promote good health and reduce certain disease risks.

Dietary Reference Intake (DRI) – a plan that presents the recommended goals of nutrient intakes for various age and gender groups.

digestion – the process by which complex nutrients in foods are changed into smaller units that can be absorbed and used by the body.

direct contact – coming in direct or immediate contact with infectious material.

discipline – training or enforced obedience that corrects, shapes, or develops acceptable patterns of behavior.

disorientation – lack of awareness or ability to recognize familiar persons or objects.

distention – the state of being stretched or enlarged.

DNA – deoxyribonucleic acid; the substance in the cell nucleus that codes for genetically transmitted traits.

Down syndrome – a genetic disorder that is characterized by unique facial features, intellectual disability, and motor delays.

E

electrolytes – substances that, when in solution, become capable of conducting electricity; examples include sodium and potassium.

elevate – to raise to a higher position.

emotional abuse – repeated humiliation, ridicule, or threats directed toward another individual.

emotional or psychological neglect – failure to meet a child's psychological needs for love and attention.

endocrine – refers to glands that produce substances called hormones that are secreted directly into the bloodstream.

energy – power to perform work.

enriched – adding nutrients to grain products to replace those lost during refinement; thiamin, niacin, riboflavin, and iron are nutrients most commonly added.

environment – the sum total of physical, emotional, cultural, and behavioral features that surround and affect an individual.

enzymes – proteins that catalyze body functions.

essential amino acids – amino acids that can only be obtained from protein food sources.

essential nutrient – nutrient that must be provided in food because it cannot be synthesized by the body at a rate sufficient to meet its needs.

ethnic – pertaining to races or groups of people who share common traits or customs.

evaluation – a measurement of effectiveness for determining whether or not educational objectives have been achieved.

F

failure to thrive – a term used to describe an infant whose growth and mental development are severely slowed due to lack of nurturing or mental stimulation.

fat-soluble vitamins – vitamins that are dissolved, transported, and stored in fat.

fecal-oral transmission – the process in which germs are transferred to the mouth via hands contaminated with fecal material.

fever – an elevation of body temperature above normal; a temperature over 99.4°F or 37.4°C orally is usually considered a fever.

First-In-First-Out (FIFO) inventory method – a method of storage in which the items stored for the longest time will be retrieved first.

fluorosis – white or brown spots that form on children's teeth due to excessive fluoride intake.

food infections – illnesses resulting from the ingestion of live bacteria in food.

food insecurity – uncertain or limited access to a reliable source of food.

food intolerance – unpleasant reactions to particular foods that do not involve an immune response and are usually outgrown.

food intoxications – illnesses resulting from the ingestion of food containing residual bacterial toxins in the absence of viable (live) bacteria.

food-borne illness – a disease or illness transmitted by the ingestion of food contaminated with bacteria, viruses, some molds, or parasites.

food-borne illness outbreak – two or more persons become ill after ingesting the same food and laboratory analysis confirms that food is the source of the illness.

fruit drinks – products that contain 0–10 percent real fruit juice, added water, and sugar.

full-strength – undiluted (as in 100 percent fruit or vegetable juice).

G

gestational diabetes – a form of diabetes that occurs only during pregnancy; affects the way the mother's body utilizes sugars in foods and increases health risks for the baby.

Good Samaritan Law – legal protection afforded to an individual who renders emergency or first aid care in a reasonable manner.

gram – a metric unit of weight (g); approximately 1/28 of an ounce.

growth – increase in size of any body part or of the entire body.

H

hands-on – active involvement in a project; actually doing something.

Hazard Analysis Critical Control Point (HACCP) – a food safety and self-inspection system that highlights potentially hazardous foods and how they are handled in the food service department.

head circumference – distance around the largest part of the head; used to monitor brain growth and development.

health – a state of wellness. Complete physical, mental, social, and emotional well-being; the quality of one health element affects the state of the others.

health assessment – the process of gathering and evaluating information about an individual's state of health.

heat exhaustion – overheating that occurs when a person is exposed to high outdoor temperatures and humidity during vigorous activity.

heat stroke – failure of the body's sweating reflex to function properly during exposure to high temperatures; causes body temperature to rise.

hemoglobin – the iron-containing, oxygen-carrying pigment in red blood cells.

heredity – the transmission of certain genetic material and characteristics from biological parents to a child at the time of conception.

hormones – special chemical substances produced by endocrine glands that influence and regulate specific body functions.

hyperglycemia – a condition characterized by an abnormally high level of sugar in the blood.

hyperopia – farsightedness; a condition of the eyes in which an individual can see distant objects clearly but has poor close vision.

hypertension – elevation of blood pressure above the normally accepted values.

hyperventilation – rapid breathing often with forced inhalation; can lead to sensations of dizziness, lightheadedness, and weakness.

hypothermia – below-normal body temperature caused by overexposure to cold conditions.

I

immunized – a state of becoming resistant to a specific disease through the introduction of living or dead microorganisms into the body, which then stimulates the production of antibodies.

impairments – a condition or malfunction of a body part that interferes with optimal functioning.

incidental learning – learning that occurs in addition to the primary intent or goals of instruction.

inclusion – the practice of including and integrating children of all abilities in a classroom and individualizing instruction to meet each child's unique learning needs.

incomplete proteins – proteins that lack required amounts of one or more essential amino acids.

incubation – the interval of time between exposure to infection and the appearance of the first signs or symptoms of illness.

indirect contact – coming in contact with infectious material that is transmitted via surfaces, animals, or insects.

individualized educational plan (IEP) – a plan that identifies specific developmental and academic goals and intervention services for a child or youth 3 to 22 years of age who has special needs.

individualized family service plan (IFSP) – a plan that outlines specific goals and intervention services for children 0 to 3 years of age who have special needs and their families.

individualized health services plan (IHSP) – a plan that identifies and addresses a child's special health care needs during school hours.

infection – a condition that results when a pathogen invades and establishes itself within a susceptible host.

ingested – the process of taking food or other substances into the body through the mouth.

inservice – educational training provided by an employer.

intervention – practices or procedures implemented to modify or change a specific behavior or condition.

intestinal – pertaining to the intestines and intestinal tract.

iron-deficiency anemia – a failure in the oxygen transport system caused by too little iron.

irradiation – food preservation by short-term exposure of the food to gamma rays.

L

latch-key – a term that refers to school-age children who care for themselves without adult supervision before and after school hours.

lethargy – a state of inaction or indifference.

liability – legal responsibility or obligation for one's actions owed to another individual.

licensing – the act of granting formal permission to conduct a business or profession.

linoleic acid – a polyunsaturated fatty acid that is essential (must be provided in food) for humans; also known as omega-6 fatty acid.

linolenic acid – one of the two polyunsaturated fatty acids that are recognized as essential for humans; also known as omega-3 fatty acid.

listlessness – a state characterized by a lack of energy or interest in one's affairs.

low-birthweight (LBW) – weighing less than 5.5 pounds (2,500 grams) at birth.

Lyme disease – bacterial illness caused by the bite of infected deer ticks found in grassy or wooded areas.

lymph glands – specialized groupings of tissue that produce and store white blood cells for protection against infection and illness.

M

macrocytic anemia – a failure in the oxygen transport system characterized by abnormally large immature red blood cells.

malnutrition – prolonged inadequate or excessive intake of nutrients and/or calories required by the body.

megadose – an amount of a vitamin or mineral at least ten times that of the RDA.

metabolism – all chemical changes that occur from the time nutrients are absorbed until they are built into body tissue or are excreted.

microbial – refers to living organisms, such as bacteria, viruses, parasites, or fungi that can cause disease.

microcytic anemia – a failure in the oxygen transport system characterized by abnormally small red blood cells.

microgram (mcg or µg) – a metric unit of measurement; one microgram equals one-millionth of a gram.

milligram (mg) – a metric unit of weight (mg); approximately 1/1,000 of a gram.

minerals – inorganic chemical elements that are required in the diet to support growth, repair tissue, and regulate body functions.

misarticulations – improper pronunciations of words and word sounds.

mixed hearing loss – a disorder that involves a combination of conductive and sensorineural hearing losses.

Mongolian spots – patches of blue-grey skin located on the lower back; more common among children of Asian, Native American, and Middle Eastern ethnicities.

mottling – marked with spots of dense white or brown coloring.

MUFAs – monounsaturated fatty acids; fatty acids that have one double hydrogen bond; nuts, avocados, and olive oil are high in this form of fat.

myopia – nearsightedness; an individual has good near vision but poor distant vision.

N

neglect – failure of a parent or legal guardian to properly care for and meet the basic needs of a child under 18 years of age.

negligence – failure to practice or perform one's duties according to certain standards; carelessness.

neophobic – fear of things that are new and unfamiliar.

neurological – pertaining to the nervous system, which consists of the nerves, brain, and spinal column.

neuromuscular – pertaining to control of muscular function by the nervous system.

neurons – specialized cells that transmit electrical impulses or signals.

non-essential amino acids – amino acids that are produced in the body.

normal – average; a characteristic or quality that is common to most individuals in a defined group.

norms – an expression (e.g., weeks, months, years) of when a child is likely to demonstrate certain developmental skills.

notarized – official acknowledgment of the authenticity of a signature or document by a notary public.

nutrients – the chemical substances in food.

nutrition – the study of food and how it is used by the body.

nutrition claims – statements of reduced calories, fat, or salt on the food labels.

nutrition education – activities that impart information about food and its use in the body.

O

obese – a BMI over 30.

objectives – clear, meaningful descriptions of specific behavioral outcomes; can be observed and measured.

observation – to inspect and take note of the appearance and behavior of other individuals.

odd-day cycle menus – menus planned for a period of days other than a week that repeat after the planned period; cycles of any number of days may be used. These menus are a means of avoiding repetition of the same foods on the same day of the week.

ophthalmologist – a physician who specializes in diseases and abnormalities of the eye.

optometrist – a specialist (nonphysician) trained to examine eyes and prescribe glasses and eye exercises.

overweight – a BMI greater than 25.

P

pallor – paleness.

palmar grasp – using the entire hand to pick up objects.

paralysis – temporary or permanent loss of sensation, function, or voluntary movement of a body part.

pasteurization – the process of heating a food to a prescribed temperature for a specific amount of time necessary to destroy disease-producing bacteria.

pathogen – a microorganism capable of producing illness or infection.

peer – one of the same rank; equal.

Percent Daily Values (% DV) – measures of the nutritional values of food; used in nutrition labeling.

person first language – a manner of addressing an individual first and then their disability; e.g., a child with autism.

physical abuse – injuries, such as welts, burns, bruises, or broken bones, that are caused intentionally.

physical neglect – failure to meet children's fundamental needs for food, shelter, medical care, and education, including abandonment.

pincer grip – using the thumb and finger to pick up an object.

plasticity – the brain's ability to organize and reorganize neural pathways.

Prader-Willi syndrome – a chromosomal disorder that causes learning and behavior problems, poor muscle tone, short height, and overeating that can lead to obesity.

precipitating – factors that trigger or initiate a reaction or response.

predisposition – having an increased chance or susceptibility.

preplan – outline a method of action prior to carrying it out.

preventive health – personal and social behaviors that promote and maintain well-being.

procurement – the process of obtaining services, supplies, and equipment in conformance with applicable laws and regulations.

prodromal – the appearance of the first nonspecific signs of infection; this stage ends when the symptoms characteristic of a particular communicable illness begin to appear.

protein – class of nutrients used primarily for structural and regulatory functions.

PUFAs – polyunsaturated fatty acids; fatty acids that contain more than one bond that is not fully saturated with hydrogen.

punishment – a negative response to what the observer considers to be wrong or inappropriate behavior; may involve physical or harsh treatment.

R

recovery position – placing an individual in a side-lying position.

referrals – directing an individual to other sources, usually for additional evaluation or treatment.

registration – the act of placing the name of a child care program on a list of active providers; usually does not require on-site inspection.

regulations – standards or requirements that are set to ensure uniform and safe practices.

regurgitation – the return of partially digested food from stomach to mouth.

reprimand – to scold or discipline for unacceptable behavior.

resilience – the capacity to endure or overcome difficult conditions.

resilient – the ability to withstand or resist difficulty.

resistance – the ability to avoid infection or illness.

respiratory tract – the nose, throat, trachea, and lungs.

resuscitation – to revive from unconsciousness or death; to restore breathing and heartbeat.

retention – the ability to remember or recall previously learned material.

risk management – measures taken to avoid an event such as an injury or illness from occurring; implies the ability to anticipate circumstances and behaviors.

RNA – ribonucleic acid; the nucleic acid that serves as messenger between the nucleus and the ribosomes where proteins are synthesized.

S

safe haven – a designated place, such as a hospital or fire station, where parents can leave their infant and give up parental rights without fear of criminal charges.

salmonellosis – a bacterial infection that is spread through contaminated drinking water, food, or milk or contact with other infected persons. Symptoms include diarrhea, fever, nausea, and vomiting.

satiety – a feeling of satisfaction or fullness.

sedentary – unusually slow or sluggish; a lifestyle that implies inactivity.

seizures – a temporary interruption of consciousness sometimes accompanied by convulsive movements.

self-concept – a person's belief of who they are, how they are perceived by others, and how they fit into society.

self-esteem – an individual's sense of value or confidence in himself or herself.

sensorimotor – Piaget's first stage of cognitive development, during which children learn and relate to their world primarily through motor and sensory activities.

sensorineural loss – a type of loss that occurs when sound impulses cannot reach the brain due to damage of the auditory nerve, or cannot be interpreted because of prior brain damage.

sensory qualities – aspects that appeal to sight, sound, taste, feel, and smell.

serrated – saw-toothed or notched.

sexual abuse – any sexual involvement between an adult and child.

shaken baby syndrome – forceful shaking of a baby that causes head trauma, internal bleeding, and sometimes death.

skeletal – pertaining to the bony framework that supports the body.

skinfold – a measurement of the amount of fat under the skin; also referred to as fat-fold measurements.

sleep apnea – temporary interruptions or stoppages in breathing during sleep.

speech – the process of using words to express one's thoughts and ideas.

spina bifida – a neural tube defect that occurs during early fetal development; a malformation (gap or opening) in the spinal column that affects the nerves and spinal cord.

sterile – free from living microorganisms.

strabismus – a condition of the eyes in which one or both eyes appear to be turned inward (crossed) or outward (walleye).

submerge – to place in water.

supervision – monitoring the behaviors and actions of children and others.

supplementary proteins – a complete protein mix resulting from combining a small amount of a complete protein with an incomplete protein to provide all essential amino acids.

susceptible host – an individual who is capable of being infected by a pathogen.

symptomatic control – treatment that controls symptoms but does not cure the condition.

symptoms – changes in the body or its functions that are experienced by the affected individual.

T

temperature – a measurement of body heat; varies with the time of day, activity, and method of measurement.

thermal – caused by heat.

thermic energy of food – energy required to digest, absorb, transport, and metabolize nutrients in food.

toxic stress – stress over which children have no control or adult support; it is intense, frequent, and often prolonged.

trans-fats – unsaturated fats that have been converted to a solid by a process called hydrogenation.

tympanic – referring to the ear canal.

U

undernutrition – an inadequate intake of one or more required or essential nutrients.

underweight – a BMI of less than 18.5.

unintentional injury – an unexpected or unplanned event that may result in physical harm or injury.

universal infection control precautions – special measures taken when handling bodily fluids, including careful hand washing, wearing disposable gloves, disinfecting surfaces, and proper disposal of contaminated objects.

urination – the act of emptying the bladder of urine.

V

values – the beliefs, traditions, and customs an individual incorporates and utilizes to guide behavior and judgments.

verbal abuse – to attack another individual with words.

W

water-soluble vitamins – vitamins that are dissolved and transported in water/fluids; cannot be stored.

weekly menus – menus that are written to be served on a weekly basis.

well child – a child who enjoys a positive state of physical, mental, social, and emotional health.

whole grains – grain products that have not been refined; they contain all parts of the kernel of grain.

Index